The Indepe   Guid

Britain and Europe

Edited by
Sam Dalley &
Bob Oldfield

The Backpackers Press

ISBN 978-0-9536185-7-6

Independent Hostel Guide 2008: Britain and Europe

17th Edition

Editors : Sam Dalley and Peter Oldfield (a.k.a Bob)

British Library Cataloguing in Publication Data
A Catalogue record for this book is available from the British Library
ISBN 978-0-9536185-7-6
Published by: The Backpackers Press, Speedwell House,
Upperwood, Matlock Bath, Derbyshire, DE4 3PE
Tel: +44 (0) 1629 580427
Email: Sam@BackpackersPress.com

Printed by: Pindar, Preston (01772) 620999
Cover Artwork : Mulberry Square Ltd (01509) 416544
Maps : Contour Design

Distributed in the UK by:-
          Cordee Books and Maps, 3a De Montfort Street.
          Leicester, LE1 7HD, Tel: (0116) 2543579

Distributed overseas by:-
          Global Exchange, Australia, Tel: (02) 4929 4688

Cover Photographs provided by the Independent Hostels.

CONTENTS

Printed on paper manufactured from
100% recycled materials.

SYMBOLS

Mixed dormitories

Single sex dormitories

Private rooms

Blankets or duvets provided

Sheets required

Sleeping bags required

Hostel fully heated (including common room)

Common room only heated

Drying room available

Showers available

Cooking facilities available

Shop at hostel

Meals provided at hostel (with notice)

Breakfast only at hostel (with notice)

Meals available locally

Clothes washing facilities available

Public telephone

Facilities for less-able people.

Internet facilities

Within 1 mile of a Sustrans cycle route

Within 3 miles of a Sustrans cycle route

Within 5 miles of a Sustrans cycle route

Affiliated to Hostelling International

Accommodation only for groups

pp	per person
GR	Ordnance Survey grid reference
€	Euros
£	Pounds Sterling
CHF	Swiss Francs
US$	United States Dollars
C$	Canadian Dollars
LT	Lithuanian Lita
ZT	Polish Złoty

TELEPHONE CODES

Phone numbers are presented as required for calling from anywhere within the UK. International dialling codes are included for addresses outside the UK. To phone UK accommodation from overseas remove the first 0 and prefix with 44.

INDEPENDENT HOSTELS

Independent Hostels provide friendly, comfortable accommodation at prices that are hard to beat. They benefit from shared common areas: these are perfect places to meet new friends or for your group to socialise if you have booked sole use. Most hostels have cooking and dining facilities, many offer private rooms and family apartments as an alternative to dormitories. All the accomodation in this guide is independently-owned and includes some hostels sold by the YHA which are starting out a new life as independently-run hostels.

Independent hostels have no membership requirements.

The first Independent Hostel Guide (IHG) was produced in 1992 as a booklet containing 15 hostels. It has grown with each annual update and now features 326 great places to stay. In 2003 the IHG expanded onto the web as **www.IndependentHostelGuide.co.uk** and up-to-date details of all the hostels in the guide can always be found on this website. In 2007 the IHG, now widely regarded as the ultimate independent hostel reference for the UK, become the handbook of the non profit-making network Independent Hostels UK (IHUK).

The aims of IHUK are to promote independent hostels and to support hostel owners. It is part-funded by the UK government under the DEFRA Rural Development Scheme, and has its own website:- **www.IndependentHostelsUK.co.uk**

FEEDBACK

Enter your experiences into IHUK's Quality Assurance system by completing the form below and sending to IHUK, Speedwell House, Upperwood, Matlock Bath Derbyshire, DE4 3PE.

Accom Name			
Date / Year of Visit			
You stayed as:-	Group Individual	Group Individual	Group Individual
Overall Rating Please consider:- value for money, location, facilities, comfort, cleanliness, friendliness and everything else.	Brilliant Very Good OK Poor Very Poor	Brilliant Very Good OK Poor Very Poor	**Brilliant Very Good OK Poor Very Poor**

Did you know that
everything in this book
is also on this website ?

WWW.INDEPENDENTHOSTELGUIDE.CO.UK

UPDATED DAILY

Links to hostel managers email
Links to hostels own websites
Online booking - coming soon !

Independent Hostel Guide
BY MAIL ORDER

The Backpackers Press, Speedwell House, Upperwood,
Matlock Bath, Derbyshire, DE4 3PE, UK
Tel/Fax +44 (0) 1629 580427

Cheques payable to the Backpackers Press

Book	Price	No	Total
2008 IHG	£4.95		
2009 IHG (available Jan 09)	£4.95		
UK P&P	£1 + 50p each extra book.		
Overseas P&P	£2 + £1 each extra book.		
TOTAL			

OR BUY ONLINE
www.IndependentHostelGuide.com

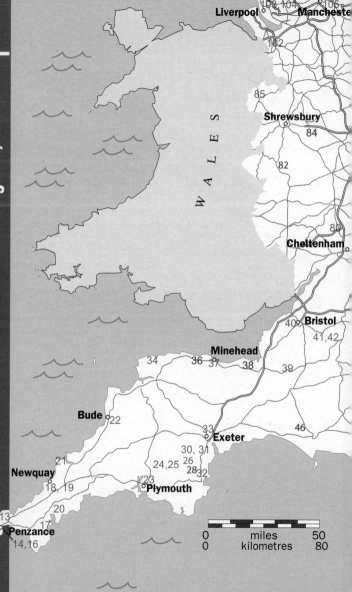

South England/Midlands

KEY

45 - **Hostel page number**

45 - **Page number of group only accomodation**

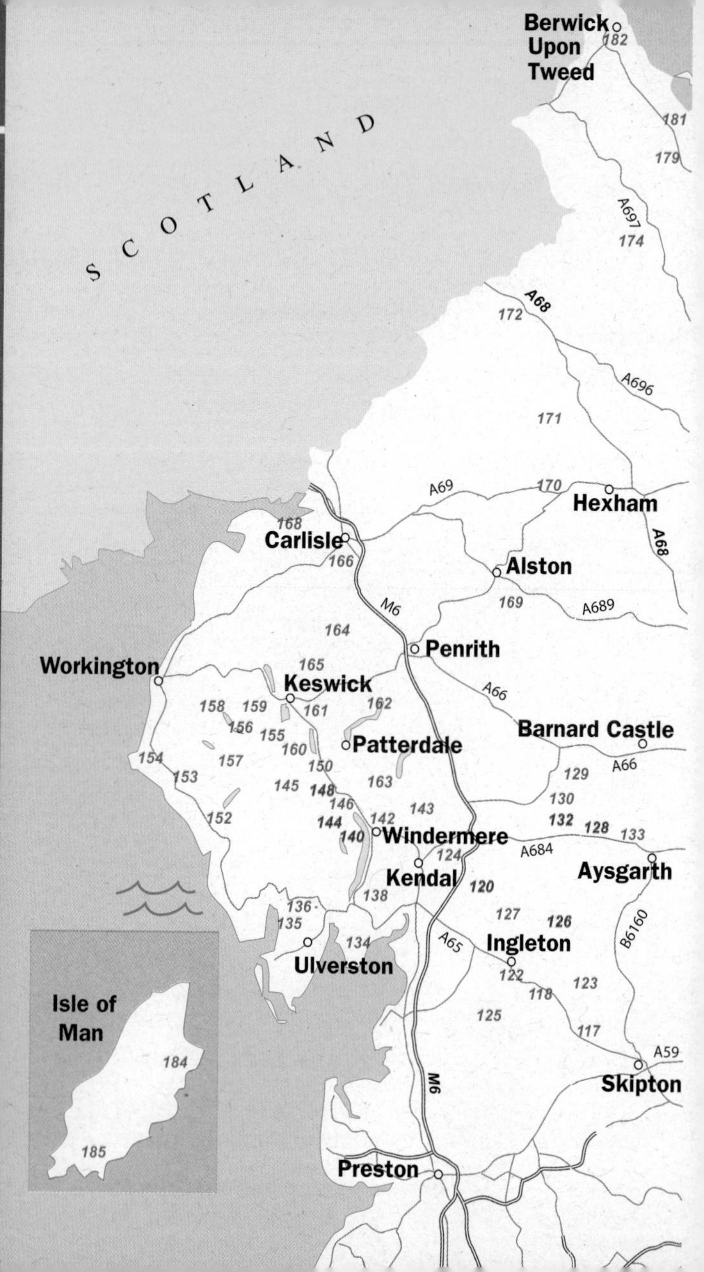

Berwick
Upon
Tweed
182

181

179

S C O T L A N D

A697

174

A68
172

A696

171

A69 *170*   Hexham

168
Carlisle
166

Alston

M6   *169*   A689

A68

164   Penrith

Workington

Keswick   *165*

158 *159*   *161*   *162*

156   *155*   Barnard Castle

154   *160*   Patterdale   A66

153 *157*   *150*   *163*   *129*

145 *148*   *146*   *130*

152   *144* *142*   *143*   *132* *128* *133*

140   Windermere   A684

124   Aysgarth

Kendal   *120*

136   *138*   *127* *126*   B6160

135   Ingleton

134   A65   *122* *123*

Ulverston   *118*

125   *117*

A59

Isle of
Man

184   M6   Skipton

185

Preston

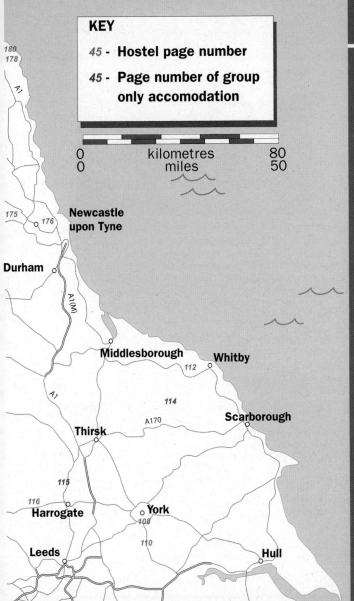

KEY

45 - Hostel page number

45 - Page number of group
only accomodation

0   kilometres   80
0   miles   50

180
178

A1

175   176   Newcastle
upon Tyne

Durham

A1(M)

A1

Middlesborough   Whitby
                112
            114
        A170
Thirsk   Scarborough

115
116
Harrogate   York
                108

            110

Leeds   Hull

KELYNACK
BUNKBARN

Kelynack Bunkbarn nestles in the secluded Cot Valley, one mile from the Atlantic Coast in the heart of the Land's End Peninsula Area of Outstanding Natural Beauty. The Barn has one twin room, two two-bedded and one four-bedded bunkroom. Blankets and pillows are provided. There is a toilet/shower room and communal kitchen with full cooking facilities. Adjacent is the bike store and a laundry/drying room shared with the campers on site. We also have a small shop for essentials.

St Just, a mile away, has plenty of food shops and a selection of pubs and take-aways. Kelynack is ideal for coast and moorland walking, spending time on the beaches, birdwatching, rock climbing and exploring the ancient villages, standing stones and tin mining heritage of unspoilt West Penwith.

DETAILS

- **Open** - All year, arrive after 2pm, vacate by 10am. 24 hr access.
- **Number of beds** - 10: 1 x 4 : 3 x 2.
- **Booking** - Booking is advised (25% deposit)
- **Price per night** - £10 per bed (£12 High season). Exclusive use £90 per night. No meters.
- **Public Transport** - There is a frequent bus from Penzance Rail Station to St Just. Hostel is one mile south of St Just. Free transport from St Just by prior arrangement.
- **Directions** - GR 373 301. The hostel is 200 yards east of the B3306, 1 mile south of St Just, 5 miles north of Land's End and 20 mins walk from coastal path

CONTACT: Francis or Wendy Grose
Kelynack Camping Park, Kelynack, St Just, Penzance, Cornwall, TR19 7RE
Tel: (01736) 787633
francis&wendy@kelynackholidays.co.uk

Zennor is a small picturesque village situated between St Ives and Land's End and is a haven for walkers, bird watchers and anyone who wants a taste of the rural way of life or just simply to relax! The hostel is located very close to the pub and St Ives is nearby for shopping, clubbing, cinemas, restaurants and some of the finest beaches in Cornwall.

The Old Chapel Backpackers has been converted to a very high standard and is perfectly situated for clear views over the sea and moorland. We have four rooms that sleep six people, one room that sleeps four and a family room with double bed. There are washbasins in every room and the hostel is centrally heated throughout. We can offer self-catering and we can provide breakfast, packed lunches and evening meals if required. There is also a café on the premises serving delicious soup, rolls and cakes

DETAILS

- **Open** - All year, winter by prior arrangement, all day
- **Number of beds** - 32: 4 x 6 : 1 x 4 : 1 x family room
- **Booking** - Booking is advisable, 20% deposit
- **Price per night** - From £15 per person all year
- **Public Transport** - There are train stations at St Ives (4 miles) and Penzance (10 miles). Local buses run to/from St Ives every few hours. The taxi fare from St Ives is approximately £5.
- **Directions** - Approximately 4 miles from St Ives on Coastal Road heading towards Land's End.

CONTACT: Paul or Hetty
Zennor, St Ives, Cornwall, TR26 3BY
Tel: (01736) 798307
zennorbackpackers@btinternet.com www.backpackers.co.uk/zennor

PENZANCE
BACKPACKERS

Penzance, with its mild climate, its wonderful location looking across to spectacular St Michael's Mount, with all the coach and rail services terminating here, is the ideal base for exploring the far SW of England and the Scilly Isles. Whether you are looking for sandy beaches and sheltered coves; the storm lashed cliffs of Land's End; sub-tropical gardens; internationally acclaimed artists; the remains of ancient cultures; or simply somewhere to relax and take time out, Penzance Backpackers is for you. We are situated in a lovely tree-lined road close to the sea front, with the town centre, bus station and railway station only a short walk away. Accommodation is mostly in small bunk-bedded rooms with bed-linen. Fully equipped self-catering kitchen, hot showers, comfortable lounge, lots of local information and a warm welcome all included.

DETAILS

- **Open** - All year, 24 hours
- **Number of beds** - 30: 2 double, 1x 4 (double+2bunks), 3x6, 1x7.
- **Booking** - It's best to phone.
- **Price per night** - From £14 per person. Discount for long stays.
- **Public Transport** - Penzance has a train station and National Express service. 15 mins walk from train/bus station or catch buses 1, 1a, 5a or 6a from Tourist Information/bus/train station. Ask for top of Alexandra Road.
- **Directions** - From Tourist Information/bus/train station either follow Quay and Promenade to mini-roundabout, turn right up Alexandra Rd, we are a short way up on the left; or follow main road through town centre until second mini-roundabout, turn left down Alexandra Rd; we are on right.

CONTACT:
The Blue Dolphin, Alexandra Road, Penzance, TR18 4LZ
Tel: (01736) 363836
info@pzbackpack.com www.pzbackpack.com

Y M C A CORNWALL
(PENZANCE)

West Cornwall is famous for it's rugged coastlines, secret coves and long sandy beaches. It offers the chance to relax and unwind, to surf, rock climb, walk, deep sea dive, fish, horse ride and to visit galleries, small harbours and villages. There are many attractions such as the famous Minack open air theatre.

The YMCA is more than just a hostel, we offer sporting facilities as well as an internet café. Our facilities provide the ideal location for school/youth groups of any size, for short weekends or for longer holidays. Sports and conference facilities also available. The YMCA has been serving the community of Penwith since 1893, providing an ideal base for you to discover all the area has to offer.

DETAILS

■ **Open** - All year, 8am to 10pm (except by prior arrangement)
■ **Number of beds** - 52: 6x5, 5x4, 1x2
■ **Booking** - booking not essential but advisable in Summer
■ **Price per night** - Accommodation prices from 1 Jan 08 to 23 March from £15.40pp. From 24 March to 31 December prices from £16.40 pp. Discount for parties of 15+. 10% discount for students in dormitories.
■ **Public Transport** - Penzance Train Station 15 min walk. Penzance Bus Station bus service numbers 6A and 6B. Taxi from Penzance centre approx £3.
■ **Directions** - From the train / bus stations, turn left towards the centre of town onto Market Jew Street. Turn left and follow Market Jew Street until it becomes Alverton Road. Go straight over the roundabout until you see our sign on the left (approx 200M).

CONTACT: Frank Aldous
International House, The Orchard, Alverton, Penzance, TR18 4TE
Tel: (01736) 334820
admin@cornwall.ymca.org.uk www.cornwall.ymca.org.uk

FALMOUTH LODGE
BACKPACKERS
ENGLAND

Falmouth's beautiful natural harbour provides a picturesque background to the main street of charming shops, restaurants, cafés and pubs; good opportunity to sample Cornish cream teas, pasties, local seafood and real ales. Falmouth is renowned for it's sandy beaches, Pendennis Castle, exotic gardens, the Falmouth Arts Centre and the Princess Pavilion. Go sightseeing on passenger ferries to St Mawes, Truro, Flushing and the Helford Passage. On a rainy day visit Ships and Castle leisure pool and the new National Maritime Museum. Take advantage of watersports, fishing trips, sailing, diving, with tuition and equipment hire. Falmouth Lodge Backpackers is conveniently situated next to Princess Pavilion, 200 metres from main beach, coastal footpath and minutes to town, harbour and castle. Relax in a friendly, clean, homely, smoke free atmosphere. Owner managed, by experienced world traveller. Guests have use of a well-equipped kitchen, dining room and TV lounge; games, bikes, frisbee, boogie board and stunt kite.

DETAILS

- **Open** - Closed December. 9am to 12pm and 5pm to 10pm.
- **Number of beds** - 18: 1 x 2 : 1 x 3 : 2 x 4 : 1 x 5 (some seaviews)
- **Booking** - Telephone or email in advance
- **Price per night** - From £17 per person
- **Public Transport** - Train - change Truro for Falmouth Town Station 250 mtrs. National Express to Falmouth. Air - London Stansted/Gatwick to Newquay
- **Directions** - From M5, A30 over Bodmin Moor to Truro, A39 to Falmouth, stay on A39 until Gyllyngvase Road on right, left into Gyllyngvase Terrace.

CONTACT: Charlotte
9 Gyllyngvase Terrace, Falmouth, Cornwall TR11 4DL
Tel: (01326) 319996, mobile 07940 390072
charlotte@mitchell999.fsworld.co.uk www.falmouthbackpackers.co.uk

ORIGINAL
BACKPACKERS

Overlooking one of Newquay's finest beaches, we offer low cost accommodation in the heart of town for international travellers and surfers. We offer mainly dorm style accommodation, however two twin rooms are available.

We have hot showers and board/bike storage can be arranged. There is no curfew, just come and go as you please. Being centrally based, The Original Backpackers is ideally located for the beaches, the town's many pubs and clubs.

A relaxed atmosphere is guaranteed.

DETAILS

■ **Open** - All year, 24 hour, check in 11am-9pm or by prior arrangement
■ **Number of beds** - 32:   3 x 6 : 2 x 5 : 2 x 2
■ **Booking** - Booking is recommended for both groups and individual travellers, although individual spaces may be available on arrival.
■ **Price per night** - Off peak from £10.00 pp, peak times from £20.00 pp. Long stay and group discounts available off peak.
■ **Public Transport** - Newquay has a train station and is served by National Express and an airport
■ **Directions** - If driving, head towards Fistral Beach, turn right at Tower Garages. Follow this road following outbound traffic, take the second left, signposted Beachfield Ave & The Crescent. Pass in front of The Central, turn right, Beachfield Ave is at the bottom of this road, the hostel is on the right.

CONTACT: Manager
Towan Beach, Beachfield Ave, Newquay, Cornwall, TR7 1DR
Tel: (01637) 874668
originalbp@hotmail.com www.originalbackpackers.co.uk

Newquay is about having fun - and the fun starts here! The Lodge has been open for twelve years and still offers the same easygoing relaxed atmosphere. Newquay is an all year round mecca for surfers, students and travellers, with dramatic cliffs, idyllic beaches and attractions galore. The backpackers is situated at the highest point of the town, only five minutes walk from Central Square with its nightlife and shops. Fistral Beach and the Town beaches are all within ten minutes walk.

All the rooms are clean and comfortable, many with seaview or en-suite facilities. Rates include breakfast, tea/coffee all day and unlimited hot showers. There is a fully equipped kitchen, no curfews, a licensed bar which has good music and 100s of DVDs, plus a games room with library, games and pool table.

DETAILS

■ **Open** - All year, 24 hours
■ **Number of beds** - 49: 4 x 6 : 3 x 4 : 1 x 3 : 5 x twin/double
■ **Booking** - Recommended for weekends and peak season, but not essential. First night's fee required as deposit.
■ **Price per night** - From £8 (or £10 for en-suite seaview), £15/£20 July, August and bank holidays. £45 pw available from September to June.
■ **Public Transport** - Local train and bus station. Free pickup when available.
■ **Directions** - From coach station walk up St George's Rd, turn right at top. From Train Station turn left and left again opposite Victoria Hotel onto Berry Rd which leads onto Mount Wise

CONTACT: Matt
110 Mount Wise, Newquay, Cornwall, TR7 1QP
Tel: (01637) 874651
matt@surflodge.co.uk www.surflodge.co.uk

TRURO
BACKPACKERS LODGE

Truro Backpackers Lodge provides welcoming, family-run accommodation in the heart of Cornwall. Here you will find a comfortable environment and ideal base for your visit to this wonderful county. The house is a rambling 1840's building with many original features and great period charm. There is a large fully equipped kitchen, with an Aga, for residents' use.
Tea and coffee making facilities are available all day and there is a large comfy lounge with Sky TV to relax in.

The city of Truro provides many attractions and facilities, plus rail and bus links to many other parts of Cornwall. Truro is the capital city of Cornwall and has excellent transport links with the rest of the county, making it a good base for touring. The bus station is just a 5 minute walk away. In addition to the historic Cathedral and popular Theatre the City boasts many bars and restaurants. Because the hostel is small advanced booking is essential.

DETAILS

- **Open** - All year, all day
- **Number of beds** - 15: 1x5, 1x4, 1x3, 1x2, 1x1)
- **Booking** - Book in advance by phone.
- **Price per night** - Dorm £15pp, Double Room £35, Single Room from £20pp
- **Public Transport** - Truro has a train station. Bus station is 5 mins walk. Bus links to many parts of Cornwall.
- **Directions** - See map on website.

CONTACT: Robert Nolan
10 The Parade, Truro, Cornwall, TR1 1QE
Tel: (01872) 260857 or 07813755210
trurobackpackers@aol.com www.trurobackpackers.co.uk

Chyvarloe Basecamp is part of the National Trust owned Penrose Estate, and located close to the legendary Loe Pool (Cornwall's largest freshwater lake), reputed to hold King Arthur's sword. Converted from redundant farm buildings, the basecamp is limited to use by conservation and education groups and is surrounded by the dramatic and varied natural beauty of the Lizard Peninsula.

There are two main dormitories equipped with bunks, mattresses and blankets (sleeping bags required) The modern kitchen is equipped for groups. The washrooms and showers take advantage of heat from three solar panels on site, and there is an adapted toilet and shower for wheelchair users. The basecamp is heated by a combination of a log burning stove and storage heaters. Separate leader's accommodation is also available.

DETAILS

- **Open** - All year, all day
- **Number of beds** - 18:
- **Booking** - Please phone or email to confirm availability.
- **Price per night** - £120 per group. Conservation groups undertaking work receive substantial discount.
- **Public Transport** - Railway station at Penzance (12 miles) and Redruth (10 miles). Bus station at Helston (4 miles).
- **Directions** - SW653235 (OS map no. 203). Situated within Chyvarloe Hamlet, south of Loe Bar. Enquire for directions

CONTACT: Jacqui Laity, Property Administrator
Chyvarloe Basecamp, Chyvarloe, Gunwalloe, Helston, Cornwall
Tel: (01326) 561407, Fax: 01326 562882
jacqui.laity@nationaltrust.org.uk www.nationaltrust.org.uk

NORTHSHOREBUDE
ENGLAND

You can make your stay whatever you want it to be. A relaxed place with a variety of bedrooms, large garden, close to town, beaches and South West Coastal path. An ideal base to see the South West's attractions: The Eden Project, Tintagel Castle, The Tamar Lakes, Dartmoor, Bodmin Moor and the South West Coastal Path. There are competition standard surfing beaches nearby. Families with children aged over 5 welcome.

Meet old friends or make new ones, on the deck, in the lounge or around the dining room table after cooking up a storm in the fully fitted kitchen.

DETAILS

■ **Open** - All year except Christmas week, 8.30am to 1pm and 4.30pm to 10.30pm
■ **Number of beds** - 43: 2x6 : 5x4 : 1x3 : 1x2 : 3xDbl
■ **Booking** - Advisable, credit card secures booking. Photo ID at check in.(Groups 6 or more by prior booking)
■ **Price per night** - From £12pp dorm rooms (single night supplement)
■ **Public Transport** - To Bude: From Exeter Via Okehampton X9. From Plymouth X8. From Newquay X10 (changing at Okehampton). From Bideford 85.
All buses- First Bus Company. There are train and bus links from London to Exeter.
■ **Directions** - From A39, head into Bude down Stratton Rd past Morrisons on your right, follow the road down past Esso garage. Take the second road on the right, Killerton Road (before the Bencollen Pub). Continue up to the top of the road and Northshorebude is on the corner on your left. Turn into Redwood Grove and parking is the first on the left.

CONTACT: Sean or Janine
57 Killerton Road, Bude, Cornwall, EX23 8EW
Tel: (01288) 354256 or 07970 149486
northshorebude@btconnect.com www.northshorebude.com

PLYMOUTH
GLOBE BACKPACKERS ENGLAND

Globe Backpackers Plymouth is located just five minutes walk from the ferry port, where boats leave for Roscoff and Santander. The hostel is close to all amenities and a short stroll to the famous Barbican waterfront, Mayflower Steps and city centre. Also near to the bus and railway stations. Excursions to Dartmoor, canoeing on the Tamar River, local boat trips, sailing and walking the coastal paths can be arranged from Plymouth. The theatre, sports/leisure centre, ice-skating rink and National Aquarium are a short walk from the hostel. Globe Backpackers Plymouth has 4, 6 and 8 bedded dorms, plus 4 double rooms. Bedding and linen included in the price. Fully equipped self-catering kitchen, TV lounge, separate social room and courtyard garden. NO ID. NO STAY (Brits and Overseas all need to produce valid ID to be able to stay.)

DETAILS

■ **Open** - All year, reception 8am-11pm, less in Winter. No curfew.
■ **Number of beds** - 48
■ **Booking** - Phone ahead to secure booking
■ **Price per night** - From £13pp. Weekly deals available. 50p surcharge for card payments.
■ **Public Transport** - National Express, local buses and various rail networks.
■ **Directions** - From train station walk up Salt Ash Road to North Croft roundabout. Turn right along Western Approach to Pavilions on your left. From bus station walk up Exeter Street, across roundabout to Royal Parade. Cross road to Union Street, Pavilions on your left. From Plymouth Pavilions walk towards the Hoe, turn left up Citadel Road, the hostel is in 100 metres on the right hand side.

CONTACT:
172 Citadel Road, The Hoe, Plymouth, PL1 3BD
Tel: (01752) 225158, Fax: (01752) 207847
info@plymouthbackpackers.co.uk www.plymouthbackpackers.co.uk

The Plume of Feathers Inn is situated in the moorland village of Princetown which is the main village in Dartmoor National Park. The park covers 368 square miles and is famous for it's rugged beauty, quaint villages, prehistoric remains, and its many peaks, such as High Willhays (2039ft) and Yes Tor (2030ft). The Plume is a traditional, family-run Inn dating from 1785, it has log fires, real ale and plenty of atmosphere. The Alpine bunkhouse and New bunkhouse provide comfortable low cost accommodation. The Inn also has B&B en-suite accommodation and a 75 tent camping area with toilets and showers. There is a wide range of activities available in the Dartmoor area including: sailing, fishing, riding, abseiling, white water canoeing, climbing, pony trekking and walking. PLEASE CONTACT THIS HOSTEL BY PHONE OR POST.

DETAILS

- **Open** - All year, all day
- **Number of beds** - 42: 2 x 10 5 x 4 1 x 2 1x4
- **Booking** - To secure beds, book in advance with 50% deposit. For weekends 3 to 4 months in advance is advised.
- **Price per night** - From £12pp (Bunkhouse), £6.50pp (Camping), B&B from £45pp.
- **Public Transport** - Nearest train and National Express services are in Plymouth (17 miles) and Exeter (26 miles). The Transmoor Link bus service between Plymouth and Exeter stops at Princetown, bus fare is £5 - £6. Taxi fare from Plymouth approx £18, from Exeter approx £25.
- **Directions** - The Plume of Feathers Inn is in Princetown village square, next to the Dartmoor National Park, High Moorland Centre.

CONTACT:
Princetown, Yelverton, Devon, PL20 6QQ
Tel: (01822) 890240, Fax: (01882) 890780
sam@backpackerspress.com

FOX TOR
CAFÉ AND BUNKHOUSE ENGLAND

Princetown on Dartmoor is an ideal base for anyone wishing to spend time on Dartmoor whether it is to walk, climb, cycle, kayak or just relax and enjoy the spectacular scenery. Fox Tor Café and Bunkhouse is situated near the centre of the village of Princetown - famous for the prison !

The bunkhouse offers self-catering accommodation for up to 12 in 3 rooms of 4. It is newly decorated, has central heating and a kitchen equipped with microwave, fridge, kettle, toaster and sink. There are separate male and female showers and toilets with underfloor heating. Bunkhouse guests also have the option to use the drying room/store room (big enough for bicycles).

Bunkhouse users can book packed lunches and breakfasts for an early start. No smoking inside.

DETAILS

- **Open** - All year, all day. Arrive from 4pm, leave by 10.30am.
- **Number of beds** - 12: 3x4
- **Booking** - Advisable with 50% deposit.
- **Price per night** - From £9.50 per person. Sole use £100.
- **Public Transport** - Trains at Exeter and Plymouth. DevonBus 98 Tavistock-Princetown. Devon Bus 82 Exeter-Plymouth. First 272 Gunnislake-Newton Abbot.
- **Directions** - GR 591 735. Just off the mini roundabout in the centre of Princetown on the Two Bridges road (B3212). 20 mins drive from Tavistock, 15 mins Yelverton, 35 mins Ashburton.

CONTACT: Sam Rockey
Two Bridges Road, Princetown, Yelverton, Devon, PL20 6QS
Tel: (01822) 890238
foxtorcafe@aol.com www.foxtorcafe.co.uk

DARTMOOR
EXPEDITION CENTRE

Great for walking, climbing, canoeing, caving, archaeology, painting or visiting places of interest nearby. Dartmoor Expedition Centre has two 300-year-old barn bunkhouses with cobbled floors and thick granite walls. Simple but comfortable accommodation with bunk beds and a wood burning stove. Radiant heaters (two in each area) and night storage heating (one in each barn). Kitchen area equipped with fridge, water heater, electric stoves and kettles. All crockery and pans provided, and there is freezer space available. Electric appliances are coin operated (£1 coins). Solar hot water system for free showers in wash rooms. House Barn has the living area downstairs and upstairs sleeps 9 plus 5 in an inner cubicle. Gate Barn (groups of 4+ only) sleeps 11 downstairs and 10 upstairs. There are two upgraded rooms (1 double, 1 twin). Beds provided with sheet/pillow/pillowcase, sleeping bags needed.

DETAILS

- **Open** - All year, 7.30 am to 10.30 pm
- **Number of beds** - 37: 1 x 1 : 1 x 2 : 1 x 8 : 1 x 5 : 1 x 11 : 1 x 10
- **Booking** - Book in advance with 25% deposit.
- **Price per night** - £12.00pp (£14.00 per person in upgraded room).
- **Public Transport** - Newton Abbot is the nearest train station. In summer there are buses to Widecombe (1.5 miles from hostel). Taxi fare from station £20.
- **Directions** - GR 700 764. Come down Widecombe Hill into the village. Turn right 200yds after school and travel up a steep hill past Southcombe onto the open moor. Continue for one mile until you reach crossroads. Turn right and take first left after 400yds. Hostel is 200yds on left.

CONTACT: John Earle
Widecombe-in-the-Moor, Newton Abbot, Devon, TQ13 7TX
Tel: (01364) 621249
earle@clara.co.uk www.dartmoorbase.co.uk

South Dartmoor Bunkhouse is situated in the centre of Buckfastleigh, on the southern flanks of the Dartmoor National Park. This magnificent area of 360 sq. miles offers a range of outdoor pursuits including walking, climbing, caving, canoeing, mountain biking and horse riding. Within short walking distance of the bunkhouse are five pubs, shops, cash point, fish & chip shop / restaurant, pizza, kebabs, Chinese and tea shop. The non-smoking bunkhouse has a common room with open plan newly refurbished fully equipped kitchen. A separate area contains the shower, toilet, and washbasin. There is a store / changing area and a drying room. Upstairs has wooden bunks for 16 people in a refurbished area. Electricity is by a £1 slot meter.

DETAILS

■ **Open** - All year, keys available by prior arrangement
■ **Number of beds** - 16 : 1 x 12, 1 x 4
■ **Booking** - Bookings with £20 per night non-refundable deposit (payable to Devon Speleo Society) is essential.
■ **Price per night** - £6.00 per person, £72.00 sole use.
■ **Public Transport** - Trains: Newton Abbot or Totnes. Local Buses and Taxis.
■ **Directions** - GR 735 660. Enter Buckfastleigh at the A38/A384 junc. at mini roundabout, turn left, past garage on right. Pass 2 turns to Buckfastleigh, (first is NO ENTRY). Continue for 500m taking next right into town, signposted 'Town Centre'. Continue past car park on right. At junction immediately ahead turn left (signed Town Hall), straight on is NO ENTRY. Pass the Town Hall on left & school on right, after 300m turn right at "T" junc. into Crest Hill. Bunkhouse is approx 85m on the left.

CONTACT: Jon (8am - 8pm)
11 Crest Hill, Buckfastleigh, Devon, TQ11 0AN
Tel: (01626) 859005 or 07748 762580
js.whiteley@btinternet.com   www.southdartmoorbunkhouse.co.uk

SPARROWHAWK
BACKPACKERS

This small, friendly 'green' vegetarian hostel is located within Dartmoor National Park, in the village of Moretonhampstead, 14 miles west of Exeter. Formerly a farm, visitors are accommodated in a beautifully converted stable. High open moorland is close by for great walking, climbing and cycling country. Magnificent Tors, stone circles and burial sites of ancient civilizations together with wild ponies, buzzards, flora and fauna are all here to be explored. There are year round guided talks and walks organised locally and by the National Park. Moretonhampstead village has shops, cafés, pubs, good food, live music, an outdoor heated swimming pool, and footpaths leading to the open moors. Easily accessible by public transport, on the Dartmoor Way route, and CTC End to End. There is a secure place for your bikes. This hostel aims to be environmentally alert and has a dedicated policy of being vegetarian and recycling waste.

DETAILS

- **Open** - All year, all day
- **Number of beds** - 18: 1 x 14 plus double/ family (up to 4) private room
- **Booking** - Book ahead if possible
- **Price per night** - Adults £14. Under 14 £6. Private room £32/£42 for 4.
- **Public Transport** - Direct from Exeter Bus 359 or 82. Direct from Plymouth Bus 82. From Okehampton or Newton Abbot Bus 173 or 179. Enquires Tel 0870 6082608.
- **Directions** - From Exeter, take the B3212 signposted on the one-way system at Exe Bridges. From Plymouth head towards Yelverton and then B3212. The hostel is on Ford Street (A382) 100 metres from tourist office.

CONTACT: Alison
45 Ford Street, Moretonhampstead, Dartmoor, Devon, TQ13 8LN
Tel: (01647) 440318 - 07870 513570
ali@sparrwohawkbackpackers.co.uk www.sparrowhawkbackpackers.co.uk

Steps Bridge Hostel is a detached wooden chalet in secluded woodland overlooking the Teign Valley on the eastern edge of Dartmoor. It is an ideal base for exploring rugged high Dartmoor and the delightful lower slopes rich in wild flowers, butterflies and birds. The surrounding native woodland and nature reserve are home to badgers, deer and otters. There are walks straight from the door (come and see the daffodils in spring) and fishing, golf and cycling nearby. Local attractions include Castle Drogo, The Miniature Pony Centre, Canonteign Falls and picturesque thatched villages. The cathedral city of Exeter is 8miles away and the beaches of South Devon are 40 minutes drive. Steps Bridge Hostel provides flexible accommodation in cosy rooms sleeping between 2 and 8 people in bunks. The hostel is ideal for use by families and groups who can book exclusive use of the whole hostel, part of the hostel or a private room. There are 2 fully equipped self catering kitchens, lounge/dining room with wood burning stove, drying room and picnic areas. Duvets provided.

DETAILS

- **Open** - All year, all day by arrangement
- **Number of beds** - 24: 1x2, 2x4,1x6,1x8
- **Booking** - Booking is essential. Deposit required.
- **Price per night** - Sole use from £150 per night (discounts for longer stays). Rooms from £25 per night. Longer stays welcomed.
- **Public Transport** - Trains Exeter. Bus 359 from Exeter + 82 on summer wk ends
- **Directions** - On the B3212 between Exeter and Moretonhampstead, 1 mile outside of Dunsford. Approx 150m up road from Steps Bridge, opposite car park.

CONTACT: John Wain
Steps Bridge Hostel, Blytheswood, Dunsford, Exeter, Devon EX6 7EQ
Tel: (01647) 252435
info@stepsbridgedartmoor.co.uk www.stepsbridgedartmoor.co.uk

TORQUAY
BACKPACKERS

Torquay is on the English Riviera, famous for warm weather and Mediterranean atmosphere. Turquoise sea, red cliffs, long sandy beaches and secret shingle coves combine to create one of the UK's most beautiful coastlines. It is renowned as a watersport mecca with sailing, water-skiing, windsurfing, diving etc and nightlife with pubs, clubs and restaurants a mere stagger from the hostel which is in the heart of Torquay.

Hostel activities include beach barbecues, jam nights, international food nights and video evenings. There are also trips to Dartmoor exploring emerald river valleys where pixies dwell and the open tor-dotted moors. The hostel offers travellers a friendly, almost family atmosphere. Those who find it hard to leave can easily find work.

DETAILS

- **Open** - All year, 24 hrs. Check in 9-11am and 5-9pm.
- **Number of beds** - 46: 1 x double, 3 x 4, 1 x 5, 2 x 6 ,1 x 7, 1 x 8.
- **Booking** - Advised at all times.
- **Price per night** - £8 to £14 per night. £60 to £85 per week.
- **Public Transport** - Torquay can be reached by coach or train from all major towns. From London take a train from Paddington/Waterloo,or a coach from Victoria/ Heathrow.
- **Directions** - Drivers: follow signs to sea front. Turn left. At junction with lights and Belgrave Hotel, bear left up Sheddon Hill. Next T junction is Abbey Road. Turn left. Hostel is 200m on right.

CONTACT: The Manager
119 Abbey Road, Torquay, Devon, TQ2 5NP
Tel: (01803) 299924
jane@torquaybackpackers.co.uk www.torquaybackpackers.co.uk

EXETER
GLOBE BACKPACKERS ENGLAND

A city centre hostel within easy walking of everything: the beautiful old port, Cathedral, shopping district and wonderful mix of pubs, clubs, live music, restaurants and café scene. We therefore attract the young and "young at heart" and have the comings and goings reflecting a vibrant city centre. We will not suit those requiring a guaranteed quiet location, or young families.

We are 20 minutes drive to Exmouth with its 2 miles sandy beach; great for all sail sports, and the same to Dartmoor National Park; great for walking, rock climbing, cycling and horse riding. Exeter is also an excellent place to find work and just 2½ hours by train to London. All nationalities must produce identification – NO ID NO STAY! We do not permit the following to stay: DSS, hens and stags, unaccompanied under 18's and families with children under 16.

DETAILS

- **Open** - All year, 8am - 11pm only. No curfew once checked in.
- **Number of beds** - 57: 1 x 2/4 : 3 x 6 : 2 x 8 : 2 x 10
- **Booking** - To secure booking phone ahead.
- **Price per night** - From £14 pp. Weekly rates available. 50p surcharge for cards.
- **Public Transport** - National Express, local bus companies and rail networks.
- **Directions** - Bus Station: Cross road, take side turning Southernhay East. Stay on LH side until Southgate Hotel. We are diagonally opposite on other side of junction. From Central rail station go down Queen St to High St, turn right and at 1st set of lights, turn left South St, continue to junction at bottom of hill. Cross at lights, we are on right.

CONTACT:
71 Holloway Street, Exeter, EX2 4JD
Tel: (01392) 215521, Fax: (01392) 215531
info@exeterbackpackers.co.uk www.exeterbackpackers.co.uk

OCEAN
BACKPACKERS

Ocean Backpackers is a homely hostel with a laid back atmosphere and no curfew. Situated in a quaint North Devon town built around an ancient fishing harbour. Central to the harbour itself, the bus station, high street, pubs, restaurants and many beaches including surfers favourites: Croyde, Saunton and Woolacombe. If the surf is down, don't despair just try the other activities available; quad biking, paint balling, kayaking, adventure swimming, mountain biking, horse riding and microlighting. Adrenalin not your thing? then take a trip to Lundy Island, spot rare birds, seals, basking sharks and dolphins. Wonderful walking country, the coastal path between Woolacombe and Lynton is breathtaking and Exmoor has an abundance of walks through Britain's most spectacular scenery. The Hostel facilities include a communal lounge, self-catering kitchen, surf board storage and a car park. Ilfracombe has plenty of summer work so why not come and hang out here for a while?

DETAILS

- **Open** - All year, reception 9am-12 & 4.30-10pm. No curfew.
- **Number of beds** - 44:- 1x8, 5x6, 1 x double, 1 x double & bunk.
- **Booking** - Booking advised but not essential.
- **Price per night** - From £10- £12 in dorm. Double/Twin £32 per room.
- **Public Transport** - Direct coaches from London Victoria/Heathrow/Plymouth/ Exeter. By train take the Tarka line to Barnstaple then bus to Ilfracombe.
- **Directions** - From M5 take A361. From Cornwall take A39 to Barnstaple then follow the signs to Ilfracombe. Ocean Backpackers is by the harbour opposite the bus station. For more detailed directions go to our website and click on directions.

CONTACT: Chris and Abby
29 St James Place, Ilfracombe, Devon, EX34 9BJ
Tel: (01271) 867835
info@oceanbackpackers.co.uk www.oceanbackpackers.co.uk

EXMOOR
BASECAMP

Exmoor Basecamp is a converted barn giving comfortable, high standard bunkhouse accommodation. There are 2 large dormitories each sleeping 8 in bunkbeds and a 2 bedded leaders' room. There are excellent hot showers, drying room, lounge/eating area, fully equipped kitchen and a barbecue. The Basecamp is situated at Countisbury on the North Devon coast. The surrounding countryside includes the dramatic Watersmeet Valleys, moors of Exmoor and coastal paths. Lynton and Lynmouth are the nearest villages and the Atlantic surf beaches are within easy reach. The Basecamp is owned and managed by The National Trust and a free night's accommodation can be earned for each day's conservation work arranged with local wardens. Other local activities are walking, horse riding, boat trips, fishing and cycling. However you spend your time the basecamp is ideal for getting away from it all.

 GROUPS ONLY

DETAILS

- **Open** - All year, 24 hours
- **Number of beds** - 18: 2x8, 1x2
- **Booking** - Booking essential with £45 deposit
- **Price per night** - £110 winter, £150 summer. 10% discount for 4+ nights (except Easter, Christmas & New Year).
- **Public Transport** - The nearest train and coach stations are in Barnstaple (approx. 20 miles), from there take a local bus to Lynton. Buses to Countisbury are very limited and summer only. Taxis from Lynton approx £5.
- **Directions** - From Minehead follow A39 to Countisbury. We are on the left after the Sandpiper Inn. From Lynmouth we are first building on right. Car Park is opposite.

CONTACT: Karen
Countisbury, Lynton, Devon, EX35 6NE
Tel: (01598) 741101 / 07974 829171
Karen.elkin@nationaltrust.org.uk www.nationaltrust.org.uk/basecamps

BASE
LODGE

ENGLAND

Base Lodge is ideally situated for exploring Exmoor, The Quantocks and The North Devon Coast by mountain bike or foot. Excellent off and on road mountain biking for all levels. Guided mountain biking and secure lock up facilities.

Exmoor affords excellent scenic moor and coastal views and the 600+ mile-long South West Coastal Path starts here in Minehead. Other activities can be arranged including mountain biking, navigational training, climbing, surfing, pony-trekking and natural history walks and talks. Base Lodge is clean, comfortable and friendly, providing a shared fully equipped kitchen and dining room. Local pubs and restaurants are all within walking distance.

DETAILS

■ **Open** - All day access once booked, bookings taken by e-mail or phone or take a chance and call in, all day access, reception open from 3pm
■ **Number of beds** - 25: 2x7: 1x5: 1x3: 1x2 :1x1
■ **Booking** - Advisable. Deposit required for groups or exclusive use.
■ **Price per night** - Dorms £12.50, private twin or single £15pp, private double £16pp. Exclusive use of Base Lodge from £250.
■ **Public Transport** - Coach station 5 min walk. Buses from Taunton, Exeter and Tiverton. Train station: Taunton (26 miles). Steam railway from Taunton to Minehead.
■ **Directions** - With the sea behind you, drive/walk up The Parade until you reach Park Street, continue straight on until you reach a fork. Take the right hand into The Parks (Baptist Church on your right). Only limited parking is available.

CONTACT: Wendy or Graham
16 The Parks, Minehead, Somerset, TA24 8BS
Tel: (01643) 703520 or 07731651536
togooutdoors@hotmail.com www.togooutdoors.com

CAMPBELL ROOM
ACTIVITY CENTRE

The Campbell Room has a sheltered rural position at the mouth of an attractive wooded valley leading to heart of the Quantock Hills, an Area of Outstanding Natural Beauty. Many routes for walking, mountain biking or horse-riding with extensive views from moorland tops. Suitable for D of E, also ideal for natural history of heath, conifer and oak woodlands. Transport needed for easy access to rocky beaches (pools and fossils), West Somerset Railway (steam and diesel), Cannington Countryside Visitor Centre, Tropicana at Washford. Well placed for exploring Wells (Cathedral), Wookey Hole and Cheddar (caves), Taunton (county town), Cricket St Thomas (wildlife park), Dunster (historic village), Exmoor and Minehead. Indoor swimming ¼ mile away and Bridgwater fun pool. Accommodation consists of a main hall with 18 good mattresses, two rooms sleeping 3 each, washrooms and showers, a fully equipped kitchen, and drying room. A small grassed area has room for 1 or 2 tents and a campfire.

DETAILS

- **Open** - All year, by arrangement
- **Number of beds** - 24: 1 x 18 : 2 x 3
- **Booking** - Essential, one month with deposit.
- **Price per night** - £3.95pp   (2 leaders free for groups over 12)
- **Public Transport** - Train and bus stations Bridgwater, bus No 15/15A to Nether Stowey, (1 mile to Centre).
- **Directions** - GR ST 187 381. M5 junction 23 or 24 Bridgwater. A39 west to Nether Stowey, follow signs to Over Stowey. From church follow road 300m east, then 400m south (toward Forest Trail Ramscombe). Centre at T junction.(W of Aley).

CONTACT: Pat Briggs
36 Old Rd, North Petherton, Bridgwater, Somerset TA6 6TG
Tel: (01278) 662537
campbellroom@tiscali.co.uk http:/myweb.tiscali.co.uk/mcleans/campbellroom

Glastonbury Backpackers is the place for budget accommodation in Glastonbury. Shrouded in legend and myth, the burial place of Arthur and Guinevere. Now famous for it's religious, cultural and musical events including the Glastonbury Music Festival. The hostel is a 16th-century coaching inn which has been renovated to provide a unique and lively place to stay. Accommodation is in backpackers' dorms and twin and double rooms, most with en-suite.

There is free bed linen, self-catering kitchen, TV and video lounge, and adjacent parking There is a café bar and public bar with happy hours and live music on most Friday nights. The town centre boasts many shops and restaurants, all with the unique style and atmosphere that is Glastonbury.

DETAILS

- **Open** - All year, 24 hours
- **Number of beds** - 42
- **Booking** - Phone with credit card
- **Price per night** - From £14
- **Public Transport** - National Express and the cheaper Bakers Dolphin coaches do daily returns to London Victoria, dropping outside the hostel. Nearest train stations are Castle Cary and Bristol. From Bristol catch 376 bus from end of Station Drive to outside of hostel.
- **Directions** - At the bottom of Glastonbury High Street, adjacent to the market cross. The hostel is painted bright blue.

CONTACT: Reception
4 Market Place, Glastonbury, Somerset, BA6 9HD
Tel: (01458) 833353, Fax: (01458) 835988
info@GlastonburyBackpackers.co.uk www.GlastonburyBackpackers.co.uk

BRISTOL
ENGLAND BACKPACKERS HOSTEL

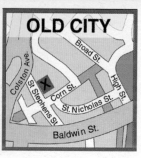

City Centre hostel
- clean & comfy beds - free linen & hot showers - big kitchen
- free tea, coffee & hot choc - indoor bicycle storage
- late night basement bar - piano & guitar room - dvd lounge
- cheap internet machines - free laptop wireless access
- luggage storage room - laundrette
- run by backpackers for backpackers -
mixed/single sex dorms - private rooms -
no curfew after check in

DETAILS

■ **Open** - All year, reception hours 0900 - 2330 (No curfew)
■ **Number of beds** - 90: Bunk bed accommodation in private twin, private triple or 6, 8 and 10 bed dorms.
■ **Booking** - Most cards, phone or walk in.
■ **Price per night** - £14pp. Private rooms from £35. See website for discounts.
■ **Public Transport** - See below.
■ **Directions** - Located in 'Old City' the historic centre of Bristol. From 'Bristol Central Bus Station 'Marlborough St' 7 mins walk. Follow pedestrian signs to 'Old City' then see map above. From 'Bristol Temple Meads Train Station' 12 mins walk. Follow pedestrian signs to 'Old City' then see map above. Or take bus number 8 or 9 (£1.30) to the 'Centre Promenade'. Disembark when you see all the fountains on your left. Hostel is on the 2m high map by the fountains. From Airport take the 'Shuttle' to the Central Bus Station. By road follow signs for Baldwin Street in the city centre.

CONTACT:
17 St Stephen's Street, Bristol, BS1 1EQ
Tel: (0117) 9257900
info@bristolbackpackers.co.uk www.bristolbackpackers.co.uk

Bath Backpackers is the closest hostel to Bath's railway and bus station. Centrally located to all amenities and shops and close to all historic sites. During the week, there are organised walking tours around the area, taking in the River Avon and town centre.

Bath Backpackers is in an historic Georgian building that is over 250 years old. It is the only independent hostel in Bath with a self-catering kitchen, social room, rooms with key code locks, shower rooms and sound system throughout the hostel. Bath Backpackers is a totally fun packed place to stay for international travellers. No curfews. Discounts given when booking ahead to Oxford Backpackers.

DETAILS

■ **Open** - All year, 24 hr access, service 8am to 12 midnight
■ **Number of beds** - 54
■ **Booking** - Booking is advised
■ **Price per night** - From £14 per person. Long term rates. Discount when you book ahead to Oxford Backpackers Hostel. Tel (01865) 721761.
■ **Public Transport** - Bus and Train Stations are in the heart of town, close to the Hostel.
■ **Directions** - From Bath railway station:- walk straight out of the entrance and follow Manvers Street, 200m past police station, Manvers Street runs into Pierrepont Street. Bath Backpackers hostel is on the left.

CONTACT: Manager
13 Pierrepont Street, Bath, BA1 1LA
Tel: (01225) 446787
bath@hostels.co.uk www.hostels.co.uk

BATH
YMCA

Bath YMCA offers a warm welcome and the best value accommodation. From its central location all the sights of this World Heritage City are easily reached on foot. Bath is also an ideal base for the explorer. Staying longer brings Stonehenge, Wookey Hole Caves, Cheddar Gorge, the southern reaches of the Cotswolds, and more exciting destinations all within reach. With a total of 202 beds, we have a great deal of experience in making all our guests feel comfortable. We have a fully air conditioned lounge area, colour TV and restaurant which offers a varied lunch menu at special YMCA subsidised prices. Laundry, lockers, pool and football table, telephone fax and internet facilities are available. The Health and Fitness suite provides a steam and sauna room and new equipment with a qualified staff team who have worked hard to create a club atmosphere. 'Fitness with Fun' is our motto. Couples, families, groups and backpackers' are all welcome, you don't have to be young or male. All these facilities and the YMCA's traditional sense of community will make your stay a truly memorable one.

DETAILS

- **Open** - All year, 24-hour reception
- **Number of beds** - 202: 1x20, 1x14, 1x12, 2x10, 7x3, 38x2, 26x1
- **Booking** - Credit card guarantees.
- **Price per night** - From £14pp dorm bed, inc. light breakfast.
- **Public Transport** - Bath has a train station and is served by National Express.
- **Directions** - Located approximately ½ mile from rail and bus station. Broad Street is located near the Podium Shopping Centre off Walcott Street.

CONTACT: Reception
International House, Broad Street Place, Bath, BA1 5LH
Tel: (01225) 325900, Fax: (01225) 462065
stay@bathymca.co.uk www.bathymca.co.uk

SWANAGE AUBERGE
BUNKHOUSE

ENGLAND

Swanage Auberge, the bunkhouse that cares, is a refuge for climbers, walkers and divers. Situated at the eastern end of the Jurassic Coast with excellent walking, diving and rock climbing on the doorstep. The bunkhouse is in the centre of Swanage town, a stones throw from the South West Coast Path and all local amenities - pubs, shops, restaurants etc. Swanage Auberge is totally self contained with central heating, fully equipped self catering kitchen, drying and laundry facilities and a meals service if required. There are two bunk rooms, one with 4 standard bunks and the other with 6 alpine style places (3 and 3). There is also accommodation for 3 (single bunks) in the adjoining house. Pillow and towel provided and bedding is available for hire. There are two showers, loos and washrooms and an area to hang and wash wetsuits. There is a rucksack and boot rack in the entrance corridor. Sandals are provided. Parking for 2 vehicles is usually available when booking (first come first served basis). Price includes cereal breakfast and beverages. English breakfast, packed lunches and evening meals available (see website for further details).

DETAILS

- **Open** - All year, opens 5.30pm (all day once booked in)
- **Number of beds** - 13: 1x6, 1x4 1 x 3
- **Booking** - Book by phone or email. Booking form online. 20% deposit required.
- **Price per night** - £16 pp including cereal breakfast and free tea or coffee. Group rates available. Hire of duvet with sheets £2.50 per week. Credit cards not accepted.
- **Public Transport** - Bus from Poole or Wareham. Train service to Wareham.
- **Directions** - At the end of the first left hand alley off Mount Pleasant Lane.

CONTACT: Pete or Pam
45 High Street, Swanage, Dorset, BH19 2LX
Tel: (01929) 424368, mobile 07711117668, Fax: (01929) 424368
bookings@swanageauberge.co.uk www.swanageauberge.co.uk

HOOKE COURT
RESIDENTIAL CENTRE

Hooke Court, a 15th Century manor house set in 14 acres of stunning grounds in rural West Dorset, provides an ideal base from which to explore Dorset's finest attractions and most notably the World Heritage Jurassic Coast, just 11 miles away. Fossil hunting in Charmouth, sailing in Weymouth , re-living the Roman invasion at Maiden Castle and exploring the quaint seaside town of West Bay are among the many exciting opportunities that are easily accessible. If guests choose to enjoy a leisurely day on site then the grounds contain a lake, woodlands, children's adventure play area, lawns and playing field. In addition, a range of exciting on-site activities including living history days, archaeology and team building exercises can be arranged. The accommodation at Hooke Court is organised into 4 separate self-contained units each containing a kitchenette, lounge area and a number of bunk-bedded dormitories and bathrooms. The Centre will provide fully catered breaks or alternatively guests can choose to self-cater. Dormitories range from 2 to 10 beds per room.

DETAILS

- **Open** - All year, all day
- **Number of beds** - Greenleaf 1x10, 4x8, 1x6, 3x2, 2x1; Honeypot 3x8, 1x6, 1x4, 4x2, 1x1; Gatehouse 1x10, 1x8, 1x6, 2x2; Court 1x8, 4x6, 3x4, 2x2, 1x1
- **Booking** - Book by phone or email
- **Price per night** - Please call/e-mail for a quote
- **Public Transport** - Dial-a-ride bus to Bridport and Maiden Newton; train service from Crewkerne and Maiden Newton/Dorchester
- **Directions** - On the outskirts of Hooke village. Directions supplied on request.

CONTACT: Reception
Hooke, Nr Beaminster, Dorset, DT8 3NX
Tel: (01308) 862260
info@hookecourt.co.uk www.hookecourt.co.uk

Britain's only island city, Portsmouth is a unique blend of seaside resort and naval heritage. Portsmouth and Southsea Backpackers is the city's only independent hostel for travellers. It offers a friendly cosmopolitan atmosphere within easy reach of the major tourist attractions including the ships (Victory, Mary Rose and Warrior), the D Day museum, and the new Gunwharf Quays. It is only 150m from the beach and in an area containing an excellent variety of pubs, restaurants and clubs. The accommodation is mostly in small dorms for 4 people, but there are also twins, doubles and family rooms, some with en-suite facilities. All hot showers are free. We have a large social area which has sky TV, an internet facility, pool, darts and a dining area. There is a large fully equipped kitchen, BBQ, seating in the garden area and secure cycle storage.

DETAILS

- **Open** - All year, service: 8am to 11pm
- **Number of beds** - 68: 1x8, 1x6, 10x4, 7x2
- **Booking** - Advisable, groups require deposit
- **Price per night** - From £13pp, £30-£34 per room (double/twin)
- **Public Transport** - From any bus or train station catch a bus to Southsea and get off at the Strand. Walk back the way the bus has come and Florence Road is 2nd left. If there are 2+ people get a taxi. Ferries from Portsmouth go to France, Spain, the Channel Islands, and the Isle of Wight.
- **Directions** - From the M27 take the M275 to Portsmouth and follow signs to the seafront. Drive along the seafront until blue glass building (The Pyramids) and turn left. Turn right at mini roundabout and Florence Road is then 1st on the left.

CONTACT: Sammi
4 Florence Road, Southsea, Portsmouth, Hants, P05 2NE
Tel: (023) 92832495, Fax: (023) 92832495
portsmouthbackpackers@hotmail.com www.portsmouthbackpackers.co.uk

WETHERDOWN
HOSTEL

On top of the South Downs is Wetherdown Hostel, an award-winning example of an eco-renovation & a comfortable place to stay, just a few steps from the South Downs National Trail. A clean, bright, friendly hostel, open to all. Ideal for family get-togethers, walkers, cyclists, business away-days and wedding parties.

The hostel has spacious communal areas, comfortable bedrooms with hand basins & all linen provided & separate bathrooms / toilets throughout. A 'help yourself' breakfast is included in the price, available from 8am. There is a small fully equipped self-catering kitchen. Packed lunches available by order. Within 2 miles of the hostel are 4 country pubs, local shops, Chinese, Indian & Pizza takeaways. Whatever your reason for staying a warm welcome is guaranteed!

DETAILS

- **Open** - All year, limited access 10pm to 5pm. Check in from 5.
- **Number of beds** - 34: 10 x 3, 2 x 2
- **Booking** - Book by telephone or online.
- **Price per night** - Shared rooms (twin/triple) £20.00pp Group booking (8+) £17.50pp. All prices include linen & breakfast.
- **Public Transport** - Trains at Petersfield, 6 miles (£10 by taxi). From station 38 bus to Clanfield or the 52 or 67 to East Meon. Call to arrange a lift from bus stop.
- **Directions** - GR 676 189. From A3 take Clanfield turn (brown sign). Turn right after Rising Sun in Clanfield. At top of hill, turn left signed Droxford.

CONTACT: Tori
The Sustainability Centre, Droxford Road, East Meon, Hampshire, GU32 1HR
Tel: (01730) 823 549, Fax: (01730) 823 168
hostel@earthworks-trust.com www.earthworks-trust.com

The Camping Barn is a traditional Surrey timber barn in Puttenham village on the North Downs Way and Sustrans NCN22 cycle route. It is located in the Surrey Hills Area of Outstanding Natural Beauty with delightful cycling and walking routes all around. There is a fully equipped self-catering kitchen, a shower, toilets and foam covered sleeping platforms, all to a high standard. Electricity and hot water included but bring your own towels and sleeping bag (or hire one - £2.50 a stay). Evening meals are available in the village. The Barn has many sustainable features including solar panels and rainwater collection for flushing toilets. The Barn is wardened. NO CARS ON SITE. Excellent cycle shed. Young people under 18 are welcome but must be accompanied by a responsible adult.

DETAILS

■ **Open** - Easter to October,, 1700 to 1000
■ **Number of beds** - sleeping platforms for 11
■ **Booking** - booking is essential
■ **Price per night** - £10 adults, £8 under 18. Sole use negotiable. £1 'green' discount if arriving by foot, bicycle or public transport.
■ **Public Transport** - Trains (08457 484950) at Wanborough (3.5 km), Guildford (7 km) and Farnham (9 km). The X64 Stagecoach bus (0845 1210180) from Guildford and Farnham drops you within 1 km of the barn. Alight at Puttenham turn (Hogs Back) and walk south to village.
■ **Directions** - GR SU 933 479. Turn off A31 south onto B3000 then take first right into village. The Camping Barn is signposted immediately opposite the church.

CONTACT: Sarah Hart
The Street, Puttenham, Nr Guildford, Surrey, GU3 1AR
Tel: (01306) 877 964, Fax: (01306) 877964
tanners@yha.org.uk www.puttenhamcampingbarn.co.uk

THE GLADE
AT BLACKBOYS

The Glade is a quiet retreat in the heart of rural East Sussex, only an hour's drive from central London and 25 mins from the south coast. This former YHA hostel is set in an acre of its own grounds close to the intersection of the Weald and Vanguard Ways and 20 mins drive from the climbing crags at Harrisons Rocks and Bowles outdoor centre. The small dorms and private location make it ideal for sole-use, for family re-unions, parties or corporate team-building groups. When the hostel is open to all, the pleasant lounge/dining room makes a great place to socialise. The Glade has recently been refurbished with brand-new showers and wet-rooms (one of which is disabled-friendly), and a make-over on the lounge/dining room including a new wood burning stove. Kitchen facilities include cooker with oven and additional hob and grill, fridges, freezer, toasters and microwaves. All bedding is provided. Outside there is a spacious secure bike shed, a cosy camping field and picnic benches which are great for al-fresco eating. There is also woodland parking space for several cars.

DETAILS

- **Open** - All year, closed between 10am and 5pm (when not in sole use)
- **Number of beds** - 30:1x6,1x5, 2x4,3x3, 2x1
- **Booking** - Please enquire by phone or email.
- **Price per night** - Sole use £350 per night. At all other times, £15 per adult and £10 for under 16s. Family room discounts available.
- **Public Transport** - Stagecoach Bus 318 stops at Blackboys Village 0.5 miles from hostel. Trains at Buxted 2.5 miles away. National Express at Uckfield 4 miles away.
- **Directions** - From Blackboys village take Gun Road and look for signs.

CONTACT: Alan
YHA Blackboys, Gun Road, Blackboys, Uckfield, Sussex, TN22 5HU
Tel: (01825) 890607, Fax: (01825) 890104
blackboys@yha.org.uk www.blackboysyouthhostel.co.uk

GUMBER
BOTHY

Gumber Bothy is a converted traditional Sussex barn on the National Trust's Slindon Estate in the heart of the South Downs. It provides simple overnight accommodation or camping for walkers, riders and cyclists, just off the South Downs Way. The bothy forms part of Gumber Farm and is 5 minutes walk from Stane Street, the Roman Road that crosses the South Downs Way at Bignor Hill. Facilities include platforms in 3 dorms sleeping up to 30, good hot showers and basins, kitchen/diner with gas hob and washing up facilities, a few pots and pans provided, and breakfast foodstuffs available to order in advance. Paddock for friendly horses and racks for bikes. Wheelchair accessible (please phone for details). Sorry, but as we're a sheep farm no dogs and most definitely NO CARS. Not suitable for under fives.

DETAILS

- **Open** - July to October (inclusive), flexible
- **Number of beds** - 30: 1 x 16 : 1 x 6 : 1 x 4 plus overflow area
- **Booking** - Booking by telephone. Booking required for groups with 50% deposit.
- **Price per night** - £8.00 (adult), £4.00 (under 16s).
- **Public Transport** - Train stations, Arundel (urban) 5 miles, Amberley (rural) 5 miles, Chichester (8 miles). National Express stop at Chichester. Bus service 700 from Chichester bus station (opposite train station) stops at Royal Oak pub on A27 every 30mins Monday to Friday. The Royal Oak is a 3 mile walk from the hostel. Taxi fare from Arundel to Northwood Farm is £10, followed by a 2 mile country walk.
- **Directions** - OS Sheet 197 GR 961 119 (Bothy), GR 973 129 (Nearest car park). No vehicular access. One mile off South Downs Way on Stane Street bridleway

CONTACT: Warden (phone between 6 and 7.30pm)
Gumber Farm, Slindon, Near Arundel, West Sussex, BN18 0RN
Tel: (01243) 814484, Fax: 814484
mark.wardle@nationaltrust.org.uk

COLDBLOW FARM
BUNKBARNS
ENGLAND

Coldblow Farm is situated on the Kent Downs just north-east of Maidstone. The farm today provides a range of self-catering accommodation for both people and horses! The long distance trail, the North Downs Way, runs along the southern boundary of the farm and the Pilgrims Way is just a short distance away. The farm is surrounded by a network of public footpaths, bridleways and byways. The accommodation comprises: two Bunkhouse Barns, sleeping 10 (3 rooms, 2, 4 & 4) or 41 (7 rooms, 4 x 8 bunks, 3, 2 & 4 beds); Camping Barn sleeping 15 on sleeping platforms; Flint Cottage (studio style, sleeping two); a Camping Paddock and 18 Stables for horses and ponies. All Barns have fully equipped kitchen/dining rooms and central heating. Log burners in the Camping Barn and Flint Cottage. Toilets and showers (on meters) in all Barns and for Camping Paddock, but the Camping Barn shares washing facilities of small bunk barn.

DETAILS

- **Open** - All year, reception 8am till 8pm
- **Number of beds** - New Barn 41: 4x8, 1x4, 1x3, 1x2, Old Barn 10: 2x4, 1x2 , Camping Barn 15: 1x15, Cottage for 2.
- **Booking** - Advanced booking essential, with full payment.
- **Price per night** - Camping Barn £7, Bunkhouses £12, Cottage £50 (for 2).
- **Public Transport** - Bearsted is the nearest train station (2 miles by road or path).
- **Directions** - From Thurnham at the Black Horse Pub crossroads take the Pilgrims Way signposted to Hucking. Turn next left at staggered crossroads into Coldblow Lane, Coldblow Farm is half a mile up hill on right. If towing or in large vehicle ring us

CONTACT: Booking Office,
Coldblow Lane, Thurnham, Maidstone, Kent, ME14 3LR
Tel: (01622) 202900
coldblow-bookings@blueyonder.co.uk www.coldblow-camping.co.uk

PALACE FARM
HOSTEL

Palace Farm Hostel is a relaxing and flexible hostel on a family run arable and fruit farm. It is situated in the village of Doddington, which has a pub, in the North Kent Downs Area of Outstanding Natural Beauty. The area is great for walking, cycling (cycle hire available £5 a day) and wildlife. The location is central for exploring Canterbury, Rochester, Chatham, Leeds Castle and the many other historic towns, villages and castles in Kent. The accommodation in converted farm buildings, consists of six fully heated en-suite rooms sleeping up to 30 guests. The rooms surround an attractive courtyard garden with lawns, patio and barbecue area, ideal for families and groups. The en-suite rooms cater for all age groups and those with disabilities. There are quality double beds and 3' bunk beds. Duvets, linen and continental breakfast included. Small tent only campsite. Green Tourism Business Scheme GOLD Award winner.

DETAILS

- **Open** - All year, 8am to 10pm flexible, please ask
- **Number of beds** - 30: 1x8, 1x6, 2x5, 1x4, and 1x2
- **Booking** - Advised, not essential mid week.
- **Price per night** - From £12 child, £16 adult. Reduction for groups (small or large) staying for 3 or more nights, please ask.
- **Public Transport** - Trains at Sittingbourne (London Victoria to Dover). Buses from Sittingbourne station to Doddington two hourly (Mon-Sat), last buses 16.30 & 17.30.
- **Directions** -   From A2 between Sittingbourne and Faversham turn south at Teynham, signed to Lynsted. Go through Lynsted and over M2 bridge, take 2nd turning right into Down Court Rd. Farm is 90 metres on left.

CONTACT: Graham and Liz Cuthbert
Down Court Road, Doddington, Sittingbourne / Faversham, Kent ME9 0AU
Tel: (01795) 886200
info@palacefarm.com www.palacefarm.com

KIPPS
INDEPENDENT HOSTEL

Recommended by Lonely Planet and Lets Go travel guides, Kipps is an ideal home from home for travellers, visitors or small groups looking for self-catering budget accommodation in Canterbury. Only a short walk from the city centre, Kipps is the ideal place to stay to experience the area's numerous pubs, restaurants, shops, cafés and historical sites, including the renowned Canterbury Cathedral. Canterbury also makes an ideal base for day trips to Dover, Leeds Castle and the many local beaches. Everyone is welcome to enjoy the facilities on offer :- large conservatory with seating for up to 20 diners, TV lounge and fully equipped kitchen, a small shop offering breakfast and other food items, bicycle hire (advice on the must-see pubs and villages). Free WIFI & broadband access. Rooms include single/double/twin/family & dorms of up to 8 beds (most en-suite). Camping available in Summer. Free on-street parking.

DETAILS

- **Open** - All year, no curfew, reception 7.30am to 11pm
- **Number of beds** - 50:- 2 x 1, 2 x 2, 1 x 3,1 x 5, 1 x 7, 3 x 8, 1 x 10
- **Booking** - Advance booking recommended.
- **Price per night** - Dorms £15pp, Singles £20pp, Doubles £35, Quads £45. Weekly and Winter rates available. Credit cards accepted.
- **Public Transport** - Canterbury East train station on London Victoria to Dover line, is ½ mile by footpath (phone hostel for directions). The local C4 bus stops by the door of the hostel. Taxi from coach/rail stations is £3.
- **Directions** - By car :- Take B2068 to Hythe from City Ring Road (A28). Turn right at first traffic lights by church. KiPPS is 300 yds on left.

CONTACT: Lee Parsons
40 Nunnery Fields, Canterbury, Kent, CT1 3JT
Tel: (01227) 786121
info@kipps-hostel.com   www.kipps-hostel.com

PALMERS
LODGE

Palmers Lodge is a unique Grade II listed building. A three million pound refurbishment has turned this house, the former home of Samuel Palmer (Huntley & Palmers) into a stunning new hostel. Guests can enjoy modern facilities, such as FREE internet, whilst admiring the beautiful oak flooring, fireplaces and ceilings! The Lodge has a 24hr reception, bar, restaurant, large lounge, full security card access, generous car park and plenty of showers! With Swiss Cottage tube just across the road the heart of the city is just minutes away whilst, if you fancy a really late night, we are also on the Night Bus route from Trafalgar Square. Winner Silver Award, Visit London best hostel 2006. Nominated for Visit London best hostel 2007. Constantly in Hostels.com top 10 hostels worldwide since July 2006.

DETAILS

- **Open** - All year, 24 hours, 24 hours
- **Number of beds** - 273 : 3x2 6x4,4x6,4x8,2x10,3x12,3x14,1x19,1x18,1x24,1x28
- **Booking** - Booking is advised but not essential. Deposit for first night is preferred. Photo ID is required at check in.
- **Price per night** - £14.00 to £24.00 per person, including breakfast.
- **Public Transport** - Next to Swiss Cottage and Finchley Road stations. Leave Swiss Cottage tube exit 2, At the top of the stairs turn to face the main road. College Crescent goes up on your right. Also on bus routes for Stansted and Luton airports.
- **Directions** - Palmers Lodge is located just off the A41 which can be accessed from the M1, M25 or A1. Simply stay on the A41 towards central London and turn left just before Swiss Cottage tube; drive round to the left along College Crescent.

CONTACT: Reception
40 College Crescent, Swiss Cottage, London, NW3 5LB
Tel: (0207) 483 8470, Fax: (0207) 483 8471
reception@palmerslodge.co.uk www.palmerslodge.co.uk

ASHLEE
HOUSE

Stay in stylish, modern cheap accommodation with great facilities and relaxing lounge areas. Feel right at home with a diverse mixture of international travellers. You'll also find yourself a stone's throw from the British Museum, Covent Garden, Bloomsbury and Camden Market or just minutes away from the bright lights of Piccadilly Circus and Leicester Square.

Security is excellent with coded entrances to the building and the rooms. There is also a fully equipped self-catering kitchen. And we can even get you on the guest list of some of London's hottest nightclubs! So if it's the real London experience you're looking for come to Ashlee House and start living it!

DETAILS

- **Open** - All year, 24 hours - no curfew or lockouts
- **Number of beds** - 3 large dorms, 6 dorms, 12 small dorms and 4 private rooms
- **Booking** - Advanced booking recommended.
- **Price per night** - From £9pp including FREE breakfast. Group discounts.
- **Public Transport** - Kings Cross has excellent public transport: underground, local buses and direct links with all major airports - Heathrow, Gatwick, Luton and Stansted. Only 20 mins from Waterloo International and Victoria.
- **Directions** - King's Cross station is 2 mins away by foot. From the station take the exit for Grays Inn Road, departing the exit McDonald's will be on right. Keep McDonald's right, walk straight ahead, passing an exchange bureau, the police station and KFC. The road curves to the right - this is Grays Inn Road - the hostel is 200 metres up the road on the right, opposite The Royal Throat Nose and Ear Hospital.

CONTACT:
261-265 Gray's Inn Road, King's Cross, London, WC1X 8QT
Tel: (020) 7833 9400, Fax: (020) 7833 9677
info@ashleehouse.co.uk www.ashleehouse.co.uk

Located in trendy Kensington, Central London, Ace Hotel sets a new standard for budget accommodation in the UK. The hotel spans four beautiful Victorian town houses, has it's own bar, garden, hot-tub and provides the latest amenities, security and comfort for the independent traveller. Ace Hotel, London's latest contemporary budget accommodation offers a clean, friendly and vibrant place to stay at a very reasonable price. We offer a wide range of bunk-bedded rooms varying from 2 beds to 8 beds, many en-suite. We also have private double rooms available, some of which are en-suite. Our 2 bed rooms have television, bathrobes, fridge, and private patio. All rooms have security lockers, high quality beds and electronic swipe card access making them comfortable, modern and secure. Come and stay with us and see for yourself why Ace Hotel is an ACE place to be.

DETAILS

- **Open** - All year, 24 hours
- **Number of beds** - 157: 1x8, 9x6, 17x4, 1x3, 11x2, 1xDouble.
- **Booking** - Credit card guarantees bed, full payment upon arrival. Groups (10+) 50% deposit and the remaining balance paid 1 month prior to arrival
- **Price per night** - Winter £15-£40pp. Summer £17- £45pp. Weekly rates available.
- **Public Transport** - 5 mins walk from West Kensington and Barons Court tube sts.
- **Directions** - From West Kensington turn right out of tube station onto North End Rd. Cross and continue down North End Rd, take next left Gunterstone Rd. From Barons Court turn left out of the station and cross over the main road. Walk straight down the road past the college and take the first right down Gunterstone Road.

CONTACT:
16-22 Gunterstone Road, West Kensington, London, W14 9BX
Tel: (0207) 602 6600, Fax: (0207) 602 1021
reception@ace-hotel.co.uk www.ace-hotel.co.uk

DOVER CASTLE
ENGLAND HOSTEL AND FLATSHARES

The Dover Castle Hostel is a friendly, privately run hostel offering the best value accommodation for backpackers in central London. We have 65 beds in bright dormitory style rooms which range in size from 4 to 12 persons. We offer daily and weekly rates and prices include breakfast, taxes and free luggage lock-up. The hostel has great facilities, including it's own late licensed bar, free WiFi internet, kitchen, lockers and a laundry service. There is no curfew - you may party all night, sleep all day! Hostel guests get a discount card for cheap food and drink. For longer term guests, we offer house/flatshares in central London, zones 1 & 2. Single rooms are from £95 a week and twin rooms from £65 per person per week. The apartments are clean, furnished and with free WiFi internet. More information and booking online at www.london99.com. Hope to meet you soon ! Member of Visit London.

DETAILS

- **Open** - All year, 24 hours
- **Number of beds** - 65: 1x3 : 1x4 : 2x6 : 3x8 : 1x10 : 1x12
- **Booking** - Booking advisable in summer. Credit card secures bed.
- **Price per night** - £10-£15 per person including breakfast
- **Public Transport** - Nearest main line station is London Bridge. Take underground Northern (black) Line to Borough. The hostel is opposite Borough underground station between London Bridge and Elephant and Castle. We are located 10 mins from Waterloo International Station.
- **Directions** - From Borough Underground Station cross the road to Great Dover Street, we are 1 minute walk and located on the right hand side.

CONTACT: Martin
6 Great Dover Street, Borough, London, SE1 4XW
Tel: (020) 74037773, Fax: (020) 77878654
dovercastle@hotmail.com www.dovercastlehostel.co.uk

GENERATOR
LONDON

Just minutes from Covent Garden and Leicester Square The Generator is located in the heart of Bloomsbury. It is the UK's largest backpacker hostel with over 800 beds and is famous for it's party atmosphere.

We are open 24 hours a day, 365 days a year with friendly staff who are always on hand to help. There is a late bar (open 6.00 pm to 2.00 am) which provides the perfect environment to meet young travellers from all over the world.

Other facilities include a laundry, games room with pool tables and satellite TV, internet café, safety deposit boxes and free luggage storage on departure. Breakfast is free for everyone, as are bed sheets, towels and 24 hour hot showers. Accommodation is available in singles, twins, triples, quads plus both small and large dorms and the hostel is generally suitable for 18-35s.

DETAILS

■ **Open** - All year, 24 hours
■ **Number of beds** - 840:
■ **Booking** - With credit card- 48 hr cancellation.
■ **Price per night** - From £15 per person in a dorm room.
■ **Public Transport** - Kings Cross/Euston Station are both approx 5 minutes walk from the hostel. The nearest National Express station is Victoria and the closest tube station is Russell Square.
■ **Directions** - From Russell Square Tube cross onto Marchmont Street, walk to traffic lights and turn right onto Tavistock Place - the hostel is at number 37.

CONTACT:
Compton Place, (off 37 Tavistock Place), Russell Square London, WC1H 9SE
Tel: (0207) 388 7666
res@generatorhostels.com www.generatorhostels.com

CLINK
HOSTEL

Clink is all about reinvention. Not only have we restored a 200 year old courthouse to create a stylish backpackers, but we have also set out to change the traditional perception of youth hostels. With its utterly cool interior, modern facilities and high-tech pod beds, Clink is a far cry from the generic budget accommodation.

What makes us exceptional? :- The Courtroom Lounge... chill out where The Clash were on trial ; The Prison Cells...sleep it all off in an authentic prison cell, whether in solitary confinement or with your partner in crime ; The Internet Lounge... write your own story from the place that inspired Charles Dickens to create Oliver Twist. Each pod bed has a personal light, a safety locker and a storage box combining comfort, security and privacy.

Stay and judge for yourself...

DETAILS

■ **Open** - All year, 24 hours - no curfew or lockouts
■ **Number of beds** - 350+ mixed of 4-21 bedded room, triple, twin, single basic or en suite and cell rooms (for 2).
■ **Booking** - Advanced booking recommended
■ **Price per night** - From £10pp including FREE breakfast. Group discounts.
■ **Public Transport** - We're just around the corner from King's Cross Station with its direct links to Heathrow, Luton, Gatwick, Victoria, the Eurostar and only one change to Stansted.
■ **Directions** -   King's Cross station is 5 mins away by foot. Exit the station, walk down King's Cross Road for 500m and you'll find us on your left.

CONTACT: Reception
78 Kings Cross Road, King's Cross, London, WC1X 9QG
Tel: (020) 7183 9400, Fax: 020) 7713 0735
info@clinkhostel.com www.clinkhostel.com

Cheap accommodation in central London. Backpacking on a budget? Globetrotter Inns provides cheap accommodation for backpackers, students and independent travellers that's gloBEtroTTER than anywhere else. The overnight prices include sparkling clean linen, all taxes and continental breakfast. Luxury comfortable bunks are available in twin, double, quad and 6-bed rooms. Facilities include steaming hot showers, immaculate clean bathrooms, self-catering kitchen, in-house supermarket, gym, laundry, internet, cinema, TV. The bar is open 24 hours and in hot weather you can spill out into the garden for a BBQ. Other facilities include CCTV, Smart cards, 24 hour reception and travel desk.

DETAILS

■ **Open** - All year, all day
■ **Number of beds** - 396 : 34x6, 20x4, 6x4 en-suite, 23xtwin en-suite, 13xdouble en-suite
■ **Booking** - Book online, by phone, fax or email.
■ **Price per night** - From £19pp (6 bed room), £22pp (4 bed room), £22pp (4 bed en-suite), £30pp (double/twin en-suite), £24pp (family room en-suite). Surcharge Fri/Sat.
■ **Public Transport** - Located in Hammersmith, a short tube ride from Heathrow airport. Close to Victoria Station and all central London's best attractions. The nearest tube station is Stamford Brook (District Line).
■ **Directions** - When you arrive just turn left out of the station and then next right onto Ravenscourt Gardens - you'll find us 150 metres on the left.

CONTACT: Reception
Ashlar Court, Ravenscourt Gardens, Stamford Brook, London, W6 0TU
Tel: (0208) 746 3112, Fax: (0208) 748 9912
london@globetrotterinns.com www.globetrotterinns.com

HOSTEL 639

Hostel 639 offers clean, cheap, budget accommodation and is part of London's Number 1 Budget Accommodation Group. From only £10 a night get a good night's sleep in spacious 6 and 8 bedded dorms with hot showers in each room, heating, clean bedding and a free breakfast. Hostel 639 has mixed, male or female dorms, quads, triples and twin rooms. There are self-catering kitchens on every floor (utensils available with deposit). Relax and enjoy a drink in the Moroccan style lounge bar, dine in the Brazilian restaurant or grab a baguette in the coffee shop. Thursday nights are Karaoke night. There are weekly pool competitions, a variety of arcade games, table tennis and TV room with 100s of movies and Sky TV. Low rate international calls, internet facilities, safe hire, towel hire and luggage storage available. Hostel 639 is twenty minutes walk from the famous Portobello Road and Notting Hill Market.
Hostel 639 has 24 hour reception, 24 hour security and 24 hour cleaning staff.

DETAILS

■ **Open** - All year, 24 hours
■ **Number of beds** - 300: 10x8, 16x6, 30x4(3), 2x2, 1x1
■ **Booking** - Book online
■ **Price per night** - Dorms £10 to £12. Private rooms from £13pp to £35pp. All prices include free breakfast. Weekly, monthly and group booking rates available.
■ **Public Transport** - For free courtesy coach pick-up from Victoria Coach Station call 07908 080 345. Hostel is opposite Kensal Green tube. No18 bus stops outside.
■ **Directions** - From Ladbroke Grove turn left onto Harrow Road and turn right at the traffic lights. Walk about 300m from the junction. Hostel 639 is on the left.

CONTACT: Reception
639 Harrow Road, Kensal Green, London, NW10 5NU
Tel: (0208) 964 4411, Fax: (0208) 964 0022
hostel639@hostel639.co.uk www.hostel639.co.uk

SMART
HYDE PARK INN

Smart Hyde Park Inn is London's award winning Hostel which consistently is voted in the top ten hostels in the WORLD! It has also been voted best located hostel in LONDON, so stay with us and your journey to London will start with an experience that you won't forget.

The hostel is located in London's buzzing Bayswater and is set in a stunning grade I listed building. Hyde Park Inn is a clean, safe and secure place to stay with 24-hour access to the hostel facilities and your room. Each of our staff is highly trained, so they know what you are looking for and are there to assist you during your stay.

DETAILS

- **Open** - All year, 24 hours (no curfew or lockouts)
- **Number of beds** - 223: 3x1, 5x2, 1x3, 6x4, 7x6, 9x8, 3x10, 2x12
- **Booking** - Book by phone, fax, email or online www.smartbackpackers.com
- **Price per night** - From £9 per person (inclusive of breakfast and linen)
- **Public Transport** - Tube Stations: Bayswater (Circle and District line) and Queensway (Central line). Train Stations: Victoria, Paddington, Kings Cross, and Euston. Bus station: Victoria. Easy links from all major airports - Heathrow, Gatwick, Luton, City & Stansted.
- **Directions** - From Bayswater Station cross the road and walk down Inverness Place, at the end of the road is Hyde Park Inn. From Queensway Station turn left onto Bayswater Road, cross the road and take the first right into Inverness Place. At the end of the road is Hyde Park Inn.

CONTACT:
48-50 Inverness Terrace, Bayswater, London, W2 3JA
Tel: (020) 7229 0000, Fax: (020) 7229 8333
hpibookings@smartbackpackers.com www.smartbackpackers.com

Smart Camden Inn is one of London's premier hostels and is located in London's legendary Camden Town area, set in a stunning building. Smart Camden Inn is a clean, safe and secure place to stay with 24-hour access to the hostel facilities and your room. All the rooms have washing facilities en-suite. There are many bath and shower rooms in our building with unlimited piping hot water.

We cater for all travellers, from groups to backpackers and provide the perfect place to meet and mix with like-minded people from all over the world. Camden Inn's staff are highly trained, so they know what you are looking for and are there to assist you during your stay.

DETAILS

- **Open** - All year, 24 hours (no curfew or lockouts)
- **Number of beds** - 108: 1x14 : 9x6 : 10x4
- **Booking** - Book by phone, fax or email or online www.smartbackpackers.com
- **Price per night** - From £9 per person including breakfast
- **Public Transport** - Tube Stations: Camden Town (Northern Line). Train Stations: Euston, Kings Cross, Liverpool Street & Paddington. Bus station: Victoria. Easy links from all major airports - Heathrow, Gatwick, Luton, City & Stansted.
- **Directions** - From Camden Town take the left exit. Walk down Bayham Street, which is opposite the station. We are on the right side of the street approx. 2 min from the station.

CONTACT:
55-57 Bayham Street, London, NW1 0AA
Tel: 020 7388 8900, Fax: (020) 7388 2008
scibookings@smartbackpackers.com www.smartbackpackers.com

SMART
HYDE PARK VIEW

Hyde Park View is our newest hostel located in the buzzing area of Bayswater and a stone's throw away from Hyde Park and lots of other tourist attractions. It has also been voted in the top ten hostels in the WORLD! So stay with us and your journey to London will start with an experience that you won't forget. Hyde Park View is a stunning listed building. It is a clean, safe and secure place to stay with 24-hour access to the hostel facilities and your room. Each of our staff is highly trained, so they know what you are looking for and are there to assist you during your stay.

DETAILS

■ **Open** - All year, 24 hours
■ **Number of beds** - 104: 2 x 4, 16 x 6
■ **Booking** - www.smartbackpackers.com online booking or phone. Deposit required for groups.
■ **Price per night** - From £9.00 per night per bed (inclusive of Breakfast and Linen).
■ **Public Transport** - Tube Stations: Bayswater (Circle and District line) and Queensway (Central line). Train Stations: Victoria, Paddington, Kings Cross, and Euston. Bus station: Victoria. Easy links from all major airports - Heathrow, Gatwick, Luton, City & Stansted.
■ **Directions** - From Bayswater Tube Station cross the road (Queensway Road) and turn right. Walk for 2 minutes till you hit the Bayswater road. Turn left and walk for 5 min and turn left into Leinster Gardens Road. Keep walking and you will see Craven (Gardens) Hotel on your right. Take the turn just after the hotel and you will see Hyde Park View Hostel.

CONTACT: Reception
11 Craven Hill Gardens, Bayswater, London, W2 3EU
Tel: (020) 7262 3167, Fax: (020) 7262 2083
hpvbookings@smartbackpackers.com www.smartbackpackers.com

THE 1912 CENTRE
GROUP HOSTEL
ENGLAND

The 1912 Centre is a 26 Bed Hostel in the heart of Harwich heritage area, only 50 metres from the sandy beach, promenade and harbour. It was built in 1912 as the Town Fire Station and the old engine garage now forms the central dining and recreational area. The upper floor has access to four cabin style sleeping areas, two with two berths and two with six berths. The ground floor has two cabins, one six berth, and one four berth with ensuite facilities. All cabins have bunk beds.

The Centre is centrally heated and has a fully equipped kitchen, showers, a drying room and ground floor facilities for the disabled. Bring sleeping bags or hire duvets. The housekeeper can provide booked meals, or you can self cater. The 1912 Centre is situated within the Harwich conservation area. The Town is built on a narrow spit of land between the sea and two rivers and owes much of its charm to medieval origins.

GROUPS ONLY

DETAILS

- **Open** - All year, all day
- **Number of beds** - 26: 3x6, 1x4, 2x2
- **Booking** - Book by phone or email. Enquiry form online.
- **Price per night** - £176.25 sole use. Weekly £894.47. Mon to Fri £703.23. Fri to Sun £343.45. Duvet hire £6.50 per person. All meals £14.50 per person per day.
- **Public Transport** - Harwich Town train and bus station are a few minutes walk away. Follow signs to Electric Palace cinema which is next door to hostel.
- **Directions** - Follow A120 to Harwich. Follow signs past Harwich Quay until you come to a large painted wall mural then take 1st Right and the centre is on your right

CONTACT:
Cow Lane, Off Wellington Road, Harwich, Essex, C012 3ES
Tel: (01255) 552010, Fax: (01255) 552010
1912@harwichconnexions.co.uk www.harwichconnexions.co.uk

HARLOW
ENGLAND INTERNATIONAL HOSTEL

Harlow International Hostel is situated in the centre of a landscaped park and is one of the oldest buildings in Harlow. The town of Harlow is the ideal base from which to explore London, Cambridge and the best of the South East of England. The journey time to central London is only 35 minutes from the hostel. National Cycle Route One passes our front door. We are the closest hostel to Stansted Airport. There is a range of room sizes from single to eight bedded, many with their own washing facilities. Self-catering facilities, refreshments and a small shop are all available. During your visit you can relax with a book from our large collection or enjoy a board game with other guests. A children's zoo, assault course, swimming and outdoor pursuit centre are available in the park. Meals provided for groups.

DETAILS

■ **Open** - All year, 08:00 - 24:00 (check in 16:00 - 22:30)

■ **Number of beds** - 36: 2x1 : 2x2 : 3x4 : 3x6

■ **Booking** - Advance booking (can be taken 18 months in advance) is recommended. Deposit of £1pppn of stay.

■ **Price per night** - £12.50 per adults, Family rooms £44 (sleeps 4), £55 (sleep 5), £66 (sleep 6). Please contact hostel for group discounts.

■ **Public Transport** - The rail station is only 600m from hostel with links to London, Cambridge & Stansted Airport. Buses connect to London and airports.

■ **Directions** - J7 of M11 take A414 into Harlow. At the 4th roundabout take 1st exit (First Ave). Drive to 4th set of traffic lights. Immediately after lights turn right (School Lane). Hostel is on left opp Greyhound Pub.

CONTACT: Richard or Iku
13 School Lane Harlow, Essex, CM20 2QD
Tel: (01279) 421702
mail@h-i-h.co.uk www.h-i-h.co.uk

WENDOVER HOUSE ENGLAND

Wendover House is a residential school set in the heart of the Chiltern Hills, right on the Ridgeway Path. At weekends and school holidays the Ramblers' Retreat welcomes walkers and holiday makers into the school. The retreat has one dormitory with five curtained bedspaces, a private room for one, a well-equipped kitchen and plenty of washing facilities. The school is situated around an 18th Century Manor House with 22 acres of land. It is easily accessible by road and there is a direct rail link to London Marylebone only a few minutes walk away. Wendover Village is an old market town set in an area of Outstanding Natural Beauty. It has lots of historic buildings with excellent pubs and restaurants only 5 minutes walk from the school. As well as the Ridgeway Path there are 33 miles of public rights of way crisscrossing the parish

DETAILS

- **Open** - Weekends and school holidays, all day
- **Number of beds** - 6: 1 x 5, 1 x 1
- **Booking** - Book minimum of 24 hours in advance. No deposit required (Payment by cash or cheque only).
- **Price per night** - £12 per person. Optional bedding pack (inc towel) £3
- **Public Transport** - Wendover station, on the Marylebone to Aylesbury line, is 6 mins walk. Trains run approximately twice an hour. Local bus service from Aylesbury runs twice an hour and hourly at weekends.
- **Directions** - Wendover House is just off the A413 in the centre of Wendover. If arriving from Aylesbury, travel through Wendover in the direction of Amersham. Look for turning signed "St Mary's Church". Drive past the church and look for school.

CONTACT:
Wendover House School, Church Lane, Wendover, Bucks, HP22 6NL
Tel: (01296) 622157 (school hours), (01296) 626065 or (01296) 625319
office@wendoverhouse.bucks.sch.uk www.wendoverhouse.bucks.sch.uk

THE COURT HILL
CENTRE

Just 2 miles south of Wantage, and only a few steps from the historic Ridgeway National Trail, The Court Hill Centre enjoys breathtaking views over the Vale of the White Horse. Reclaimed barns surround a pretty courtyard garden, on the site of a disused rubbish dump! Offering accommodation to families, groups and individuals, a popular year-round destination. we offer evening meals, breakfasts, and picnic lunches, all prepared using as much local produce as possible. Meals are served in the beautiful high-roofed dining room which retains the impressive proportions and atmosphere of the old barn. Before and after your meal relax in the cosy sunken lounge with a log fire when it's chilly. We offer a limited number of pitches for small tents, and can accommodate small groups by arrangement. Our 2 tipis sleeping 5/6 each are available from April to the end of August. A meeting/classroom and bike hire are also available.

DETAILS

■ **Open** - From Good Friday to the end of October. Bookings accepted 48 hours in advance at all other times if possible, Office 08:00-11:00 & 17:00-22:00
■ **Number of beds** - 59: 1x10+, 1x9, 1x6, 1x5, 7x4
■ **Booking** - Essential 48 hours in advance. Payment required to guarantee booking
■ **Price per night** - Adult £16, Under 18 £11.50
■ **Public Transport** - Train, Didcot Parkway 10 Miles. Stagecoach, 32/A, X35,36 from Didcot Parkway to Wantage 2 Miles. There is no direct connection to the centre.
■ **Directions** - From the M4 Jct 14, follow signs to Wantage. From Oxford A420 and A338 through Wantage. The Courthill Ridgeway Centre is accessed from the A338 close to Letcombe Regis

CONTACT: Reception
Courthill, Letcombe Regis, Wantage, OX12 9NE
Tel: (01235) 760253
info@Courthill.org.uk www.Courthill.org.uk

OXFORD
BACKPACKERS

UNDER NEW MANAGEMENT. Oxford Backpackers is a purpose built hostel, in the heart of Oxford, the leading university town of England. The hostel is two minutes walk from the train and bus stations and close to the Tourist Information Centre and all the City's attractions. It is safe, clean and friendly. Small dorms with individual pin code locks, fully equipped kitchen, well supplied bar, laundry, games room, internet access and organised activities add to the experience.

Oxford City is steeped in history and culture. You can explore Christ Church, Magdalen and New College of the University, the Bodleian Library, the Oxford Story and Britain's oldest museum the Ashmolean Museum. Or explore the canals and quiet villages of the Cotswolds.

DETAILS

■ **Open** - All year, 24 hour access, service 8am until 12 midnight
■ **Number of beds** - 120
■ **Booking** - Booking is advised in summer (April to Sept), 7 days in advance with deposit by credit card.
■ **Price per night** - From £13 per person. Discounts for longer stays and groups. Discounts when you book ahead to Bath Backpackers hostel (01225) 446787.
■ **Public Transport** - Oxford has train and National Express services. Hostel is 100m from train station and easy walking distance from the coach station.
■ **Directions** - From train station turn left and walk 100 metres, hostel is on your right. From Oxford coach station turn right, hostel is over the bridge 100 metres on your left. By road follow signs to the train station.

CONTACT:
9a Hythe Bridge Street, Oxford, OX1 2EW
Tel: (01865) 721761, Fax: (01865) 203293
oxford@hostels.co.uk www.hostels.co.uk

CENTRAL
BACKPACKERS OXFORD ENGLAND

Central Backpackers is conveniently situated right downtown on one of Oxford's liveliest streets, lined with 8 bars, 3 clubs and 5 restaurants! Just a few minutes walk away are tourist information, universities, museums, tour bus pick up, supermarkets, cinemas, theatres, canal walks and the recently refurbished Oxford Castle and Prison Complex. Oxford is also a great start for touring nearby Cotswold villages and Blenheim Palace. This newly opened, smoke free hostel offers clean, new beds and a helpful team with advice and local knowledge. The hostel is equipped with a self-catered kitchen (offering free tea and coffee), dining room, cosy TV lounge (with satellite TV and DVDs), outdoor deck and BBQ. There are also lockers for all guests, swipe card access to dorms, free map, free internet and wireless access throughout and a laundry service. Families and groups welcome. ID required.

DETAILS

- **Open** - All year, 24 hours. No curfew
- **Number of beds** - 50: 1x12, 3x8, 1x6, 2x4
- **Booking** - Advisable, essential in high season.
- **Price per night** - From £14 per person.
- **Public Transport** - Oxford Tube bus company leaves London every 12 mins and costs £12-15 return, Oxford Express buses offer direct services to and from Heathrow, Gatwick and London Airports. Trains from Paddington every 10-20 mins.
- **Directions** - Bus: (3 mins) turn right onto George St, follow the road around to the left. Take first right onto Park End St. Train: (3 mins) Look to your left and see Royal Oxford Hotel. Park End St runs down the right side of the hotel. Give us a call if lost.

CONTACT: Reception
13 Park End Street, Oxford, OX1 1HH
Tel: (01865) 242288
oxford@centralbackpackers.co.uk www.centralbackpackers.co.uk

BERROW HOUSE
ENGLAND BUNKHOUSE & CAMP SITE

Berrow House is situated in Hollybush between Rugged Stone Hill and Midsummer Hill in the Malvern Range. It is ideally suited for families, groups and individuals (including those with special needs) who want easy access to the countryside. The Forest of Dean, the Welsh border and the start of the Worcestershire Way Walk are near, with the towns of Malvern, Ledbury, Tewkesbury, Worcester, and Gloucester, all within a half hour drive. The Bunkhouse has sleeping accommodation for 5 in the main room and 3 more beds on the upper floor. The main room has heating and easy chairs. The adjacent kitchen/dining room has hot water, cooker, cutlery, crockery and cooking utensils. Toilets, dryer and shower are adjacent. The Fold is a separate building which has sleeping accommodation for 4 in two rooms, a fully equipped kitchen, heating, toilet, shower and a cloakroom. The Nook (caravan) has a double and single bed and uses the bunkhouse facilities. Camping, picnic area, water garden and car park are also available.

DETAILS

- **Open** - All year, 24 hours
- **Number of beds** - 8 (Bunkhouse), 4 (The Fold), 3 (The Nook) and 8 tents.
- **Booking** - Not required for individuals
- **Price per night** - £8 per person.
- **Public Transport** - Nearest train station and National Express service are in Ledbury, which is 3 miles from the hostel and would cost approx. £3 in a taxi.
- **Directions** - Take A449 from Ledbury towards Malvern. Turn right on to A438 through Eastnor. Berrow House is behind phone box in Hollybush (campsite sign).

CONTACT: Bill or Mary Cole
Hollybush, Ledbury, Herefordshire HR8 1ET
Tel: (01531) 635845, Fax: 635845
william@holybush.fslife.co.uk www.berrowhouse.co.uk

BERROW HOUSE

CAMPING

CARAVANS

BUNKHOUSE

BISHOP MASCALL
CENTRE

The Bishop Mascall Centre has developed from a former church school and provides hostel-style accommodation for up to 48 people. The residential area has sixteen single and four twin rooms, plus two dormitories each sleeping twelve people in bunk beds. Rooms have wash-hand basins. Showers, toilets and a bathroom are located on each floor. A range of good home-cooked food is available in the Centre's dining room. Other facilities include a fully licensed bar, free internet connection, TV / video, audio-visual equipment, a library and chapel. A short walk away is the centre of the ancient market town of Ludlow, where you can wander medieval streets to the Norman Castle and the splendid church of St Laurence . The surrounding excellent walking country and varied geology make it an ideal base for outdoor enthusiasts. The Centre offers flexible meeting spaces, good food, simple, comfortable accommodation and a personal service. It belongs tor the Diocese of Hereford, but it is open to all.

           GROUPS ONLY

DETAILS

- **Open** - All year, all day
- **Number of beds** - 48: 2x12 + singles and twins.
- **Booking** - Book by phone or email.
- **Price per night** - Accommodation including all meals from £38pp (dorm), £46pp (twin) and £44pp (single). Prices are based on group sizes over 12. Please enquire for smaller groups or B&B/half board prices.
- **Public Transport** - Ludlow train station is on the Cardiff to Manchester route. Buses operate from Birmingham, Shrewsbury and Hereford.
- **Directions** - We are in the heart of Ludlow, about 5 minutes' walk from the station

CONTACT: House Manager
Lower Galdeford, Ludlow, Shropshire, SY8 1RZ
Tel: (01584) 873882, Fax: (01584) 877945
info@thebmc.org.uk www.thebmc.org.uk/

Looking for a place to stay in Birmingham within walking distance of top attractions, easy on your wallet, and a great place to meet new friends? Birmingham Central Backpackers is ideally located in the heart of the city, a short walk from Digbeth Coach Station and New Street Station and steps from buses to the airport and the NEC; the best choice for clean, friendly budget accommodation in England's second city. Most of the dorms sleep between 5 and 8 and have shower, sink and storage lockers. Friendly staff from around the world strive to make our guests feel at home providing map and directions, recommending attractions, and doing their best to make your stay all it can be. Warm up by the fire, read a book from our library, play board games, watch films on our sofas, surf the internet or visit our guest-only bar or coffee shop. There's free Wi-Fi, a pool table, big screen Nintendo, guest kitchen and garden patio.

DETAILS

- **Open** - All year, check-in from 2pm-11pm. Common area open 8am-12am
- **Number of beds** - 58: 10 rooms of 5-8 beds, 1x2
- **Booking** - Book by phone, email or online. 2% credit card fee, 40p debit card fee.
- **Price per night** - £15 weekdays, £16 Fri and Sat., inc. linen & light breakfast.
- **Public Transport** - Digbeth coach station and New Street train station near by.
- **Directions** - From Digbeth Coach Station take Milk Street (Big Bulls Head on corner). Hostel located above Billy's Bar, one block down. From New Street Station, walk down New Street through the Bull Ring and down the steps to the markets. Take a left at the markets and go to the traffic light. Cross over the light to the Digbeth High Street. Walk 4 blocks, and turn left onto Milk Street.

CONTACT: Ian and Jen Randall
58 Coventry Street, Digbeth, Birmingham, B5 5NH
Tel: (0121) 643-0033, Mobile: 0775-682-9970
info@birminghamcentralbackpackers.com www.birminghamcentralbackpackers.com

STOKES BARN
BUNKHOUSE

Stokes Barn is located on top of Wenlock Edge, an Area of Outstanding Natural Beauty and in the heart of Shropshire countryside. The barn offers comfortable, centrally heated, dormitory accommodation for a wide range of groups. 'The cottage' in the courtyard is often used for leaders, teachers or families.

Stokes Barn is an ideal base for field study groups, universities, schools, walkers or just a relaxing reunion with friends. The Ironbridge World Heritage Site is only 6 miles away and is a great attraction. Walk to the historic town of Much Wenlock to visit shops, pubs and sports facilities. Situated only a few miles from Church Stretton and the Long Mynd the barn is in a walking/cycling haven. Have a relaxing and enjoyable stay. Many activities available.

DETAILS

■ **Open** - All year, 24 hours with prior notice
■ **Number of beds** - 43:1x14,1x12,1x10,1x7 + Cottage 6: 2x2,2x1
■ **Booking** - Deposit required.
■ **Price per night** - £9 pp plus £3 duvet charge. Minimum charges apply.
■ **Public Transport** - Trains at Telford (10 miles) and in Shrewsbury (10 miles). National Express coaches call at Shrewsbury from London, call (0839) 142 348 for information. Midland Red buses stop in Much Wenlock, enquires (01952) 223766.
■ **Directions** - GR 609 999. From the M6 take M54 Telford following Ironbridge Gorge signs. A4169 to Much Wenlock, joining A458 for Shrewsbury. The Barn is signed at Newton House Farm (TF13 6DB) on the Much Wenlock to Shrewsbury Rd.

CONTACT:
Stokes Barn, Newtown Farm, Much Wenlock, Shropshire TF13 6PP
Tel: (01952) 727491, Mob: 07973 329887, Fax: 728130
info@stokesbarn.co.uk www.stokesbarn.co.uk

Springhill Farm is a 130 acre organic hill farm in an area unspoilt by modern life, overlooking the beautiful Ceirog Valley and the Berwyn Mountains. With rights of way and open access just yards from our door, Springhill is ideal for walking and other activity-based breaks or just relaxing with friends and family.

The Bunkhouse sleeps up to 22 in 5 bedrooms, with a seperate double ensuite next to the main building. It has underfloor heating, a modern kitchen, dining and sitting rooms, 4 bathrooms and a large entrance area with WC and drying room. Outside is a large patio and lawn with hot tub, BBQ, table tennis etc.

We have horse riding on site suitable for all abilities, from 1hour to 3day trail rides. Cycle hire available, and other activities nearby. Pets and horses welcome on request.

DETAILS

- **Open** - All year,, all day (please don't phone after 9pm)
- **Number of beds** - 22 + 2: 1x5/7, 1x6, 1x4, 1x2, 1x1 + double en-suite
- **Booking** - Advisable, deposit required
- **Price per night** - £15pp (including bedding but not towels)
- **Public Transport** - Nearest train station Chirk (8 miles). Nearest bus service is in the village Glyn Ceiriog (2.5 miles). Transfer can be arranged.
- **Directions** - On the A483 from Wrexham, take the third exit on the first roundabout (Macdonalds), at the next roundabout take the first exit, continue into Chirk, and then turn right for Glyn Ceiriog. After 6 miles you will arrive at Glyn Ceiriog. At the mini roundabout turn left, go over the bridge, and then straight away turn right into a small lane. This continues up the hill for about two miles, do not turn off.

CONTACT: Sue Sopwith
Springhill Farm, Selattyn, Oswestry, Shropshire, SY10 7NZ
Tel: (01691) 718406
sue@atspringhill.co.uk www.atspringhill.co.uk

THE IGLOO
BACKPACKERS HOSTEL

Within walking distance of the city's historical sights and entertaining sounds, the Igloo is Nottingham's most popular choice for the budget-minded traveller. On offer to overseas jobseekers, backpackers and youth groups is a clean, safe and warm overnight stay in a large, listed Victorian house. Just £14.50 pp per night buys a whole host of homely comforts; bunk bed dorms, hot power showers, lounge with TV, films, games and free internet, fully-equipped kitchen, free tea & coffee, laundry facilities and good company. Open in outlook and open all day all year, it is the ideal home-from-home for hostellers seeking rest and recuperation before pursuing the exploits of Robin Hood or enjoying the energetic nightlife of this popular university city. Check out our web site.

DETAILS

■ **Open** - All year except 22/12 to 03/01, all day
■ **Number of beds** - 36: 1x6; 1x8; 1x10; 1x12
■ **Booking** - Essential during Summer months. Groups must confirm in writing with deposit.
■ **Price per night** - £14.50 pp. £58 per week after 7 nights stay.
■ **Public Transport** - Direct, regular trains from London etc. National Express to Broadmarsh bus station. From bus/train stations 20mins walk, £4 taxi ride or catch tram to Trent Uni (4th stop), take next R (Peel St) follow to Golden Fleece pub.
■ **Directions** - From the Tourist Information Centre (Market Square) turn right out of TIC, take next left onto Cumber Street, keep walking straight on for ten mins, past the Victoria Shopping centre, untill you reach the Golden Fleece Pub. The igloo is directly opposite. Entry is on the side of the buidling.

CONTACT: Igloo
110 Mansfield Road, Nottingham, NG1 3HL
Tel: (0115) 9475250
reception@igloohostel.co.uk www.igloohostel.co.uk

OLD RED LION

ENGLAND

Visitors to Castle Acre are entranced by the special atmosphere of this medieval walled town which lies within the outer bailey of an 11th-century castle. Castle Acre is on the Peddars Way, an ancient track now a long distance path.

The Old Red Lion, a former pub, is centrally situated and carries on the tradition of serving travellers who seek refreshment and repose. Guests can stay in private rooms or dormitories, where bedding and linen are provided free of charge. There are quiet areas (with wood burning stoves) for reading, meeting other guests and playing. There are two large areas and studio space (one with kitchen and toilet) which are ideal for group use, courses and retreats. Sole occupancy of entire premises may be hired; rates negotiable. Drying facilities. Good local shops, pubs etc. Tourism concern supporter. No smoking.

DETAILS

- **Open** - All year, all day access. Arrival times by arrangement.
- **Number of beds** - 24: 1x10 : 1x6 : 2xdouble (1en-suite) : 2 twin
- **Booking** - Useful but not essential
- **Price per night** - £17.50 - £25, en-suite £30 (inc. bedding and breakfast). One night supplements.
- **Public Transport** - Train stations at King's Lynn & Downham Market (14 miles). Buses from King's Lynn to Swaffham. Daily National Express coach between Victoria Coach Station & Swaffham. Norfolk Bus info (0500) 626116. Taxi from Swaffham £4.
- **Directions** - GR 818151. Castle Acre is 3.5 miles north of Swaffham (A47) on the A1065. The hostel is on left, 75yds down from Bailey Gate in village centre.

CONTACT: Alison Loughlin
Bailey Street, Castle Acre, Norfolk, PE32 2AG
Tel: (01760) 755557
oldredlion@yahoo.co.uk www.oldredlion.here2stay.org.uk

DEEPDALE GRANARY ⁸⁹
GROUP HOSTEL
ENGLAND

A perfect base for groups to stay, explore and absorb the stunning North Norfolk coast. Deepdale Granary is a self-contained 17th century building sleeping 18 in four bedrooms with a fully fitted kitchen and dining/sitting room. Part of the award winning Deepdale Farm, right on the coast in the heart of an Area of Outstanding Natural Beauty. We have excellent pubs nearby, both traditional and chic. Great restaurants and miles of unspoilt beaches and dunes. The Norfolk coast is perfect for walking and cycling with miles of coast path and picturesque villages. Take time to discover our heritage sties including the Sandringham and Holkham estates or enjoy birdwatching in the tranquil beauty of the unique saltmarsh. The Granary is fully heated, has showers, a drying room and solar water heating. Next-door Dalegate Market has shops, a supermarket, and a brilliant café serving locally sourced food. Camping and Tipis also available.

 **GROUPS ONLY**

DETAILS

- **Open** - All year, all day. Collect key from Deepdale Information.
- **Number of beds** - 18: 2 x 6 : 1 x 4 : 1 x 2.
- **Booking** - Essential, 20% deposit, balance in advance. See website for details
- **Price per night** - £155 midweek, £210 wk-end/bk-holiday. Weekly rates available.
- **Public Transport** - Trains / coaches at King's Lynn (25 miles) then excellent Coastal Hopper bus to Burnham Deepdale. Coastal Hopper services the coast from King's Lynn to Cromer, including Sandringham. Travelline 0870 608 2 608.
- **Directions** - GR 803443. On A149 coast road, halfway between Hunstanton and Wells-next-the-Sea. Beside Deepdale Garage & opposite Deepdale Church.

CONTACT:
Deepdale Farm, Burnham Deepdale, Norfolk PE31 8DD
Tel: (01485) 210256
info@deepdalefarm.co.uk www.deepdalefarm.co.uk

DEEPDALE
BACKPACKERS

Eco friendly award winning backpackers hostel on the beautiful north Norfolk coast. Escape the smog of the cities to this stunning part of the world. We offer private ensuite rooms and dorms. There's so much to do here, adrenaline sports, great pubs and restaurants, miles of sandy beaches. Deepdale is a perfect base for walking and cycling with miles of coast path, the famous big skies and quaint fishing harbours. Or just come and chill. Our facilities are second to none, all rooms are en-suite, we have a fully equipped farmhouse kitchen and a really cosy lounge with a TV and a woodburner for those cooler nights. There's a lovely courtyard with barbeques for summer evenings.

Deepdale is a working farm and eco-friendly with recycling, underfloor heating and solar water. Next-door Dalegate Market has shops, a supermarket, and a brilliant café serving locally sourced food. Camping and Tipis also available.

DETAILS

- **Open** - All day every day, collect key from Deepdale Information.
- **Number of beds** - 50
- **Booking** - Pre-booking recommended. Max group size 12. See website.
- **Price per night** - From £10.50 (£63 per week) dorm room. £28 twin/double room.
- **Public Transport** - Train and coaches at Kings Lynn (25 Miles). Coast Hopper bus to Burnham Deepdale on the coast road from Kings Lynn to Cromer, stops at Sandringham, Holkham and Titchwell Bird Reserve. Travelline 0870 6082608
- **Directions** - GR 803443 On A149 Coast road halfway between Hunstanton and Wells-next-the-Sea. Beside Dalegate Market, opposite Deepdale Church.

CONTACT:
Deepdale Farm, Burnham Deepdale, Norfolk, PE31 8DD
Tel: (01485) 210256
info@deepdalefarm.co.uk www.deepdalefarm.co.uk

MOORSIDE FARM
BUNKHOUSE
ENGLAND

Moorside Farm is a 300-year-old farmhouse set 1200 feet up in the beautiful Peak District National Park on the Derbyshire/Staffordshire border and approximately five miles from the historic town of Buxton. Sleeping accommodation is provided in two areas, one for 14 - this is alpine style with pine clad ceiling and a pine floor with bunk beds. The second area has 6 beds, also in bunks and is an ideal room for a small group or family. Downstairs there are showers, toilets and a large dining/general room. The farmhouse has full central heating and drying facilities are available. We provide a three course breakfast, a packed lunch and a substantial dinner in the evening, vegetarians are catered for. A small kitchen is available for making tea and coffee. Ample parking space is provided. The farmhouse has a current fire certificate. All bookings have sole use of the accommodation.

DETAILS

- **Open** - All year, 24 hours
- **Number of beds** - 20: 1 x 14 : 1 x 6
- **Booking** - Booking with deposit required with two weeks' notice
- **Price per night** - £25.00 per person, bed, breakfast and evening meal included. £17.00 per person bed and breakfast. (min 4 persons)
- **Public Transport** - Nearest train station Buxton. Take bus to Longnor or Travellers Rest. Bus enquiries (01332) 292200
- **Directions** - GR SK 055 670. Leave A53, Buxton to Leek road, at Travellers Rest, take 4th lane on left, down to T junction, take first left, Moorside Farm is first right entrance.

CONTACT: Charlie
Hollinsclough, Longnor, Buxton, Derbyshire SK17 0RF
Tel: (01298) 83406
moorsidefarm@yahoo.co.uk www.moorsidefarm.com

SHEEN
BUNKHOUSE

Sheen Bunkhouse is a newly converted barn in a quiet corner of the Peak District, close to the beautiful Dove and Manifold valleys. Comprehensively equipped, it offers a large TV lounge, well-equipped self-catering facilities and two bunkrooms with wash basins. Toilets and showers are conveniently located for both rooms.

Passing close by the barn, the Manifold Valley Track, Tissington Trail and High Peak Trail provide easy access to beautiful countryside, ideal for families and cyclists. Dovedale, the Upper Dove Valley and the remote and mysterious moorlands around Flash and Longnor offer stunning scenery for walkers. Visit the markets and parks at Buxton (8 miles), Leek (10 miles) and Bakewell (12 miles) for a great day out. Other attractions include Alton Towers (35mins by car) and the famous Opera House and show caves at Buxton.

DETAILS

- **Open** - All year, 24 hours access, reception 8-10am, 5-9pm
- **Number of beds** - 14: 1x8, 1x6
- **Booking** - Book by phone or email
- **Price per night** - Adults £12.00, Under 18's £8.00.
- **Public Transport** - Train station at Buxton. Daily bus operated by Bowers from Buxton to Hartington passes close to bunkhouse.
- **Directions** - On the B5054 between Hartington and Hulme End take the turning to Sheen (also signposted for 'Staffordshire Knott'). The bunkhouse is on the right 200yds after the pub.

CONTACT: Graham Belfield
Peakstones, Sheen, Derbyshire, SK17 0ES
Tel: (01298) 84501, Fax: (01298) 84501
grahambelfield@fsmail.net

BARN FARM
ENGLAND **BARNS AND CAMPSITE**

Barn Farm is a working livestock farm in the Peak District National Park with fine views over the Derwent valley. It borders the mystical Stanton Moor with its Victorian stone carvings and ancient Nine Ladies stone circle. Robin Hoods Stride and other bouldering and climbing areas are nearby and the area is excellent for walking with the Limestone Way long distance path passing close by. Birchover has a village shop and two pubs which serve food, one of which is the famous 'Druid Inn'. Barn Farm provides camping with good shower, toilet and laundry facilities and four camping barns. Sabine Hay Barn, Hill Carr Barn, Warren Carr Barn and the Stable Barn provide well appointed accommodation. Sabine Hay has 15 bunkbeds arranged around a communal space with fully fitted kitchen and table and chairs. Hill Carr barn and Warren Carr have a similar arrangement with 15 and 12 single beds respectively. Stables Barn has 6 bunkbeds. All bunkhouses have self-catering facilities, are heated and have private bathroom and shower facilities in adjacent barns.

DETAILS

- **Open** - All year, accommodation available all day.
- **Number of beds** - Hill Carr / Sabine Hay 15:1x15, Warren 12:1x12, Stables 6:1x6
- **Booking** - Booking advisable 50% deposit.
- **Price per night** - Hill Carr £140, Sabine Hay £130, Warren Carr £240, Stables Barn £100. Weekly rates available. Camping £7.50pp (£4.50 for DofE groups)
- **Public Transport** - The 172 bus from Bakewell to Matlock runs approx. hourly.
- **Directions** - From the A6 between Matlock and Bakewell take the B5056. Follow signs for Birchover, continue past the Druid Inn to farm sign at the top of the village.

CONTACT:
Birchover, Matlock, Derbyshire, DE4 2BL
Tel: (01629) 650245
gilberthh@msn.com   www.peakdistrictonline.co.uk

BUSHEY HEATH FARM
BUNK BARNS
ENGLAND

Bushey Heath Farm is a family run smallholding in the heart of the Peak District, central to all the popular visitor centres, but just off the beaten track. Offering a summer campsite, self-catering static caravan and 'top of the range' bunkbarns for up to 14 people. Incorporating a Ground Source Heat Pump, a wind turbine for electricity and rainwater harvesting for wc flushing. We have developed the farm in an environmentally sensitive way so visitors can experience practical sustainable ideas. The static caravan has two bedrooms and shower/wc and can sleep up to 6. The Hen House Bunk Barn has two bedrooms with bunks for 4 in each. The Little Barn has a large single bedroom with bunks for 6 people. Both barns have luxury shower rooms and a combined fully equipped kitchen/diner open area downstairs. Sleeping bags required. Good dogs accepted.

DETAILS

- **Open** - All year. Campsite May till October, opening hours by arrangement
- **Number of beds** - 8: Hen House, 6: Little Barn, 6: Static caravan, 80 Pitches.
- **Booking** - Camping at Bank Hols only. Bunkhouse early with deposit advisable.
- **Price per night** - Camping Adult £4, Child £2, Vehicle £2. Static Caravan £160-£285 per week, short breaks available. Hen House - sole use £120pn .Little Barn – sole use £90pn. Weekends sole use only.
- **Public Transport** - Nearest trains at Hope (4 miles), Nearest buses in Tideswell (2 miles). Bus numbers 65, 66, x67, 173, 177, 197, 202.
- **Directions** - GR SK 146 785. From Tideswell take Manchester Road past Star Pub and cross over A623, road stops at farm. Going west along A623, 11/2 mile past the Anchor Pub turn right at cross roads in 's' bends..

CONTACT: Rod Baraona or Lisa Thomas
Tideswell Moor,Tideswell, Buxton, Derbyshire, SK17 8JE
Tel: (01298) 873007, Mobile: 07710 163376
rod@baraona.freeserve.co.uk www.busheyheathfarm.co.uk

The Reckoning House camping barn has been renovated to a high standard including double glazing and insulation. It is situated on the edge of Lathkill Dale, 3 miles from Bakewell. Lathkill Dale is a nature reserve managed by English Nature to protect a variety of flora and fauna as well as some outstanding geological features. Horse riding, fishing, golf and cycle hire are all available locally. There are also many local walks including the Limestone Way. It has a cooking area, 4 calor gas rings (gas supplied) a washing up sink with hot water, a toilet, washbasin, storage heaters in all rooms and shower inside the barn. The sleeping area is upstairs and has two separate sleeping floors.

DETAILS

- **Open** - All year, by arrangement
- **Number of beds** - 12
- **Booking** - Sole use bookings only ,in advance (min 2 nights at weekends). 10% deposit, balance 2 weeks before arrival.
- **Price per night** - £8.50 per person. Sole use £85 per night, Reduction for sole use on Sun (excluding bank holidays), Mon, Tue, Wed or Thurs nights.
- **Public Transport** - Train stations at Buxton (10 miles) and Matlock (13 miles). National Express drop at Bakewell. Local buses (enquiries (01332) 292200) go to Bakewell from Monyash, Over Haddon and Buxton.
- **Directions** - GR 184 666. Take the B5055 out of Bakewell towards Monyash. Continue for 3 miles. After passing Haddon Grove Farm holiday cottages (the second set of cottages on right), take the first turn left at the signpost to Haddon Grove. Bear left at the bottom of the lane. The camping barn is the first on the left in a half mile.

CONTACT:
Mandale Farm, Haddon Grove, Bakewell, Derbyshire, DE45 1JF
Tel: (01629) 812416
julia.finney@virgin.net

HOMESTEAD
AND CHEESEHOUSE

The Bunkhouses are situated on a small mixed farm in the middle of Bamford, just 3 miles from Stanage Edge. The Derwent Dams are between 1.5 and 7 miles further up the valley. Castleton is 5 miles to the north, Chatsworth 10 miles to the south west. Both bunkhouses have individual bunks each with mattress, fitted sheets and pillow, gas central heating and drying facilities. Homestead has 22 beds in 3 rooms, and 2 bathrooms with 2 toilets and showers in each, a large dayroom with oak seating and a fully equipped kitchen with gas cooker. Cheesehouse is a self-contained bunkhouse with four bunks, ideal for a small family or group. It has a shower and toilet and is equipped with a kitchen having cooking rings, a microwave oven, toaster and kettle. The Bunkhouses are 2 minutes walk from two pubs. No dogs.
PLEASE CONTACT THIS HOSTEL BY PHONE OR POST

DETAILS

- **Open** - All year, no restriction
- **Number of beds** - Homestead 22: 1x10, 2x6. Cheesehouse 4: 1x4.
- **Booking** - Recommended for weekends.
- **Price per night** - £9 per person. Sole use: Homestead £160, Cheesehouse £34.
- **Public Transport** - Nearest train station Bamford, 10 mins walk. Bus 274 & 275 operates Sundays Bamford/Sheffield or to Castleton. Bus 272 Bamford to Sheffield and Castleton. Bus 175 Bamford/Bakewell.
- **Directions** - The farm is in the centre of Bamford on South View Lane (turn off A6013 at the 'Country Stores').

CONTACT: Helena Platts
The Farm, Bamford, Hope Valley, S33 0BL
Tel: (01433) 651298
sam@backpackerspress.com

PINDALE FARM
OUTDOOR CENTRE

The Centre is situated one mile from Castleton in the heart of the Peak District. The centre comprises a farmhouse pre-dating 1340 and lead mine buildings from the 1850s, which have been completely rebuilt from a near derelict condition. The Centre now offers 5 different kinds of accommodation. The farmhouse offers traditional bed and (an AGA cooked) breakfast. The Barn has 6 independent self-catering units, the lower 3 of these can accommodate people with certain physical disabilities. The old Lead Mine Engine House, our logo, is a self-catering unit sleeping 8. The Powder House, originally the mine's explosive store, is a small camping barn with basic facilities for up to 4 people. A campsite, adjacent to the Centre, has showers, hot water, and toilet facilities. The Centre is the ideal base for walking, climbing, caving, horse riding etc. Instruction is available if required. Well behaved pets welcome.

DETAILS

■ **Open** - All year (Camping March-October), 24 hours
■ **Number of beds** - 64 bunkbeds plus camping and B&B
■ **Booking** - Early booking (deposit) is best.
■ **Price per night** - All prices are pp, per night. Camping £4.00, Powder House £5, Engine House and Barn £8.00, B&B £25 with four poster bed, and an AGA breakfast.
■ **Public Transport** - Hope has a train station. The nearest National Express service is in Sheffield. Approximate taxi fare to Sheffield is £15-£20. On local buses ask for Hope. Hope is 15 minutes walk from the hostel.
■ **Directions** - GR 163 825   From Hope follow cement works signs, turn off main road between church and Woodroffe Arms.

CONTACT:
Pindale Lane, Hope, Hope Valley, Derbyshire, S33 6RN
Tel: (01433) 620111, Fax: (01433) 620729
pindalefarm@btconnect.com www.pindale.fsbusiness.co.uk

Thorpe Farm Bunkhouses are situated a mile northeast of Hathersage, on a family run mixed/dairy farm. It is 2 miles from Stanage Edge and other popular climbing and walking areas are nearby. Castleton is 6 miles up the Hope Valley and Eyam is 6 miles southwest. The dormitories have individual bunks each with mattress and pillow. There is some sleeping space in the sitting rooms and room for camping outside. The bunkhouses have heating, drying facilities, hot showers, toilets, electric/gas cooking, fridges, freezers, electric kettles, toasters etc. The Byre is on one level with disabled facilities.

DETAILS

- **Open** - All year, no restrictions
- **Number of beds** - Old Shippon 32: 2x12, 2x4. Byre 14: 1x6, 2x4. Old Stables 14: 1x8, 1x6. Pondside 14: 1x8, 1x6
- **Booking** - Highly recommended for weekends.
- **Price per night** - From £10pp. Sole use from £94 per night.
- **Public Transport** - Train station at Hathersage, 10 mins walk from bunkhouse. Bus service 272 operates from Sheffield to Hathersage. Weekends only bus service 257 operates from Sheffield via Stanage & Snake Pass to Hathersage. Details phone Busline (01298) 230980 or (01246) 250450.
- **Directions** - GR 223 824. If walking from A6187/A625 in Hathersage turn right (just past the George Hotel) up Jaggers Lane, turn second right up Coggers Lane and fifth turning on left (signed Thorpe Farm). If driving follow the road from Hathersage towards Hope for ¾ mile, then turn right into private drive (signposted Thorpe Farm).

CONTACT: Jane Marsden
Thorpe Farm, Hathersage, Peak District, Via Sheffield, S32 1BQ
Tel: (01433) 650659
marsdenhathersage@surfree.co.uk www.thorpe-bunk.co.uk

CHESTER
BACKPACKERS

Chester Backpackers is located just a few minutes walk from the ancient heart of the historic city of Chester in an original Tudor coaching inn (formally the Waterloo Inn). We offer clean, comfortable rooms most of which have en-suite facilities, with freshly laundered linen provided as standard. Free tea and coffee, free left luggage facilities and well-equipped rooms make Chester Backpackers an ideal base for walking the Roman walls of Chester, exploring the nearby Welsh mountains and dramatic coastline or day trips to Liverpool and Manchester. We can also assist with finding work for longer-term travellers and our attractive long-term rates make it an ideal location to spend time in this beautiful city. We are open 24 hours with no curfew, and our friendly well-trained staff (travellers themselves) are on hand to offer help and advice.

DETAILS

- **Open** - All year, 24 hours , no curfew
- **Number of beds** - 32: 1 x 18 : 1 x 8 : 2 x 2 : 2 x 1
- **Booking** - Book by phone or email. Strongly recommended at weekends, 2 to 4 days notice, advisable at other times
- **Price per night** - Dorm £15pp Single £22pp Dbl/ twin £40 per room. (most rooms are en-suite). Long term rates available.
- **Public Transport** - Hostel is 10 mins walk from train station and National Express coach station. Liverpool and Manchester airports are 30 mins drive away.
- **Directions** - From train walk up City Rd, at ring road (nr Last Orders) bear left into Boughton (A41). Hostel 100 metres on left. From National Express walk up Union St with park on right, turn right at major junction. Hostel 100m on left. Car park at rear.

CONTACT:
67 Boughton, Chester, CH3 5AF
Tel: (01244) 400185
sales@chesterbackpackers.co.uk www.chesterbackpackers.co.uk

EMBASSIE
HOSTEL

ENGLAND

The Embassie is a terrace house in an unspoilt Georgian square used in the filming of 'In the Name of the Father'. The house was built in 1820 and until 1986 it was the Consulate of Venezuela. Only 15 minutes walk from city centre.

Liverpool is known for it's nightlife, a student population of 70,000 ensures a lively scene, bands start playing at 11pm and bars are regularly open till 2am. Hostellers have a key to come and go, the hostel is clean, safe and staffed 24 hours. Bedding is provided (including sheets) and free coffee, tea, toast and jam are available 24 hours, eat as much as you want.
International, or UK regional travellers only, NO LOCALS.

DETAILS

- **Open** - All year, 24 hr access with key.
- **Number of beds** - 40:
- **Booking** - Booking is not essential for individuals. Groups larger than 6 should book (20% deposit).
- **Price per night** - £15 (Sunday to Thursday), £17.50 (Friday), £20 (Saturday).
- **Public Transport** - Liverpool has a train station and is served by National Express Coaches. A £3.50 taxi fare will bring you from the train or bus station to the hostel door, (good idea if you have a heavy rucksack).
- **Directions** - From the Anglican Cathedral (the third largest in the world) continue uphill along Canning Street away from the city centre. This will bring you into Falkner Square (15-20 mins). The hostel has a red door and is by a phone box.

CONTACT: Kevin
1 Falkner Square, Liverpool, L8 7NU
Tel: (0151)7071089
kevertonm@msn.com www.embassie.com

The International Inn is a multi award-winning hostel in a converted Victorian warehouse, located in the heart of Liverpool City Centre's cultural quarter.

Liverpool has a wealth of attractions for visitors and you will find theatres, heritage, two Cathedrals as well as the City's renowned nightlife venues just a stone's throw away. The Hostel is also ideally located for visiting students, being opposite the University. The International Inn provides fully heated accommodation in en-suite dormitories of 2, 4,6, 8 and 10 beds. Private fully furnished apartments also available. Facilities include a café, fully equipped kitchen, TV/DVD/games lounge, laundry, baggage store, internet access and information desk. There are no curfews to curtail your evening's fun.

DETAILS

- **Open** - All year, all day
- **Number of beds** - 103: 4x2, 5x4, 2x5, 1x6, 1x7, 4x8, 2x10 plus apartments
- **Booking** - Advisable at the weekend
- **Price per night** - From £15 (dorm) or £18 per person in twin room. Price includes tea, coffee, toast'n'jam 24hrs.
- **Public Transport** - Liverpool Lime Street Station 10 minutes walk away. National Express Station 10-15 minutes walk.
- **Directions** - From Lime St Station take the Skelhorn St exit. Turn left up hill and continue along Copperas Hill. At Main Road jnct. turn right along Russell St, continuing along Clarence St then Rodney St. At jnct. of Hardman St (HSBC bank on corner) turn left. South Hunter St is 2nd on left. The hostel is 20m up on the right.

CONTACT:
South Hunter Street, (off Hardman Street), Liverpool, L1 9JG
Tel: (0151) 709 8135
info@internationalinn.co.uk www.internationalinn.co.uk

Recently refurbished to it's 100 year old spender and winner of the Manchester Tourism Customer Care award, The Hatters has firmly established itself as the city's favourite hostel. Located in the Northern Quarter in the heart of the city centre, this is an ideal spot to start exploring the north west of England.

Hatters caters for independent travellers and groups. It has a fully serviced kitchen with seating for groups of up to 50 and free all-day continental breakfast. There is an internet cafe and free wireless connection. Let the knowledgeable and friendly staff guide you to the best that this great city has to offer, from live music and football to restaurants, shopping, museums, pubs and clubs. Three star graded with Visit Britain.

DETAILS

- **Open** - All year, 24 hours
- **Number of beds** - 150: 1x18, 7x10, 6x8, 1x6, 2x4, 2x2, 3x1
- **Booking** - Booking recommended, essential for groups with deposit. ID is required at check in. Booking not essential for individuals.
- **Price per night** - From £14.50 in an 18 bed dorm, £15.50 in a 8 to 10 bed dorm, £17.50 in a 4 to 6 bed dorm and from £25 per person in private rooms.
- **Public Transport** - We are located only 5 minutes from Piccadilly railway station which is in the city centre. The main bus and tram station is on Piccadilly Gardens which is literally around the corner.
- **Directions** - Coming into Manchester follow signs for Piccadilly Station. Newton Street is at the top of Portland and London Piccadilly Road.

CONTACT:
50 Newton Street, Manchester, M1 2EA
Tel: (0161) 236 9500
Manchester@hattersgroup.com www.hattersgroup.com

BROOK HOUSE BARN

ENGLAND

Brook House Barn provides comfortable, self-catering accommodation ideally suited for families, groups or individuals. This high standard barn conversion has a fully equipped kitchen/dining area, drying room, utility, and a large lounge with panoramic views over the Wolds countryside. There are 2 bedrooms on the ground floor and 3 bedrooms and a small lounge on the first floor. The bedrooms have a mix of beds and bunks, bed linen is provided and all have en-suite shower rooms. A two bedroom (4/5 person) cottage converted to a similar standard (graded Visit Britain 4 *) is also available. The village of Scamblesby, at the heart of the Lincolnshire Wolds and on the Viking Way, has footpaths, bridle ways and meandering country lanes. The historic market towns of Louth and Horncastle are 10 mins drive, Lincoln, Boston and the Coastal Beaches are 1/2 hour away. Cadwell Park racing circuit, Market Rasen racecourse and the Battle of Britain and Aviation Heritage centres are nearby.

DETAILS

- **Open** - All year, flexible accesss.
- **Number of beds** - 20:
- **Booking** - Booking advisable, 20% deposit, balance 1 month prior to visit.
- **Price per night** - From £15pp, family and group rates available. Whole barn hire Fri Sat Sun, 2 nights £300 per night, 3 nights £270 per night. Mon to Thurs, 2 nights £250 per night, 3 or 4 nights £220 per night. Whole barn £1500-00 per week.
- **Public Transport** - Trains: Lincoln, Grimsby. Coaches: Louth, Horncastle. Interconnect 6 (0845 234 3344) calls at Scamblesby and other villages in the Wolds.
- **Directions** - Scamblesby village is just off the main A153 Horncastle to Louth rd.

CONTACT: The Strawsons
Watery Lane, Scamblesby, Nr Louth, Lincolnshire, LN11 9XL
Tel: (01507) 343266
enquiry@brookhousefarm.com www.barnbreaks.co.uk

YORK
BACKPACKERS

York Backpackers is situated in a magnificent historic mansion, inside the medieval city walls and just 5 minutes from Rail and Coach stations. It is a short stroll from the gothic York Minster and the world-famous Jorvik Viking Centre. Open all year round with friendly staff who are always on hand to help.

Our Dungeons Bar is open till late providing the perfect environment to meet travellers from all over the world. Breakfast, bedding (including sheets) and hot showers (available all day) are all free. There are 135 beds available in double rooms, family rooms and dorms. Other facilities include self-catering kitchen, laundry, TV and video room, internet & 24 hour security.

DETAILS

- **Open** - All year, 24 hours
- **Number of beds** - 135: 2x18,1x17,1x16,2x12,2x10,1x8,1x6, 2xfamily(5) & 1xTwin
- **Booking** - Booking is advised especially on weekends and in summer. Deposit / full payment required.
- **Price per night** - From £9pp in a dorm room (Sunday). All prices include breakfast.
- **Public Transport** - York has coach and rail stations 5 minutes walk.
- **Directions** - By Car: From A64 take A1036 into York. Continue straight past race course and into Micklegate. We're 100 metres along on the left opposite the church. From Rail station: Turn right out of the station for 300 metres. Take the first left through the medieval gate into Micklegate. From Coach Station: Head up the hill towards the traffic lights. At the end of Rougier St, turn right onto Micklegate.

CONTACT: Reception
Micklegate House, 88-90 Micklegate, York, YO1 6JX
Tel: (01904) 627720, Fax: (01904) 339350
mail@yorkbackpackers.co.uk www.yorkbackpackers.co.uk

GUINNESS
St. Patrick's
party

Events start
Friday 17th March

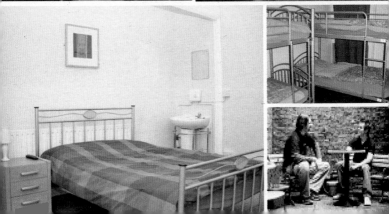

NABURN STATION

ENGLAND

Naburn Station is a converted railway station situated on the Trans Pennine Trail and Sustrans cycle route 65. It offers high quality accommodation ideal for cyclists and walkers. It also provides the perfect base for exploring the many delights of York and North Yorkshire with easy access to the city, the moors, the dales and the coast. The local village pub provides basic groceries and good food and there are other pubs and shops within easy walking and cycling distance. Cycle and boat hire are available locally and there are riding stables in the village. Facilities include a well equipped kitchen, a laundry and drying room, off road parking, secure bike storage and internet access. All bedding and towels are provided. No smoking. Pets and children welcome.

DETAILS

- **Open** - All year, 24 hours
- **Number of beds** - Singles/twins/double and up to 4 beds
- **Booking** - Advised in Summer + bank holidays
- **Price per night** - £15pp,under 14 yrs £10. Inc:bedding, towels,tea and coffee. Camping £5 per person. 10% discount for cyclists.
- **Public Transport** - Trains at York(5 miles) and Selby (10 miles). Arriva bus 42 between Selby and York stops at bottom of the drive. Collection can be arranged from either station and local bike hire is available.
- **Directions** - On A19 from York turn right at sign to Naburn just before A64 ring road junction. From A64 Selby junction follow A19 towards York. Take first left signed Naburn. Just before the village go under the old railway bridge and turn immediately left. On sustrans cycle route 65, 5mins walk from Naburn.

CONTACT: Ann
Station House, Naburn, York, YO19 4RW
Tel: (01904) 647528 mob:07775 572 130
Saturn65@btinternet.com

WHITBY BACKPACKERS
AT HARBOUR GRANGE

Harbour Grange is Whitby's long established friendly, backpackers hostel. It is beautifully situated on the River Esk, in Whitby itself, and only 5 minutes walk from train and bus stations. The hostel is all on the ground floor and has good facilities for self-catering with a dining area and a separate lounge area, both big enough to seat 24 people. There are 5 dormitories and family rooms are available on request. The hostel is open all day but so that everyone can have a chance of a good night's sleep, there is a curfew at 11.30 (quiet at midnight). The premises are non-smoking.

Whitby is a beautiful little fishing town surrounded by beaches and moorland. Here you can find stunning views from cliff walks and visit lovely villages like Grosmont where steam trains run to Pickering & Goathland where Heartbeat is filmed. Take a look at where Captain Cook lived and the Abbey that has stood as a landmark for 800 years.

DETAILS

■ **Open** - 1st April - 31st Oct. Open all year for groups booked in advance, Hostel open all day. Check in 5pm-9pm.
■ **Number of beds** - 24: 1 x 2 : 2 x 4 : 1 x 6 : 1 x 8.
■ **Booking** - Booking advised for weekends and for groups, 10% deposit.
■ **Price per night** - From £14 per person. Sole use £240 a night.
■ **Public Transport** - Whitby has a train station and a bus station.
■ **Directions** - From Whitby train and bus stations: cross the bridge and turn right. Follow the river. First right after 'The Bottom House' pub.

CONTACT: Birgitta Ward-Foxton
Spital Bridge, Whitby, North Yorkshire, YO22 4EF
Tel: (01947) 600817, Mobile 0777 9798611
backpackers@harbourgrange.co.uk www.whitbybackpackers.co.uk

BRANSDALE
MILL

Bransdale Mill is a converted Water Mill at the head of an unspoiled and hidden valley in the North York Moors. Accommodation is comfortable, but basic. It is an ideal base from which to get away from it all and to enjoy peace and tranquillity in beautiful countryside. There are many fine walks in the surrounding area, which is rich in wildlife. The nearest towns are Kirkbymoorside and Helmsley, both 10 miles away, and the North Yorkshire coast can be reached within an hour. The local pubs are 8 miles away, both of which serve food. Local attractions include the North Yorkshire Moors Railway; Heartbeat Country; National Trust properties at Nunnington, Rievaulx, Bridestones, and the Yorkshire Coast; Pickering and Helmsley Castles and Duncombe Park. The surrounding farmland is owned by the National Trust and let to tenant farmers; please respect the working life of the Dale.

DETAILS

■ **Open** - All year, but used for NT holidays at peak spring/summer times, All day
■ **Number of beds** - 13: 1 x 7 : 1 x 6.
■ **Booking** - Essential, min. 2 weeks in advance.
■ **Price per night** - £110 per group (discounts may be available for small groups - please contact for details)
■ **Public Transport** - National Express to Pickering. Local buses Malton (18 miles) and Kirkbymoorside. Taxi Kirkbymoorside approx £10.
■ **Directions** - From Kirkbymoorside Market Place left at the mini roundabout take left fork to Fadmoor continue 9 miles. Just before the head of Bransdale see a gate with sign 'Basecamp', follow track to Mill.

CONTACT: Anne Deebank
Bransdale, Fadmoor, York, YO62 7JL
Tel: (01751) 431693
anne.deebank@nationaltrust.org.uk

WHITEFIELDS
COTTAGE
ENGLAND

Situated on a medieval deer-park, Whitefields Cottage offers self-catering accommodation within the Fountains Abbey and Studley Royal Estate. Cared for by the National Trust and awarded World Heritage Site status in 1986, the estate contains a beautiful water garden, Elizabethan mansion and a Cistercian abbey. Whitefields is a 19th-century cottage on the edge of Studley Royal Deer Park, home to around 500 Red, Fallow and Sika deer. Whether you want to explore the water gardens and impressive abbey, or walk around the North York moors (1hr drive) or Yorkshire Dales, Whitefields is ideal. It is fully equipped to offer groups of up to 16 people inexpensive but comfortable accommodation.

DETAILS

- **Open** - All year, except Christmas and New Year, no restrictions
- **Number of beds** - 16: 1 x 6 : 1 x 8 : 1 x 2.
- **Booking** - Bookings required 2 weeks in advance, non refundable deposit £60
- **Price per night** - Sole use, Sun to Thurs £100, Friday and Sat £160, full week £700.
- **Public Transport** - Train station and National Express coaches at Harrogate (15 miles). Regular bus service between Harrogate and Ripon. Taxis Ripon to Whitefields £5 - Harrogate to Whitefields £20.
- **Directions** - From B6265 turn to Studley Roger. Drive through village, bear sharp right, before the National Trust sign, into deer park. Half a mile up main avenue turn right sign-posted 'estate vehicles only'. Turn right up the track at the end of this road, Whitefields is at top of track. Telephone estate office (during office hours) for gate code if arriving after 6pm Winter or 9pm Summer.

CONTACT: Joanne Hudson
Fountains Abbey and Studley Royal Park, Fountains, Ripon, HG4 3DY
Tel: (01765) 643172
joanne.hudson@nationaltrust.org.uk

WEST END
OUTDOOR CENTRE

Situated in the Yorkshire Dales amidst stunning landscape overlooking Thruscross Reservoir in a designated Area of Outstanding Natural Beauty on the edge of the Dales National Park, this self-catering accommodation centre offers excellent facilities for up to 30 people in 9 bedrooms with bunk beds. Leaders' en-suite accommodation has private catering, dining and lounge facilities. The centre is fully centrally heated. There are 4 showers, 4 hand basins and 4 toilets. There are no extra charges for heating, lighting and hot water. The well-equipped kitchen includes a 4-oven Aga cooker, two fridges and a freezer, together with all the cooking utensils and equipment. 3 star Hostel. Ideal for Team Building Courses, Schools, Scouts, Guides and family parties etc. Located only 12 miles from Harrogate and Skipton, 30 miles from the City of York. Tourist Board inspected and managed by the owners. All groups must be accompanied by an adult (25+).

DETAILS

- **Open** - All year, flexible
- **Number of beds** - 30 :- 4 x 2 : 3 x 4 : 1 x 6 : 1 x 4 en-suite
- **Booking** - Advisable at weekends
- **Price per night** - £10 pp. Sole use £250 (Sat/Sun/Bank Hol), £190 any other night, £575 for 4 nights midweek. Sunday night, if staying for 2+ nights £150.
- **Public Transport** - Nearest train stations are at Harrogate and Skipton, both 12 miles from the hostel. Taxi fare from either station would be approximately £18.
- **Directions** - GR 146 575. Leave A59 at Blubberhouses, signed West End 2.5 miles. Do not turn off, centre is on left side.

CONTACT:
West End, Summerbridge, Harrogate, HG3 4BA
Tel: (01943) 880207
m.verity@virgin.net www.westendoutdoorcentre.co.uk

Airton Quaker Meeting house was built in 1690 by William Ellis and the adjoining hostel was originally a stable for the Quakers attending the meetings. The stable was converted into a wartime evacuee hostel in 1940 and used as a holiday hostel from 1943 with a modernisation in 1983. The meeting house is still used for worship. The hostel is situated in the centre of Airton, a typical Yorkshire Dales village on the banks of the River Aire. The Pennine Way passes the village and Malham Cove, Janet's Foss and Gordale Scar are in walking distance. The hostel has a self-catering kitchen / common area and 3 rooms, 2 with 4 bunks, 1 with 6. Blankets and pillows are provided but you must bring your own sleeping bag. There is a farm shop and café at Airton (closed Mondays) and more facilities in Gargrave. Parties of children (except families) must be accompanied by two adults. No animals permitted except guide dogs.

DETAILS

- **Open** - All year, no restrictions
- **Number of beds** - 14: 2 x 4 ; 1 x 6
- **Booking** - Advance booking is recommended with a deposit of 10%.
- **Price per night** - £8 (adults) £4 (Children under 10). Exclusive use of the hostel is available for a supplement charge.
- **Public Transport** - Nearest train stations Gargrave (4.5miles), Skipton (8.5miles). Buses from Skipton to Malham pass through Airton. Approx taxi fare from Skipton £12.
- **Directions** - GR 904 592 Block of buildings at the end of Airton Village on the top of the hill leading down to the river bridge.

CONTACT: Mr or Mrs Parker
The Nook, Airton, Skipton, North Yorkshire, BD23 4AE
Tel: (01729) 830263
bobminor@aol.com

Dalesbridge is located on the A65 at Austwick, on the edge of the Yorkshire Dales National Park, just five miles from both Ingleton and Settle. It is a comfortable venue for those visiting the Yorkshire Dales, whether you are a family, a group or an individual. The six bed units have a kitchen area with a cooker, fridge, washing up sink, shower and toilet. Crockery, cutlery and cooking pots are provided and there is a seating area in the middle of the room. The four bed units have a shower and toilet, small seating area with kettle, toaster, microwave, crockery and cutlery. These rooms are ideal for the smaller group not requiring full self-catering facilities. Utilising all the units provides group accommodation for up to 40. You will need to bring your own sleeping bag and pillow, alternatively bedding is available to hire. We have a great deal to offer: bar, drying room, functions, B&B, and campsite.

DETAILS

- **Open** - All year, reception open 9:00-17:00
- **Number of beds** - 40
- **Booking** - Advance booking with deposit
- **Price per night** - £14 per person. ~ £72 - 6 bed unit ~ £48 - 4 bed unit.
- **Public Transport** - Settle railway station is 5 miles away and Clapham station 1.5 miles. There are infrequent buses but if you would like collection from either railway station please give us a call.
- **Directions** - GR 762 676. The hostel is on the main A65. When travelling from Settle towards Ingleton we are situated on the left hand side between the two turnings into Austwick.

CONTACT: Jon
Austwick, Nr Settle, LA2 8AZ
Tel: (015242) 51021
info@dalesbridge.co.uk www.dalesbridge.co.uk

LONGRIGG
RESIDENTIAL CENTRE

Longrigg Residential Centre is within walking distance of Sedbergh, only 10 miles from Kendal and less than 10 minutes from the M6, an ideal location for exploring the Lakes and the Yorkshire Dales. The centre stands in its own grounds and overlooks the unspoilt splendour of the Howgill Fells. Perfect for mixed groups or families. Walking cycling, canoeing, and caving are nearby. The centre has recently been refurbished. It has two dormitories sleeping 6 in the main building and a larger separate building sleeping 20 in dormitories of 2,4,6 and 8. There are ample shower and toilet facilities. Sleeping bags and pillowcase are required. The large kitchen is equipped for group catering. The lounge has easy chairs and gives access to the patio area. A separate games room has pool table TV and table football. There is a drying room and tumble dryer. The Centre holds an Adventure Activity Licence and can offer instruction and equipment. Entry is by a touch lock system. The centre is owned by an Education Authority and complies with relevant Health and Safety requirements.

DETAILS

- **Open** - All year, all day
- **Number of beds** - 32: 1x8, 3x6, 1x4, 1x2
- **Booking** - Book by phone or email
- **Price per night** - £13 pp, minimum of 10 people.
- **Public Transport** - Trains at Oxenholme on the West Coast Line.
- **Directions** - Longrigg Centre is located near the village of Sedbergh, which lies on the edge of the Yorkshire Dales and is just 30 minutes from the Lake District. Easy access via M6 junction 37.

CONTACT: Rob Gregory
Frostrow Lane, Sedbergh, Cumbria, LA10 5SW
Tel: (01539) 621161
longrigg.centre@kencomp.net www.longrigg.org.uk

TIMBERLODGE

ENGLAND

Timberlodge is a Scandinavian pine lodge for self-catering groups or individuals, situated half a mile from Ingleton on the edge of the Yorkshire Dales. The surrounding limestone landscape is renowned for it's excellent underground systems. The famous Gaping Ghyll system is popular with cavers and for those that like to keep dry there are show caves featuring stalagmites, stalactites and a massive 200,000-year-old ice age cavern. The Three Peaks Race route is accessible to the enthusiastic walker and from Ingleton there is a pleasant 4 mile walk on maintained footpaths through spectacular waterfall and woodland scenery. The lodge is fully double glazed and centrally heated. It has spacious bunkrooms for 3 to 6 people, hot showers, sauna, and an excellent drying room. The kitchen is well equipped with gas and electric cookers, dishwasher, fridge freezer, microwave and a food warmer which will hold 48 meals. The large dining room has a soft drinks machine and satellite television and video. There is a payphone for incoming/outgoing calls (015242) 42119.

DETAILS

- **Open** - All year, 10am - 10pm
- **Number of beds** - 48:- 4 x 3   6 x 6
- **Booking** - Booking (with deposit) is advised with as much notice as possible, particularly for groups.
- **Price per night** - £13 per person. Exclusive use available.
- **Public Transport** - Nearest train station is at Bentham (3 miles away). Local buses call at Ingleton (1 mile away).
- **Directions** - GR 699719, The hostel is ¾ mile south of Ingleton on the A65.

CONTACT: Robin and Dorothy
Pinecroft, Ingleton, Carnforth, Lancashire, LA6 3DP
Tel: (015242) 41462, Fax: 41462
enquiries@pine-croft.co.uk www.pine-croft.co.uk

The Golden Lion Bunkroom is part of the hotel and is situated in the Yorkshire Dales overlooking Pen-y-ghent. A newly-opened bunkhouse provides an extra 40 beds. These make an ideal base for the adventurous who are tackling the 'Three Peaks' or a welcome break for Pennine Way Walkers. It is believed that The Golden Lion was a coaching inn during the sixteenth century and the old coach highway can still be followed on foot. Three public bars provide a good selection of real ales and The Flag Floored Tap Room makes an ideal place for people who enjoy outdoor activities - even in wet weather there is no need to remove boots to enjoy a refreshing drink. At weekends this bar is used extensively by the local pothole clubs and singing sessions are not uncommon. Visitors with musical instruments and plenty of enthusiasm are welcome! A variety of food can provide anything from a beefburger to an à la carte menu. Vegetarian meals are also available.

DETAILS

- **Open** - All year (except Christmas Day), 11am to 11pm
- **Number of beds** - 15: (1 room in hotel) ; 40 in bunkhouse.
- **Booking** - Booking recommended with deposit of full amount £10 pp per night.
- **Price per night** - £10pp
- **Public Transport** -   Nearest train stations are Settle (6 miles) and Horton (½ mile). Three buses a day stop near to the Golden Lion Hotel. Taxi fare to Settle is approximatly £5-£6.
- **Directions** - Follow signs from Settle to Horton-in-Ribblesdale. We are opposite the church.

CONTACT: Michael Johnson
Horton-in-Ribblesdale, Nr. Settle, North Yorkshire, BD24 0HB
Tel: (01729) 860206, Fax: 860206
tricia@goldenlionhotel.co.uk www.goldenlionhotel.co.uk/

WYTHMOOR FARM
CAMPING BARN

Wythmoor Camping Barn is on the Walney to Wear coast to coast cycle route and a few hundred metres from the Dales Way long distance footpath. It enjoys great views of the Howgill fells and the distant mountains of the Central Lakes. Being only 4.5 miles from Kendal and less than 10 mins from the M6 this is an ideal location for exploring the Lake District and the Yorkshire Dales. The 19th century barn has hot water provided by solar panels, underfloor heating powered by ground source heat pump and mains electricity supplemented by wind turbine. The barn is generously sized for twelve people and includes facilities for wheelchair users, two separate heated shower rooms and a food preparation area with sinks and cooking slabs (bring your own camping stove). Kettle and microwave are provided. Local taxis available for transport to Kendal and Sedburgh. Holmescales Farm Outdoor Centre is close by.

DETAILS

- **Open** - All year, all day
- **Number of beds** - 12: 1x12 (10 single beds, 1 double)
- **Booking** - Book online, by phone or email. Booking not always required
- **Price per night** - £7 per person.
- **Public Transport** - Oxenholme (6.5 miles) and Kendal (4.5 miles) have stations.
- **Directions** - Take Appleby Road (A685) from Kendal. After 2.5 miles turn right signed 'Docker' (single track). Opposite Docker Hall farm take left fork signed Lambrigg. Follow for 2 miles, barn is on left. From M6 Junction 37 take A684 towards Sedburgh; then direct left signed Lambrigg/Beck Foot. After 1.5 miles take left signed Lambrigg and Docker (single track). Barn is on right in half a mile.

CONTACT: Bruce Withington
Wythmoor Farm, Lambrigg, Kendal, LA8 0DH
Tel: Booking office (01946) 758198, Farm mobile 07971 018567
info@lakelandcampingbarns.co.uk www.lakelandcampingbarns.co.uk

Roeburndale Camping Barn is situated in a secluded meadow on the banks of the River Roeburn, and surrounded by native woodlands. It is a mile walk from the car park through woods and over a swing bridge. It is ideal for walkers, study groups or as a quiet retreat.

There are two floors and a balcony overlooking the river. The upstairs has bunk beds for 16 people. Some double and some single beds. Downstairs there are table and chairs, gas cooker and wood burning stove (wood available at £3 per bag). Plenty of eating utensils are provided. There are simple washing and compost toilet facilities. Outside there is a field and a small fire place. Quiet wilderness camping by the river is available for up to 4 tents. There is also a 10 bed study centre for hire - ring (015242) 21880. No dogs.

DETAILS

- **Open** - March to November (inclusive), 24 hours
- **Number of beds** - 16: 1x16 + camping
- **Booking** - At weekends groups booking for 2+ nights get priority. Individuals and single night bookings available mid week and weekends at short notice (eg 1 week) .
- **Price per night** - £90 full weekend (Fri,Sat,Sun) sole use. Single night £40 sole use or £4.50 per person (only at short notice).
- **Public Transport** - Trains at Lancaster (12 miles) and Wennington (3 miles). Hourly buses from Lancaster bus station to Hornby or Wray, then 1 hour walk to barn.
- **Directions** - GR SD 611 650. 12 miles east of Lancaster, Junction 34 on M6. Take A683 then B6480 to Wray or Hornby.

CONTACT: Jane McArthur
Backs Bottom Farm, Roeburndale West, nr Wray, Lancaster, LA2 9LL
Tel: 08454 585795 or (015242) 22214
roeburndalecampingbarn@phonecoop.coop www.middlewood.org.uk

THE OLD SCHOOL
BUNKHOUSE

Situated 4.5 miles from Ingleton in Yorkshire Dales limestone country. Located between Ingleborough and Whernside with superb views of both, the bunkhouse makes an ideal base for sporting or nature holidays. The area is well known for it's scenery including the Three Peaks walk, (Ingleborough, Pen-y-ghent and Whernside), the waterfalls walk and for having some of the best caves and potholes in the country including the famous Gaping Ghyll system and the White Scar show cave.

This is a stone property, which has been converted from an old school, with much of the character remaining and provides self-catering accommodation for up to 30 people. The property comprises lounge, drying room, 3 shower rooms with hand basins and toilets, well equipped kitchen / dining room with industrial cooker, toaster, fridge, freezer, dishwasher, microwave, and payphone. Nearest pub 100 yds.

GROUPS ONLY

DETAILS

- **Open** - All year, 24 hours
- **Number of beds** - 30 (5 x 6)
- **Booking** - Early booking advised for popular times. £100 deposit for 2 nights. 25% for 3 nights or over.
- **Price per night** - Minimum of 20 people £180 per night. £9 per person over 20 and up to maximum of 30. Minimum of 2 nights at weekend.
- **Public Transport** - Ribblehead station 1 mile. Buses run from Ingleton 4.5 miles.
- **Directions** - 4.5 miles on the B6255 Ingleton to Hawes Road, just after Chapel-Le-Dale village on left hand side. 11 miles from Hawes on B6255.

CONTACT: Clare and Peter Fox
Chapel-le-Dale, Ingleton, Carnforth, Lancs, LA6 3AR
Tel: (01729) 823835, Fax: 42327
hyginbarwick@aol.com www.oldschoolbunkhouse.co.uk

The beautiful Dentdale Valley is the ideal place for walking, caving, climbing or just enjoying the stunning views.   Three good pubs and 3 cafés and a shop just a stroll away give you the best of both worlds.

The bunkhouse is set in the grounds of historic Whernside Manor, a grade 2 listed building. This is an English Tourist Board approved bunkhouse, well equipped with cooker, microwave, b/w TV, crockery and pans. All you need is food and sleeping bags (these can be hired). Everyone loves the hot shower rooms and drying rooms.   Lifts are available for groups who wish to go to the village. Barbeque and outdoor eating area for hot days, cosy and heated for colder ones.

The perfect place for a get together. Brochure available on request.

DETAILS

- **Open** - All year, 24 hours
- **Number of beds** - 12: 1 x 12
- **Booking** - Booking essential with 25% deposit
- **Price per night** - £8.50pp   Group use £70.
- **Public Transport** - Dent Station 3 miles. Coach station Kendal 15 miles. Local bus Wednesdays and Saturdays to and from Kendal and Dent.
- **Directions** - Leave M6, junction 37. Follow Sedburgh Road for approx 7 miles, then Dent for 3 miles. Whernside Manor is approx 1.25 miles along the road past the Post Office.

CONTACT: Angela Johnson
Whernside Manor, Dent, Sedburgh, Cumbria, LA10 5RE
Tel: (015396) 25213
whernsidemanor@aol.com www.whernsidemanor.com

HARRIS
HOUSE

Harris House is the outdoor pursuits centre of the William Hulme's Grammar School (Manchester). The centre occupies an old village school, with attached headmaster's house, on the edge of the hamlet of Hardraw. It is a grade II listed building built in 1875 in attractive Dales stone. Ample parking is available in the old playground and the large schoolroom is used for communal activities. The well appointed and practical accommodation is centrally heated throughout and can accommodate groups of up to 34. Hardraw has a camp site, a café and the Green Dragon Inn (adjacent to Hardraw Force waterfall). Many groups use these facilities to complement their visit. The café offers good value, substantial home cooking for groups. In the locality are opportunities for caving, rock climbing, fell walking and cycling (secure storage). The Pennine Way passes the centre. The local town of Hawes has a full range of shops. Harris House is an ideal base for Duke of Edinburgh's award expedition training or educational visits.

DETAILS

- **Open** - All year, 24 hours
- **Number of beds** - 32: 3x8, 2x3, 1x2
- **Booking** - Essential (20% deposit) but short notice bookings are often available.
- **Price per night** - £14 per person, min £140, max £200
- **Public Transport** - Garsdale Station is 8 miles away, connected by infrequent buses. Hawes, a pleasant one and a half mile walk away, has more frequent buses.
- **Directions** - Turn north off A684 1 mile to the west of Hawes and proceed for ½ mile. Harris House is at the west end of the hamlet of Hardraw.

CONTACT: Warden
The Old School, Hardraw, near Hawes, Wensleydale, North Yorkshire, DL8 3LZ
Tel: (0161) 226 2054
john.hardy@whgs-academy.org www.whgs.co.uk

Kirkby Stephen Hostel is a former Methodist church with substantial additions. The old chapel now accommodates a large dining room and kitchens, with a lounge/reading room in the gallery. The bedrooms and dormitories are in a building at the rear, with ample lavatories and showers. In addition to the original stained glass windows, pews, pulpit and organ, the hostel displays over 100 works of art, 15 grandfather clocks, antique furniture and objects of interest. This creates a peaceful country house atmosphere.

Kirkby Stephen is a pleasant market town in the upper Eden valley, situated 15 miles from Kendal, 15 miles from Hawes and on Wainwright's coast to coast path. It also enjoys easy access to Lady Anne's Walk, the Howgill Hills, the Dales National Park and the Lake District. The hostel stands prominently on the main street, with a range of restaurants, cafes, pubs, fish and chip shops and food shops on the doorstep.

PLEASE CONTACT THIS HOSTEL BY PHONE OR POST.

DETAILS

- **Open** - All year, please arrive between 5pm and 9pm
- **Number of beds** - 40: 3x8, 1x6, 1x4, 3x2
- **Booking** - Book by phone. Booking advised but not essential.
- **Price per night** - £17pp. Reductions for groups.
- **Public Transport** - One mile from Kirkby Stephen train station on the Leeds-Carlisle line. Regular buses from Penrith, Kendal and Appleby stop outside hostel.
- **Directions** - In the centre of town on main road. From M6 leave at junction 38 and follow signs to Appleby.

CONTACT: Robert Paley
Market Street, Kirkby Stephen, Yorkshire, CA17 4QQ
Tel: 0870 770 5904 or (01768) 372236 or (01768) 371793 or 0781 771 0311
sam@backpackerspress.com www.IndependentHostelsUK.co.uk

BENTS
CAMPING BARN

Bents Camping Barn was formerly a shepherds' cottage in the 1600s. You will need sleeping bags, walking boots and warm clothes. There are 2 sleeping rooms on the first floor with bunk beds. On the ground floor there is a kitchen with cooking area, a dining area with tables and benches and a WC with washbasins. Other facilities include electric lighting and power points throughout (£1 coin meter), crockery, cutlery, toaster, microwave, 3 electric cooking rings, 2 electric kettles, 2 electric convector heaters, parking. The barn is accessible from the Coast to Coast path and there is good fell walking in the Howgill Fells, Wild Boar Fell and Crosby Garrett Common. Smardale Gill Nature Reserve and Sunbiggin Tarn are nearby. The area is ideal for mountain biking and the Settle to Carlisle Railway is 5 miles away at Kirkby Stephen.

DETAILS

- **Open** - All year, all day
- **Number of beds** - 12 to 14: 1x10, 1x6
- **Booking** - Booking is essential for groups (2 weeks in advance with deposit). Individuals are advised to phone.
- **Price per night** - £7 per person. Sole use £72 per night.
- **Public Transport** - Train Station at Kirkby Stephen (5 miles). Local buses to village of Newbiggin-on-Lune.
- **Directions** - GR MY 708 065 OS map 91. From Junction 38 of the M6 take the A685 to Newbiggin-on-Lune. Take Great Asby Road on left then first right through tall gate. Follow tarmac road past Tower House and follow signs to Bents Farm up farm track.

CONTACT: Dorothy Ousby
Newbiggin-on-Lune, Kirkby-Stephen, Cumbria, CA17 4NX
Tel: Booking (01946) 758198 Dorothy (01768) 371760
info@lakelandcampingbarns.co.uk www.bentscampingbarn.co.uk

FELL END
BUNKHOUSE

Fell End consists of two 18th-century buildings: the Schoolhouse and Greenslack. They provide comfortable bunk-house accommodation for people wishing to explore this beautiful area, overlooking the unspoilt splendour of the Howgill Fells. Perfect for mixed groups, families and people with special needs. Walking, cycling, canoeing, caving nearby and the Lake District is only 1 hour away. The Schoolhouse (white building) sleeps up to 8 people in bunks in the central communal area, plus an extra bed in an adjoining room. The bathroom consists of two toilets, one electric shower and 4 wash basins. Greenslack provides a further 2 bunks and 1 single bed plus a bathroom designed for people with mobility problems. This building has no cooking facilities so cannot be booked separately. All beds have a covered mattress and pillow. The living room has a beautiful multi-fuel-stove, which also heats the radiators. There is a fully equipped kitchen with fridge/freezer and cooker. Entry is by a touch lock system. Dogs allowed under strict supervision. Fell End is owned by the Bendrigg Trust, a charity offering outdoor activities for disabled people.

DETAILS

- **Open** - All year, 24 hours
- **Number of beds** - 14: 1 x 8 : 1 x 5 : 1 x 1.
- **Booking** - Advance booking with 20% deposit
- **Price per night** - £9.00pp (minimum of £54)
- **Public Transport** - Trains at Kirkby Stephen (6 miles) on the Carlisle/Settle/Leeds line. Then take bus 564 Mon to Sat (4 per day). Tel (0870) 6082 608 for times.
- **Directions** - GR:723983(Postcode CA17 4AL). Directions given on booking.

CONTACT: Lynne Irish
Ravenstonedale, Sedbergh, Cumbria, CA17 4LN
Tel: (01539) 723766, Fax: (01539) 722446
Lynne@bendrigg.org.uk www.fellend-bunkhouse.org.uk

Marsett Barn is a back to nature experience, it is an old barn in an old landscape. The barn is basic but full of character and charm and has been sympathetically restored to retain its special place in this dales setting.

On the ground floor there is an entrance area with living and dining space, a wood burning stove, a fully fitted kitchen, a drying area, and a toilet for people with disabilities.

Upstairs there are two sleeping areas, each with platform to sleep 10 people (20 in total). Also toilets with handbasins and showers.

Activities may be available at Low Mill Outdoor Centre from £100 per session. A list of activities is available on request.

DETAILS

- **Open** - All year,
- **Number of beds** - 20 2 platforms x 10
- **Booking** - Booking is essential
- **Price per night** - £8 per person (minimum of £32 per night) includes gas.
- **Public Transport** - The nearest bus stop is Bainbridge (4 miles) and nearest train station Garsdale (11 miles).
- **Directions** - From Marsett Green, access is normally on foot or cycle. From the green, follow the track on left towards Stalling Busk. The Barn is in a field on the right, approximately ½ kilometre from the green.

CONTACT:
c/o Low Mill Outdoor Centre, Askrigg, Leyburn, North Yorkshire, DL8 3HZ
Tel: (01969) 650432
info@lowmill.com www.lowmill.com

STABLES
LODGE

Cartmel is a picturesque village located at the southern end of the Lake District Peninsula, close to the northern shore of Morecambe Bay. Cartmel is an ideal base for exploring the Lake District and surrounding areas. It is popular with families, walkers and cyclists, who appreciate a friendly relaxed environment, wonderful scenery and easy access to both mountains and the coast. The hostel provides affordable self-catering accommodation, with shower and toilet facilities, a common room and a fully equipped kitchen. All you need to bring is a sleeping bag. There is ample free parking, secure bike storage, and both children and dogs are welcome.

DETAILS

- **Open** - All year, by arrangement (office Mon -Fri 9am-4.45pm)
- **Number of beds** - 19: 3 x 2, 1 x 3, 1 x 4, 1 x 6
- **Booking** - Give 24 hours notice at weekends.
- **Price per night** - £10 per person
- **Public Transport** - Trains at Grange-over-Sands and Cark, both approximately 3 miles away, and an hourly bus service operates Monday – Saturday from each. Bus links to Grange-over-Sands are also available from Kendal and Barrow-in-Furness. Information is available from Traveline on 0870 6082608
- **Directions** - Stables Lodge is located in the grounds of Cartmel Racecourse. From the village square, turn right at the Sticky Toffee Pudding shop, and the entrance to Stables Lodge is located on your right hand side past the last house (approx 400 metres). Registration is at the Racecourse Office at the Grandstand on the opposite side of the road.

CONTACT:
The Racecourse, Cartmel, Cumbria, LA11 6QF
Tel: (015395) 36340
info@cartmel-racecourse.co.uk www.cartmel-racecourse.co.uk

DUDDON SANDS
HOSTEL
ENGLAND

The purpose-built Duddon Sands Hostel, overlooking the Duddon Estuary, stands in the grounds of The Ship Inn, built in 1691. A comfortable Lakeland pub, known for good food and real ales. Both are non-smoking but there is a beautiful beer garden where smoking is permitted. The hostel is ideally suited to walkers, bikers, bird watchers, canoeists, climbers and steam train enthusiasts, with the Cumbria Cycle Way and Coast Path running past and with many outdoor pursuits contacts locally who can advise on activities. Bike wash and storage are available. All bedding is provided, and a cot or bed cot-sides can be requested. The Ship serves home cooked meals, including children's and vegetarian, for breakfast, lunch and dinner, and packed lunches. PLEASE CONTACT BY MAIL OR PHONE.

DETAILS

- **Open** - All year, all day
- **Number of beds** - 16 : 2x4, 1x8
- **Booking** - Not essential, but recommended. Deposit if booking whole room.
- **Price per night** - From £13 per person
- **Public Transport** - By train: Change at Barrow-in-Furness or Carlisle onto Cumbrian Coast Line (request stop). By bus: Take X7 (Barrow-in-Furness to Millom). Get off at Moorland Stores Crossroads in Kirkby and follow signs for hostel.
- **Directions** - From M6 J36 take A590 Barrow-in-Furness. After Ulverston, at roundabouts on outskirts of Dalton-in-Furness turn right on A595 for Whitehaven. At Moorland Stores crossroads in centre of Kirkby turn left for Sandside and Train Station. Hostel is at bottom of hill.

CONTACT:
The Ship Inn, Askewgate Brow, Kirkby-in-Furness, Cumbria LA17 7TE
Tel: (01229) 889454
sam@backpackerspress.com www.theship1691.co.uk

FELL END
CAMPING BARN

Fell End is a traditional 18th Century Lakeland stone barn, located within its own grass courtyard approximately ½ mile from the farm. It is in the centre of a 500 acre estate in the western fells with easy access to some spectacular scenery, ideal for walkers, cyclists and wildlife enthusiasts. It is a short drive from Coniston (6 miles) and the Duddon Valley (5 miles). There are magnificent views, star-filled skies (a truly breathtaking sight) and the tranquil 'sound of silence'. Fell End Barn is lit by chandeliers and tea lights (provided) and heated by woodburing stove (a gas heater is also available for hire). There is no electricity and you will need to bring your own cooking and lighting equipment and bedding with mat. There are 2 picnic style tables, a wash basin and w.c. Ideal for campfires or BBQs. Wood is available from the farm.
Check the website www.lakelandcampingbarns.co.uk and book on line..

DETAILS

- **Open** - All year, all day
- **Number of beds** - 12: 1x12
- **Booking** - Book online. Booking in advance is essential.
- **Price per night** - £6.00 per person
- **Public Transport** - Trains: Foxfield (3 miles). Buses: Grizebeck (3 miles).
- **Directions** - Leave M6 at J36, follow the A590 towards Barrow. Near Greenodd Estuary take A5092 signed to Broughton-in Furness. Follow this road until you reach Grizebeck. Just before Grizebeck garage take lane on right signposted 'Woodland'. Follow for 2 miles, over a cattle grid, until road becomes level. Take lane on left signed 'Woodland Hall' and follow for 1 mile.

CONTACT: booking office / Jean
Thornthwaite farm, Woodland, Broughton in Furness, Cumbria, LA20 6DF
Tel: Booking office (01946) 758198, Farm (01229) 716 340
info@lakelandcampingbarns.co.uk www.lakelandcampingbarns.co.uk

LAKELAND CAMPING BARNS

The perfect place to share a yarn

Camping Barns offer a special opportunity to stay in traditional farm buildings at an affordable price (£7.00 per person per night).

You can experience Cumbria's stunning lakes and lofty peaks literally from your doorstep.

The living and sleeping areas are usually communal, so unless you book the sole use of the barn, you may have to share with others.

Facilities are usually basic but they do vary between barns. As a general rule, imagine you are camping but you don't need a tent. All barns are annually inspected.

As a minimum, they have a sleeping area, mattresses, food preparation area, tables and benches for eating, a water supply and a flush toilet. Many have basic heating, some have hot water and showers.

Walking and cycling routes between and around barns on specially produced maps are also available.

See the individual barn entries with virtual tours on our website.

Lakeland Barns Booking Office -
Tel: 01946 758198
Email: info@lakelandcampingbarns.co.uk

defra
Department for Environment
Food and Rural Affairs

ROOKHOW
CENTRE

Perhaps the best situated small hostel in the Lake District. Peaceful, in 12 acres of its own woodland, but close to the heart of the Lakes, ten minutes from Coniston Water and Windermere, and on the edge of the famous Grizedale Forest Park with its trails and sculptures. Superb area for walking, cycling and all outdoor activities. Also for quiet retreat, relaxation, study and artistic pursuits. The Rookhow Centre is within the former stables of the nearby historic Quaker meeting house which is also available for conferences and group sessions.

Guests find the centre warm, comfortable and well equipped. It has electric heating and an optional wood burning stove. There are three sleeping areas, a self-catering kitchen/dining area and picnic tables and barbecue for warm days. There is a camping area, bonfire place and barbecue.

DETAILS

- **Open** - All year, all day
- **Number of beds** - 20: 1x9 : 1x8 : plus extra on bedsettees. Also camping.
- **Booking** - Booking is essential (deposit).
- **Price per night** - From :- Adult £14.00, £7.00 for under 16's
- **Public Transport** - Grange-over-Sands train station is 11 miles from the hostel. Approximately £15 taxi fare from station.
- **Directions** - GR 332 896. From A590 leave at Greenodd (A5092) junction and follow sign for Workington for ¼ mile. Take minor road to right signed Oxen Park. Continue through Oxen Park for a further 2 miles, Rookhow is on left. From Ambleside : to Hawkshead, then to Grizedale. Continue beyond Grizedale for 3.5 miles (Satterthwaite to Ulverston Road). Rookhow is on the right.

CONTACT: Warden
Rusland, Grizedale, Cumbria, South Lakeland, LA12 8LA
Tel: (01229) 860231
straughton@btinternet.com

HIGH WRAY
BASECAMP

Situated in the heart of South Lakeland in secluded woodland, 4 miles from the village of Ambleside, High Wray Basecamp provides an ideal base for groups wishing to explore and take part in activities in the Lake District Area. Local attractions include rambling, fell walking, climbing and water sports, with the Basecamp Warden being happy to assist with information on local walks and activities. The Longland Block has two separate fully centrally heated dormitories each sleeping 8, with a separate washing and living area/kitchen block. The comfortable living area is heated by a central wood burning stove and the kitchen has a commercial gas cooker, fridge freezer, microwave and utensils. The Acland block has two separate centrally heated dormitories sleeping 8 each, with toilet and shower room attached. The kitchen/lounge area is fitted with commercial gas cooker, fridges, microwave and utensils.

DETAILS

- **Open** - All year, 24 hours
- **Number of beds** - 16 + 20
- **Booking** - Booking with deposit of £50
- **Price per night** - Longland £9.25pp, Acland £9.75pp
- **Public Transport** - Nearest train station, Windermere 8 miles. Local bus (505 'Coniston Rambler' Windermere - Hawkshead) stops 2 miles away at turning to Wray Castle (Cumbria travel-line 0870 6082608)
- **Directions** - GR: 373 995 Take A593 from Ambleside towards Coniston, bear left onto the B5286 signed Hawkshead, fork left for High Wray village, signed Wray Castle. Basecamp is ¼ mile up dirt road on the left at the end of High Wray village.

CONTACT:
High Wray, Ambleside, Cumbria, LA22 0JE
Tel: (015394) 34633
paul.kear@nationaltrust.org.uk

LAKE DISTRICT
BACKPACKERS

Situated in the heart of Windermere and central Lakeland, you will find our cosy, friendly hostel ideally situated for exploring the surrounding area. We can advise you on routes for walks and cycle rides and provide you with maps. We are often asked to help organise abseiling, canoeing, sailing, windsurfing, even caving! There is easy access to the lake and fells from our door and we are adjacent to the main 555 bus route through Lakeland.

The hostel with its small dormitories provides you with every comfort but at a budget price. We are right next to a number of pubs, restaurants and take-aways and only minutes away from the rail and bus stations. Lockers are available and internet access and Sky keep you in touch! A well equipped kitchen and comfortable common room make your stay one to remember.

DETAILS

- **Open** - All year, 24 hours
- **Number of beds** - 20:- 1x7, 2 x 4, 1x 3, 1 x2
- **Booking** - Essential, 24 hours in advance.
- **Price per night** - £14 (£12 per night for 3 nts or more) price includes self service continental breakfast and free tea/coffee.
- **Public Transport** - Windermere train station is 2 minutes walk. National Express Coach stop 2 minutes walk.
- **Directions** - Turn left out of station, walk to information centre, Hostel is opposite, next to Simpson and Parsons Insurance Company.

CONTACT: Paul
High Street, Windermere, Cumbria, LA23 1AF
Tel: (015394) 46374, Fax: (015394) 88611
enquiries@lakedistrictbackpackers.co.uk www.lakedistrictbackpackers.co.uk

Kentmere is a quiet, unspoilt valley within the Lake District National Park. It's a ramblers' paradise with woods, fields, lanes, a scattering of traditional lakeland farms and dwellings, and of course the fells with their walks so favoured by Wainwright. The Lakeland to Lindisfarne long distance path passes this way as well as the mountain bikers' and horse riders' Coast to Coast. Kentmere offers plenty of activities which include biking, riding and fishing, but most of all quiet enjoyment. A pleasant day's visit can be found at the market town of Kendal and Lake Windermere which are only 20 minutes away. The recently converted Barn has two sleeping areas, fully fitted kitchen, two showers and toilets. All you need is your sleeping bag, mattresses provided. Breakfasts and suppers are available next door at the B&B.

PLEASE CONTACT THIS HOSTEL BY PHONE OR POST.

DETAILS

- **Open** - All year, 24 hours
- **Number of beds** - 14: 1 x 4   1 x 10
- **Booking** - Recommended with 50% deposit for groups. Individuals can book but not essential
- **Price per night** - £10.00 per person or £90 sole use.
- **Public Transport** - Staveley 4 miles with train and bus service. Oxenholme train station is 10 miles (taxi £18). Kendal/Windermere National Express 8 miles.
- **Directions** - GR 462 041, MAP OS English Lakes South East. Green Quarter. Leave the A591 and come into Staveley, proceed to Kentmere for 4 miles, then take right fork to Green Quarter keeping right until you reach Maggs Howe.

CONTACT: Christine Hevey
Maggs Howe, Kentmere, Kendal, Cumbria, LA8 9JP
Tel: (01539) 821689
sam@backpackerspress.com www.smoothhound.co.uk/hotels/maggs.html

SHACKLETON
LODGE

Shackleton Lodge is the brand new Brathay Exploration Group Field Quarters, in the heart of the Lake District, just over a mile from Ambleside and four miles from Langdale. It provides accommodation for 30 people in 5 rooms of 4 bunks, 2 rooms of 2 bunks and one room with 6 mattresses on the floor. Bed linen, sleeping bags and pillows are not provided. The lodge has central heating, double glazing, showers, drying room and facilities for the disabled. There is a large common room on the ground floor together with an additional room on the first floor which provides an excellent meeting and work space. The kitchen and dining room has a large gas oven, gas rings, microwave oven, fridge-freezer and a complete range of cutlery, plates, pans etc. It is centrally heated, has a gas water heater and provides a seating area with tables and benches. There is a barbecue nearby. Shackleton Lodge, self-catering accommodation - right where it matters!

DETAILS

- **Open** - All year, 24 hours
- **Number of beds** - 30: 5x4, 2x2 and 1x6 (mattresses on floor)
- **Booking** - Booking form on website, non-refundable deposit of £100.
- **Price per night** - Sun to Thurs £245 per night (2 nights min) for up to 24 people plus £7 per extra person. Fri and Sat £575 (for both nights) plus £18 per extra person. Bookings of 5+ nights charged at midweek rate. New Years add £150.
- **Public Transport** - Trains at Windermere (6 miles). Local buses 505 runs from Windermere rail stn to Clappersgate (Traveline 0870 608 2 608)
- **Directions** - GR NY366027 1mile from Ambleside on A593/B5286 to Hawkshead.

CONTACT:
Brathay Exploration Group Trust, Brathay Hall, Ambleside, Cumbria, LA22 0HP
Tel: (015394) 33942, Fax: (015394) 33942
admin@brathayexploration.org.uk www.brathayexploration.org.uk/accom.htm

The Sticklebarn is beautifully situated amidst some of the finest mountain scenery in England. It is at the very foot of the famous Langdale Pikes and Dungeon Ghyll waterfalls and seven miles north west of Ambleside.

The Sticklebarn is privately owned and is available to the general outdoor public and traveller on foot. The bunkhouse has no common room or self-catering facilities but meals are provided in the pub. Sorry no pets. A brochure is available on request. Food served 12noon to 2.30pm and 6pm to 9.30pm. Saturdays, Sundays and bank holidays: 12noon to 9.30pm. Breakfasts available between 8.30am and 10.45am weekends, 9am and 10.30am during week. Live music every weekend from February to end of October. Check out the weather via our webcam on the Langdale Website.

DETAILS

- **Open** - All year, all day
- **Number of beds** - Winter 20, Summer 8
- **Booking** - Pre-booking is advised for weekends and groups and requires a 50% deposit.
- **Price per night** - £11.50 per person
- **Public Transport** - Bus service 516 to Great Langdale from Ambleside, ask for New Dungeon Ghyll Hotel, walk 2 mins (timetable (01946) 632222).
- **Directions** - From the A591 Windermere to Keswick road at Ambleside take the A593 turn to Coniston / Torver. After two miles take the B5343 to Great Langdale via Chapel Stile. The Bunkhouse is adjacent to the Sticklebarn Tavern.

CONTACT: Terry or Lorna Graham
Sticklebarn Tavern, Great Langdale, LA22 9JU
Tel: (015394) 37356
sticklebarn@aol.com www.langdaleweb.co.uk

AMBLESIDE
BACKPACKERS

Get away to The English Lakes National Park, one of the most beautiful scenic areas in the UK. Ambleside Backpackers is in a marvellous location with fell and mountain walks, boating, scenic drives, cycle touring, mountain biking and outdoor activities practically from the doorstep. Set just 4 minutes walking from the centre of Ambleside it is also a great centre for visiting places made famous by Wordsworth, Ruskin and Beatrix Potter. Ambleside is excellent for shopping and eating out with many outdoor equipment shops, restaurants and pubs.

With 68 beds the hostel can accommodate most sizes of groups as well as individuals in either single sex or mixed dorms. The hostel is a large, traditional Lakeland cottage featuring a great lounge with a fire and TV, dining room, large well equipped kitchen for your use - not to mention central heating, showers and washing/drying facilities. Reasonably priced, light breakfast included. Friendly helpful staff, on site manager and good public transport links makes this hostel the ideal base for exploring the Lakes.

DETAILS

- **Open** - All year, 24 hours
- **Number of beds** - 68: 1 x14, 1x12, 2 x7, 3x6, 2x4, 1x2
- **Booking** - Recommended, essential for groups, deposit required.
- **Price per night** - £16.00pp discount on 3 or more nights and special breaks.
- **Public Transport** - Windermere train station 4 miles then 555 bus to Ambleside
- **Directions** - From Ambleside bus stop: Up hill to T junction. Across Rd to Old Lake Rd. 200m up on left.– By Road – A591 Windermere to Ambleside. At Hayes Garden Ctr. turn right into Old Lake Rd. 300m on right.

CONTACT:
Ambleside BP's, Iveing Cottage, Old Lake Rd, Ambleside Cumbria, LA22 0DJ
Tel: (015394) 32340
bookings@amblesidebackpackers.com www.amblesidebackpackers.com

RYDAL HALL
BUNKHOUSE

The Bunkhouse is situated in the centre of Rydal Hall estate, sheltered on three sides by the Fairfield Horseshoe and offering access to the best of Lakeland's activities. Facilities inside provide the necessities for groups of up to 36. There are 2 dormitories sleeping 14 and 18 in bunk beds and 2 leader rooms each sleeping 2. There is a large common room which can be used for dining or recreation. A welcoming log burner provides additional warmth to the ample heating powered by our nearby water turbine. The kitchen is fully furnished for cooking en masse and there are 2 separate toilet facilities with showers. Laundry and drying facilities are close by and a games room with table tennis and pool is available on request. Users need to bring sleeping bags, pillow cases and extra blankets during winter. Rydal Hall also offers camping to organised groups and there is comfortable residential accommodation for up to 56 at the Hall in single, twin, double and family rooms.

DETAILS

- **Open** - All year, 24 hours
- **Number of beds** - Bunkhouse 36: 1x14, 1x18, 2x2
- **Booking** - Required with deposit. No bookings by email please.
- **Price per night** - Sole use Nov-Mar (excl.Xmas & New Year) £180, Apr-Oct £270 10% discount for youth groups + midweek. Individual bookings by arrangement.
- **Public Transport** - Trains at Windermere. National Express at Ambleside. Local stagecoach service (555) from Lancaster to Keswick stops 200 yards from Hall.
- **Directions** - GR 366 064. Take the A561 from Ambleside to Grasmere, Rydal is reached after 2 miles. By the church turn right up lane for 200m.

CONTACT:
Rydal Hall, Ambleside, Cumbria, LA22 9LX
Tel: (01539) 432 050, Fax: (01539) 434 887
mail@rydalhall.org www.rydalhall.org

GRASMERE
INDEPENDENT HOSTEL

This small deluxe hostel is situated on a farm right at the heart of the Lakes. See the best of Lakeland right from our doorstep. Give the car a holiday. Take the Wordsworth walk around Grasmere and Rydal Lake, or do a mountain classic, climb Helvellyn or Fairfield from our door. The Coast to Coast footpath goes right through the farm. Over 101 other local attractions and activities, including a good pub with fine bar meals just 300 yds down the road. Our English Tourism Council 4 star graded hostel has en-suite bedrooms with made up beds (sheets & duvets) lockers, bedside lights, a coin operated sauna, commercial laundry, drying room, dining room, 2 self-catering kitchens with microwaves, fridges, toasters etc. A stunning common room with large TV, a lockable bike/luggage store and private parking. We are resident proprietors. Cleanliness and friendliness assured. Totally non-smoking. Individuals, families and groups all welcome. Please always check availability by phone.

DETAILS

■ **Open** - All year (winter, subject to minimum numbers), 8am to 10pm, (keys issued)
■ **Number of beds** - 24: 1 x 3 : 1 x 4 : 1 x 5 : 2 x 6.
■ **Booking** - Advisable, credit card confirms bed.
■ **Price per night** - From 17.50pp (bedding inc). Groups please apply.
■ **Public Transport** - Train to Windermere (11 miles from hostel), catch 555 bus from Windermere or Keswick, ask for Travellers Rest Pub. There is also a National Express coach that runs between London/Grasmere daily.
■ **Directions** - GR 336 094. 1.25 miles north of village. Stay on main A591 right to our drive, 400m north of Travellers Rest Pub, on the right hand side.

CONTACT: Mr Bev Dennison
Broadrayne Farm, Keswick Road, Grasmere, Cumbria, LA22 9RU
Tel: (015394)35055
Bev@grasmerehostel.co.uk www.grasmerehostel.co.uk

MURT BARN
CAMPING BARN

Murt is a traditional farm, dating from 1728, situated in the Wasdale valley. The camping barn is a converted stone hayloft and byre, attached to the farmhouse, with stunning views to the Scafell Massif, and the surrounding fells. Sleeping accommodation and cooking area are on the first floor, reached by an internal wooden staircase. The shower, toilet and washing up facilities are downstairs. Electricity is metered (£1 coins) and provides light, water heater, hot shower, electric heater and a power point. Car parking is adjacent to the barn. You need to bring a sleeping bag/mat and stove and eating utensils if you wish to self cater. Murt is 3/4 mile from Wastwater and is an ideal base for high fell walks including Scafell Pike, Mosedale Horseshoe, Great Gable etc. There is direct access to footpaths and bridle-ways. For those interested in flora and fauna, the Wasdale valley has great variety, and coastal dune walks, Muncaster Castle and Ravensglass (for the Eskdale railway) are all only a stones throw away. There are 2 pubs in the village, 10 minutes walk from the Barn.

DETAILS

- **Open** - All year, arrive after 4pm.
- **Number of beds** - 8: 1x8
- **Booking** - Booking recommended. Book online.
- **Price per night** - £7 per person. Sole use w/ends and bank/hols £48 per night.
- **Public Transport** - Seascale station, then taxi to Wasdale.
- **Directions** - From the A595, follow signs to Santon Bridge and Wasdale. After approx. 2 miles, bear sharp left over bridge, and sharp right immediately afterwards. At junction turn right, to Wasdale Head, and Murt is the 2nd gate on left.

CONTACT:
Murt, Nether Wasdale, Seascale, Cumbria, CA20 1ET
Tel: Booking office (01946) 758198, Farm (019467) 26044
info@lakelandcampingbarns.co.uk www.lakelandcampingbarns.co.uk

This 14 bed cycling barn is situated in the heart of the historic market town of Egremont, West Cumbria. Only minutes away from the sea and some of the most beautiful lakes and mountains in the Lake District. The barn is fully heated and has electric lighting and complimentary showers. The small dorms/private rooms all have ensuite shower-wet-rooms and cost only £8 per person per night. The ground floor has a communal room for cooking and this is equipped with tables and chairs for dining. Also on the ground floor is an ensuite bedroom for disabled users with external access. The first floor has 3 ensuite four-bedded rooms. The barn is set in a walled garden. There is secure cycle storage and cleaning facilities for bikes. Plenty of shops, pubs and restaurants nearby.

DETAILS

- **Open** - All year (opening Jan 2008), 24 hour, Key code entry
- **Number of beds** - 14: 3x4, 1x2
- **Booking** - Booking essential.
- **Price per night** - £8.00pp including heating / showers
- **Public Transport** - Trains at St.Bees (2.8 Miles) and Whitehaven (5.5 Miles). Bus Stop (60 Yards) for buses to Barrow X6, Carlisle - 300/301, Keswick/Penrith X4 X5.
- **Directions** - Leave M6 at junction 40 (Penrith) and turn onto the A66 signed towards Keswick and Workington. Continue on the A66 until the A595 left junction signpost Whitehaven. Follow the A595 bypassing Whitehaven town centre. After the hospital roundabout take the 3rd exit (signed Egremont). Continue towards Egremont on the A595. At the Clints Brow roundabout go straight through. At the next roundabout take the 3rd exit for the Main Street. Hostel is on LH in 0.3 miles.

CONTACT:
Market Place, Egremont, Cumbria. CA22 2AE
Tel: (01946) 758 198
info@horseandgroomcourt.co.uk www.horseandgroomcourt.co.uk

TARN FLATT
CAMPING BARN

Tarn Flatt Camping Barn is a traditional sandstone barn on St Bees Head overlooking the Scottish coastline and the Isle of Man. It is on a working farm which also includes a lighthouse, RSPB bird reserve on 100 metre cliffs and access to Fleswick Bay - a secluded shingle cove. There is canoeing and fishing in the area and the rock climbing and boulders at the base of the cliff are superb. There are several local circular walks with panoramic views of the coast and the fells and easy access to the quieter western Lakeland fells and lakes. The award-winning historic Georgian town and harbour of Whitehaven is only 3 miles away and St Bees (the starting point of the Coast to Coast walk) is 2 miles via the coastal path. The barn has a raised wooden sleeping area on the ground floor. There is electric light, a cooking slab (please bring your own stove and utensils) and an open fire (wood available from the farm). Toilets, wash-basin and showers are in adjacent buildings. Meals are available by arrangement. Children welcome. Dogs are accepted in sole use only.

DETAILS

- **Open** - All year, 24 hours
- **Number of beds** - 12 bed spaces.
- **Booking** - Booking in advance is advised.
- **Price per night** - £7 per person.
- **Public Transport** - Trains at Whitehaven (4 miles) and St Bees (3 miles). Buses also at Whitehaven.
- **Directions** - GR 947 146. With Sandwith village green on right, pass row of houses and turn right, at phone box take private road for 1 mile.

CONTACT: Janice Telfer
Tarn Flatt Hall, Sandwith, Whitehaven, Cumbria, CA28 9UX
Tel: Detail (01946) 692162, Booking (01946) 758198
stay@tarnflattfarm.co.uk   www.tarnflattfarm.co.uk

Dinah Hoggus Camping Barn is situated on the old Packhorse route to Watendlath. It is right on the Cumbria Way and Coast to Coast routes.

The sleeping area is on the first floor and 12 mattresses are provided. There is a cooking and eating area on the ground floor with tables and benches. There is mains electricity and water, a small electric ring cooker, micro-wave, electric kettle, toaster, clothes dryer and electric heaters. The toliet/shower room is at the end of the building and has a hot electric shower and washbasin. Electricity is charged extra. Meter reading at start and end of stay.
The pub is 300yds away and village shop 200yds.

Check the website www.lakelandcampingbarns.co.uk and book on line.

DETAILS

- **Open** - All year, all day
- **Number of beds** - 12
- **Booking** - Book online
- **Price per night** - £7 per person
- **Public Transport** - The local bus service out of Keswick stops at Hazel Bank Lane End (Rosthwaite), just 100yds from the barn.
- **Directions** - The camping barn is situated on the outskirts of the village of Rosthwaite in Borrowdale. Take the B5289 road out of Keswick up the Borrowdale Valley for approx 6 miles. When you see the Rosthwaite village sign take first left (Hazel Bank Lane) over the hump bridge and into the left. Park beside the barn.

CONTACT:
Thorneythwaite Farm, Borrowdale, Keswick, Cumbria, CA12 5XQ
Tel: Booking office (01946) 758198, Farm (017687) 77237
info@lakelandcampingbarns.co.uk www.lakelandcampingbarns.co.uk

CRAGG BARN
CAMPING BARN

Cragg Barn Camping Barn is a traditional stone-built barn with stunning views of Buttermere fells. It has a kitchen and seating area with a sink and cold running water. There is a hot shower on a meter and a toilet and washbasin with hot and cold water. The sleeping area has 8 mattresses, bring your own sleeping bag. You need a stove and eating utensils if you wish to self cater. Cragg Barn is a great base for walkers of all abilities. It is also ideal for climbing, fishing and wildlife/bird-watching. There are many local tourist attractions within a short drive. Cragg House Farm also has a holiday cottage sleeping 2.
Check the websites www.buttermerecottage.co.uk or www.lakelandcampingbarns.co.uk and book on line.

DETAILS

- **Open** - All year, all day, late arrivals by arrangement.
- **Number of beds** - 8: 1 x 8
- **Booking** - Booking essential at least 24 hrs in advance. Book online.
- **Price per night** - £7 per person.
- **Public Transport** - Train stations at Penrith / Workington. Bus links from Penrith station and Workington town centre to Keswick. Bus runs seasonally from Keswick.
- **Directions** - GR NY 173 171. From Keswick follow signs to Borrowdale, continue through Rosthwaite, Seatoller and over Honister Pass. Continue past Buttermere lake into Buttermere village. Keep on main road. Cragg House Farm is on the left on the brow of the hill before you get to NT carpark. In icy conditions approach from Cockermouth town centre and continue through Lorton. Turn left to Buttermere following road signs. Cragg Farm is 1st on the right past the Buttermere village sign.

CONTACT:
Cragg House Farm, Buttermere, Cockermouth, Cumbria, CA13 9XA
Tel: Camping Barn (01946) 758198. Holiday Cottage (017687) 70204
info@lakelandcampingbarns.co.uk www.buttermerecottage.co.uk

LOW GILLERTHWAITE [157]
FIELD CENTRE
ENGLAND

Towards the head of Ennerdale valley, one of the most beautiful, least spoilt and quietest valleys in the Lake District, sitting at the foot of Pillar and Red Pike you will find Low Gillerthwaite. An ideal base for fellwalking, classic rock climbs, bird and wildlife watching, mountain biking, orienteering (we have our own permanent course), canoeing (instruction available for groups) and environmental studies. Originally a 15th-century farmhouse, the Centre has group self-catering facilities, drying room, library of environmental books and a group lecture room. Due to its remoteness the Centre generates it's own electricity and in the evening when the generator ceases lighting is supplied by gas lamps. Vehicle access is by forest track and a BT payphone is on site (most mobiles do not work here). With 40 beds Low Gillerthwaite is an ideal base for clubs, extended family groups, school and youth groups. Video available for group leaders; more information can be found on our website.

DETAILS

- **Open** - All year, except Christmas and Boxing Day, 24 hours
- **Number of beds** - 40: 2x4 : 1x8 : 1x10 : 1x14
- **Booking** - Always phone to check availability
- **Price per night** - From £8.00 per person.
- **Public Transport** - Whitehaven Station 12 miles. Buses to Ennerdale Bridge from Cleator Moor or Cockermouth (5miles).
- **Directions** - GR 139 141. From Ennerdale Bridge take road east, via Croasdale, 3.5 miles to Ennerdale Forest. Continue on forest track 3 miles. Hostel is the first building below the RH road, 200m before the YHA.

CONTACT:
Ennerdale, Cleator, CA23 3AX
Tel: (01946) 861229
Warden@lgfc.org.uk www.lgfc.org.uk

SWALLOW BARN
CAMPING BARN

Lying in the picturesque Loweswater Valley, Swallow Barn is part of a traditional set of buildings dating back to 1670 on a working beef and sheep farm. The barn accommodates 18 people on mattresses in 4 sleeping areas. There is a cooking and eating area with tables and chairs, 2 coin-operated showers and 2 toilets. Swallow Barn is an excellent base for exploring the western fells with both high and low level walks and spectacular views, or you can enjoy the peace and tranquillity of the valley. Boat hire and fishing permits are available from the farm. The coast to coast cycle route is right on the doorstep. The Kirkstyle Pub provides excellent food, just over a mile away and the market town of Cockermouth is only 8 miles.

Check the website www.lakelandcampingbarns.co.uk and book on line.

DETAILS

- **Open** - All year, all day
- **Number of beds** - 18: 1x9, 3x3
- **Booking** - Book Online. In advance, especially for school and bank holidays.
- **Price per night** - £7 per person.
- **Public Transport** - The nearest train station is Penrith with a bus to Cockermouth, then a taxi costing approximately £25.
- **Directions** - Leave the M6 at junct. 40 and follow the A66 to the Egremont turn off at Cockermouth. Follow the A5086,Egremont road for 6 miles. Turn left at Mockerkin and follow road to Loweswater. Farm is just past the Grange Hotel on the left .

CONTACT:
Waterend Farm, Loweswater, Cockermouth, Cumbria, CA13 0SU
Tel: Booking office (01946) 758198, Farm (01946) 861465
info@lakelandcampingbarns.co.uk www.lakelandcampingbarns.co.uk

Catbells Camping Barn is part of a traditional set of farm buildings dating back to the 14th century.   The barn is on the slopes of Catbells in the tranquil Newlands Valley, with magnificent views over the Lake District. The Cumberland Way passes through the farmyard. Keswick is only 4 miles away and both Borrowdale and Buttermere are in walking distance. The camping barn is on the ground floor and has sleeping accommodation for 12, with mattresses provided. Bring your own sleeping bags. The barn is heated with a multi-fuel stove (not suitable for cooking) and coal can be bought at the farm. In the adjacent building is a toilet and a cooking area suitable for a camping stove. Bring your own stove, cutlery, crockery and cooking utensils.   It is possible to walk to a pub which serves food.   Breakfast can be provided with notice.

DETAILS

- **Open** - All year, 24 hours
- **Number of beds** - 12: 1x12
- **Booking** - Advisable, groups require deposit.
- **Price per night** - £7 per person
- **Public Transport** - Trains at Penrith (20 miles). Regular buses (meet the trains) from Penrith to Keswick.   Summer bus from Keswick to Buttermere stops ¾ mile from Barn. Summer ferry from Keswick to Hawes End (3/4 mile from barn).
- **Directions** - GR 245211 Leave the M6 at Junction 40 and follow the A66 past Keswick. At Portinscale turn left, follow the Buttermere road for 3 miles. Turn sharp left at Stair, follow the sign for Skelgill, up the road for 1/2 mile and right into farmyard. Please follow these directions and not those from 'sat-nav'.

CONTACT: Mrs Grave
Low Skelgill, Newlands, Keswick, Cumbria, CA12 5UE
Tel: (01946) 758198 or 0709 2031363
info@lakelandcampingbarns.co.uk www.lakelandcampingbarns.co.uk

CAUSEWAY FOOT
CAMPING BARN

Causeway Foot Farm Camping Barn is on a small family run sheep and dairy farm set in the magnificent scenery of the Naddle Valley, just outside Keswick. The two storey barn enjoys a detached location with good access and parking. The ground floor has 8 bunkbeds, electric heaters and storage space. The upper floor has 12 bunkbeds, electric heaters, folding dining tables with bench seats and a well fitted kitchen with 6 burner gas cooker, fridge, microwave, electric kettle and toaster. The sink has hot & cold running water and there is a selection of pans, crockery and cutlery. The bunks have mattresses & pillows. There is a toilet/shower block 50 metres from the barn. The farm also has a 3 bedroomed bungalow and three holiday caravans.

With glorious views over the Lakeland fells of Skiddaw, Latrigg, Blencathra and Helvellyn, this is a popular location for those wishing to relax, whilst also making an excellent and convenient base for walkers and families.

DETAILS

- **Open** - All year, 24 hours
- **Number of beds** - 20: 1x8, 1x12
- **Booking** - Deposit, balance on arrival.
- **Price per night** - £5.00 per person, with minimum of £50 per night (10 bed spaces). Price includes gas, electricity by £1 meter.
- **Public Transport** - Trains at Penrith (16 miles). Hourly buses Penrith to Keswick.
- **Directions** - On the A591 between Keswick and Windermere, about 2.5 miles from Keswick opposite a lay-by and phone box.

CONTACT: Greg Nicholson
Causeway Foot Farm, Naddle, Keswick, Cumbria, CA12 4TF
Tel: (017687) 72290
jackie@causewayfoot.co.uk www.causewayfoot.co.uk

DENTON HOUSE

Denton House is a purpose built hostel and outdoor centre in the heart of the Lake District. The hostel is designed for group use so has plenty of hot water for showers, central heating throughout, a commercial kitchen, a large dining room and solid bunkbeds! Denton House now welcomes individuals too with upgraded facilities designed to be homely as well as functional. Denton House Outdoor Centre can provide traditional activities for groups of all ages. The centre is particularly suitable for those wanting to explore the great outdoors; we have storage for kayaks and bikes and there's access/egress to the River Greta just across the road. Qualified instructors are available to provide advice as well as to run trips and help organise expeditions.

Denton House is primarily an adult hostel; under 16s are welcome in supervised groups or in exclusive use dorms with parents. Dogs welcome in some rooms if pre-booked. Due to the large number of school, youth and military groups, corporate teambuilds and celebration weekends, early booking is advised.

DETAILS

- **Open** - All year, 24 hours
- **Number of beds** - 56: 1x4 : 2x6 : 1x8 : 2x10 : 1x12.
- **Booking** - Preferred (25% deposit for Groups)
- **Price per night** - £13 midweek, £14 weekends
- **Public Transport** - Nearest train station Penrith, buses hourly to Keswick.
- **Directions** - From centre out of town towards Windermere, keep the park on your left (approx 10mins). We are on the right after post sorting office.

CONTACT:
Penrith Road, Keswick, Cumbria CA12 4JW
Tel: (017687) 75351
sales@vividevents.co.uk www.vividevents.co.uk

ST JOHNS-IN-THE-VALE
CAMPING BARN

St Johns-in-the-Vale Camping Barn is adapted from an 18th Century stable and hayloft, in an idyllic setting overlooking St John's Beck on a peaceful hill farm. With stunning views to Blencathra, Helvellyn and Castle Rock. The Barn has a sleeping area upstairs (matttress provided) with a sitting and dining area below. Seperate toilet, shower and cooking area (bring your own equipment) are within the building. A wood-burning fire provides a focal point and warmth!

There is a BBQ and seating area outside, magical on a star-filled night as we have no light pollution. Low Bridge End Farm has a tea garden - all home baking. Breakfasts and packed lunches can be ordered in advance from the farm. To get the full picture see our virtual tour, complete details then book online at www.lakelandcampingbarns.co.uk

DETAILS

- **Open** - All year, 24 hours
- **Number of beds** - 8 : 1x8
- **Booking** - Advised in advance. Credit card booking available on (01946) 758198.
- **Price per night** - £7 per person
- **Public Transport** - Trains terminate at Windermere. From there take a 555 bus towards Keswick. Get off at Thirlmere Dam Road End (Smaithwaite). Climb over ladder stile and we are ½ mile north along a footpath.
- **Directions** - Leave M6 at junction 40. Take A66 towards Keswick for 14 miles. Turn left onto B5322 St Johns in the Vale Road. 3 miles along the road on the right.

CONTACT: Graham or Sarah
Low Bridge End Farm, St Johns-in-the-Vale, Keswick, CA12 4TS
Tel: (017687) 79242 (Bookings 01946 758198)
info@campingbarn.com   www.campingbarn.com

Swirral Barn is one of a group of mine buildings, situated at 1,000ft on the flank of the Helvellyn Mountain Range. It offers the basic necessities: hot water, toilet, tables, benches and a sleeping platform with mattresses. You will need to bring a stove and utensils if you wish to cook, a torch and a sleeping bag. The location is perfect for walking over the fells. Popular routes to Striding Edge and Swirral Edge pass the door, and there is quick access to Ullswater and the Eastern Fells. Enjoy a hike up Helvellyn and the surrounding peaks or, for less strenuous walking, try the scenic lake shore paths around Ullswater. Rowing, sailing and steam boats trips are available on Ullswater, where you can relax by the waterside. There are so many thing to do in this beautiful area. The barns facilities are: Sleeping platform on the first floor. Slate cooking area, cold tap and toilet, plus electric lighting. Nearest pub is only 1 mile away, with the nearest village store only 1.5 miles away.

DETAILS

- **Open** - All year, all day
- **Number of beds** - 8: 1x8
- **Booking** - Book online. Booking in advance is essential.
- **Price per night** - £7.00 per person
- **Public Transport** - Buses run every 2 hours from Penrith to Glenridding. It is just over 1 mile walk from bus stop to barn.
- **Directions** - From Pooley Bridge take A592 to Glenridding then to main car park. Follow the sign post to Helvellyn Youth Hostel. Swirrel Barn is 100 metres past the hostel on the left.

CONTACT: Jeanette
Striding Edge, Glenridding, Cumbria, CALL 0NR
Tel: Booking office (01946) 758198, Farm mobile 07775561512
info@lakelandcampingbarns.co.uk www.lakelandcampingbarns.co.uk

HUDSCALES
CAMPING BARN

Hudscales Camping Barn is part of a group of traditional farm buildings, situated at 1000ft on the northern-most flank of the Lakeland Fells. It overlooks the villages of Caldbeck and Hesket Newmarket and is in an ideal position for exploring the northern fells. It is situated right on the Cumbria Way.

Sleeping accommodation is on the ground floor along with a separate cooking and eating area. You will need to bring sleeping bags and mats. If you wish to cook bring a camping stove and all utensils / crockery. There is a separate toilet and washbasin and a metered shower. A woodburning stove is provided for added comfort (logs extra) and there is electric lighting plus metered power points. Breakfasts available if booked in advance.

Check the website www.lakelandcampingbarns.co.uk and book on line.

DETAILS

■ **Open** - All year, all day
■ **Number of beds** - 12: 1x12
■ **Booking** - Book online. Bookings preferred but not essential.
■ **Price per night** - £7 per person
■ **Public Transport** - Penrith station 12 miles. Carlisle station 15 miles. No buses from Penrith. Limited service from Carlisle. Taxi fare from Carlisle approx £20.
■ **Directions** - Leave M6 at J41 and take B5305 for Wigton. After approx 9 miles take left turn for Hesket Newmarket. Drive to top end of village and take left turn for Fellside. Hudscales Camping Barn is approx 1 mile on left up a lane.

CONTACT: Booking office / William or Judith
Hudscales, Hesket Newmarket, Wigton, Cumbria, CA7 8JZ
Tel: Booking office (01946) 758198, Farm (016974) 78637
info@lakelandcampingbarns.co.uk www.lakelandcampingbarns.co.uk

At 1550 feet, Skiddaw House is the highest YHA affiliated hostel in Britain. A former shooting lodge and shepherd's bothy on the Cumbria Way, it is an ideal base for exploring the little used and quiet northern fells. This is a remote and isolated place, to reflect on the wilderness, with no sign of the 21st Century in any direction. With no electricity, phones ringing or TV to distract from the vista of a clear unpolluted starry night. This is simple accommodation with log and coal fires the only heating. No noise pollution from traffic as the nearest road is 3½ miles away, yet only an hour or so's walk from civilisation. Walkers and cyclists are advised to bring a map and torch. Campers welcome.

DETAILS

- **Open** - 1st Mar-31st Oct (groups only Nov-Dec), mornings till 10am, 5pm to 11pm
- **Number of beds** - 21: 1x7, 2x5, 1x4
- **Booking** - Book in advance for groups of 5 or more, by email, text, phone or post (postal service is slow). 50% deposit required for advance bookings.
- **Price per night** - £14pp (over 21), £10 (16-21), £7pp (under 16). YHA members receive £1-3 discount. Camping £5.50. Credit / debit cards not accepted.
- **Public Transport** - Nearest trains and National express coaches at Penrith. From Penrith take X4 or X5 bus towards Keswick and Workington. Alight at the Horse and Farrier (Threlkeld). From Carlisle take 55 bus to Keswick (only 3 per day). Alight at Castle Inn (Bassenthwaite) and then walk 6 miles.
- **Directions** - No access for cars, nearest tarmac road 3½ miles. Vehicles can be left at Fell Car Park by Blencathra Centre above Threlkeld, at Lattrigg Car Park (end of Gale Rd near Applethwaite) or at Whitewater Dash Falls south of Bassenthwaite.

CONTACT: Martin or Marie
Bassenthwaite, Keswick, Cumbria, CA12 4QX
Tel: 07747 174293
skiddawhouse@yahoo.co.uk   www.skiddawhouse.co.uk

CARROCK HALLS
ENGLAND UNIVERSITY OF CUMBRIA

Carrock Halls of Residence in the centre of Carlisle provide private ensuite accommodation for individuals and groups during the college summer holidays. A short walk from Carlisle's vibrant city centre and with easy access to the Northern Lakes, Northumberland, Hadrian's Wall and the Borders of Scotland, Carrock Halls makes an ideal base for holidays and conferences.

The accommodation is in Carrock Halls, newly built with 85 en-suite bedrooms. The recently restored Victorian buildings around the hall offer an up to the minute leisure and learning environment including sports complex, café bar, display and exhibition areas and dining for up to 200 people,

DETAILS

- **Open** - June, July and August, all day
- **Number of beds** - 85 ensuite single bedrooms.
- **Booking** - Book by phone or email
- **Price per night** - From £21.00 per room (single en-suite).
- **Public Transport** - Carlisle is on the main London to Glasgow rail line and therefore readily accessible by train. The Railway Station is a ten minute walk from the campus or a £2 taxi ride. The Bus Station is approximately a twenty minute walk. The campus is on the main local bus route.
- **Directions** - At Junction 43 of the M6, take the exit for Carlisle (A69). Head in towards Carlisle along Warwick Road. Turn left at the third set of traffic lights into Greystone Road (there is a post office / grocery store on the corner). Turn right into Fusehill Street (Newsagents on the corner). Take first entrance on the right

CONTACT: Events Office
University of Cumbria, Fusehill Street, Carlisle, CA1 2HH.
Tel: (01228) 616317, Fax: (01228) 616312
conferences.carlisle@cumbria.ac.uk www.cumbria.ac.uk/hospitality

HILLSIDE FARM
BUNKBARN

Hillside Farm is a Georgian farmstead in a conservation area just steps away from Hadrian's Wall. It is located in the small village of Boustead Hill, near the Solway Coast Area of Outstanding Natural Beauty and RSPB nature reserve. The farm has stunning views over the Solway Firth Marshes towards Scotland. Hadrian's Wall National Trail and Hadrian's Cycleway pass right by. Hillside farm is a working farm and the fourth generation of a farming family welcomes you to stay in the bunkbarn or in the B&B rooms in the farmhouse. The Bunkbarn is a recent conversion of the farms Georgian stable block. It has cooking slabs, cutlery and crockery and a 2 ring gas stove. There are hot showers and towels and sleeping bags can be hired if required. There is no heating in the barn. You can arrange delivery of shopping via the farmhouse and with notice you can eat a full english breakfast at the farmhouse. Walking, cycling and family groups are most welcome.

   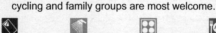

DETAILS

- **Open** - All year, all day
- **Number of beds** - 12:
- **Booking** - Book by phone.
- **Price per night** - £6 per person. £1 shower. £6 full English breakfast.
- **Public Transport** -
- **Directions** - From M6 junction 43 follow signs for A595 past the castle, turn at small rundabout onto B5307. After 1 mile turn right following signs for Burgh-by-Sands. Pass through town and cross the cattle grid onto Marsh Road. Take next left into village of Boustead Hill, then 2nd turning on left under arches into farmyard.

CONTACT: Mrs Sandra Rudd
Hillside Farm, Boustead Hill, Burgh-by-Sands, Carlisle, Cumbria, CA5 6AA
Tel: (01228) 576398
ruddshillside1@btinternet.com www.hadrianswalkbnb.co.uk

Assay House Bunkhouse and Mill Cottage Bunkhouse are situated at the Nenthead Mines Heritage Centre, a Scheduled Ancient Monument. In the 19th century it was part of the largest lead and silver mining and processing area in the country. Nenthead is in the North Pennines Area of Outstanding Natural Beauty, and is one of the highest villages in England. An ideal location for people wishing to explore the dramatic North Pennine area, with walks and the C2C cycle route passing the door, as well as the opportunity to visit the Heritage Centre. The Assay House was the laboratory of the Assay Master, who analysed ore samples and set the prices paid to the miners. Now converted to a bunkhouse it sleeps up to 12 people in two upstairs bedrooms. There is a kitchen / dining room downstairs. Mill Cottage was part of the home of the Smelt Mill manager. The Bunkhouse sleeps six in the upstairs bunkroom. Each bed is styled like a ship's cabin bunk with curtains for privacy, a light and shelf. Either bunkhouse is available for groups. Cafe on site and pub in the village.

DETAILS

- **Open** - All year. (Heritage Centre Apr-Oct.), Heritage Centre open 10.30am-5pm.
- **Number of beds** - Mill Cottage 6: 1 x 6, Assay House 12: 2 x 6
- **Booking** - Preferred but not essential. Deposit is required.
- **Price per night** - £12
- **Public Transport** - Trains at Hexham (24 miles) and Penrith (25 miles). Limited bus service (Wright Bros Buses (01434) 381200) from Hexham and Penrith to Alston.
- **Directions** - In Nenthead village, off the A689 Alston to Stanhope road. The bunkhouse is on the Nenthead Mines site.

CONTACT: Paul Mercer/ Tim Haldon
Nenthead Mines Heritage Centre, Nenthead, Alston, Cumbria, CA9 3PD
Tel: (01434) 382037 or (01434) 382726
bunkhouse@npht.com www.npht.com/nentheadmines

GIBBS HILL FARM
BUNKHOUSE

Gibbs Hill Farm Bunkhouse is a new conversion of a Hay Barn on a traditional working hill farm. The bunkhouse is designed to reduce energy consumption and is centrally heated throughout. There are 3 bunkrooms, 2 shower rooms, 2 toilets, a well equipped kitchen, comfortable sitting and dining area and a large deck where guests may enjoy the evening sun. The bunkhouse has a drying room, lockers, laundry facilities and safe cycle storage. Ideal for families who may take a whole room with private facilities. Study groups welcome and evening meals can be provided. Situated near Hadrians Wall it is an excellent base for exploring the Roman sites, Hadrians Wall Trail and Northumberland National Park. Basic items of food may be purchased and meals can be ordered in the evening for the next day. Continental Breakfast is £4, Packed lunches £5.

DETAILS

- **Open** - All year, flexible, but no check in after 9pm
- **Number of beds** - 18: 3x6
- **Booking** - Advisable, groups require deposit.
- **Price per night** - £12pp week, £14pp wk/end. Bring sleeping bag or hire linen £3.
- **Public Transport** - Trains at Haltwhistle 6 miles. Regular Bus Service along A69 between Newcastle and Carlisle, and in summer the Hadrians Wall Bus runs between Newcastle and Carlisle. Alight at Once Brewed Information Centre and walk north to farm. Last bus 5.30pm from Haltwhistle.
- **Directions** - From the A69, turn north at Bardon Mill, signed 'Once Brewed'. Follow the signs towards 'Housesteads'. At the B6318, turn right and then immediately left towards 'Steel Rigg'. Follow for 1 mile, turn right to 'Gibbs Hill'.

CONTACT: Valerie Gibson
Gibbs Hill Farm, Bardon Mill, Nr Hexham, Northumberland, NE47 7AP
Tel: (01434) 344030, Fax: (01434) 344030
val@gibbshillfarm.co.uk www.gibbshillfarm.co.uk

Demesne Farm Bunkhouse is a self-catering unit which was converted in 2004 from a barn on a working hill farm. The farm is situated on the Pennine Way, Route 68 cycle route, Reivers cycle route and is within 100 metres of the centre of the North Tyne village of Bellingham on the edge of the Northumberland National Park. The bunkhouse provides an ideal base for exploring Northumberland, Hadrian's Wall, Kielder Water and many climbing crags. It accommodates 15 and is perfect for smaller groups, individuals and families. The bedrooms are fitted with hand crafted oak man-sized bunk beds, high quality mattresses, pillows and curtains with cushion flooring. The communal living area with potbelly stove and fitted kitchen includes cooker, microwave, fridge, kettle, toaster, crockery, cutlery, cooking utensils, farmhouse tables, chairs and easy chairs. It has 2 bathrooms with hot showers, hand basins, toilets and under floor heating. Outside in the courtyard there is ample parking, bike lock up and a gravelled area with picnic tables. Linen can be hired.

DETAILS

- **Open** - All year, flexible, but no check in after 9pm
- **Number of beds** - 15: 1 x 8, 1 x 4, 1 x 3
- **Booking** - Please book in advance.
- **Price per night** - £15 per person (including linen).
- **Public Transport** - Trains at Hexham (17 miles), regular bus service from Hexham to Bellingham. Bellingham bus stop 100 metres from Bunkhouse. By car: Newcastle 45 mins, Scottish Border 20 mins, Kielder Water 10 mins.
- **Directions** - 100 metres from centre of village, located next to Northern Garage.

CONTACT: Robert Telfer
Demesne Farm, Bellingham, Hexham, Northumberland, NE48 2BS
Tel: (01434) 220258 Mobile 07967 396345
stay@demesnefarmcampsite.co.uk www.demesnefarmcampsite.co.uk

FOREST VIEW
WALKERS HOSTEL

Forest View is set in the hamlet of Byrness on the edge of Keilder Forest and Northumberland National Park. An ideal stopover on the A68 England to Scotland route. The Pennine Way runs just a few hundred yards from the hostel.

The building has just undergone a major refurbishment with new beds, curtains and carpets. The central heating is supplied by an eco-friendly wood pellet boiler and the hot water by solar panels. The log burning stoves in the quiet room and dining room keep the hostel cosy all year round.

The beds are arranged in 2, 3 & 4 bedded rooms and bed linen is supplied. Secure storage is provided for up to 10 bikes. There is a large selection of bottled beers and wines, meals can be provided or guests can use the well equipped self catering kitchen.

DETAILS

- **Open** - All year, 24hrs (coded entry system)
- **Number of beds** - 20: 2x4, 2x3, 3x2
- **Booking** - Booking is recommended
- **Price per night** - Adult £16, Under 16s £14
- **Public Transport** - Nearest rail station Newcastle-Upon-Tyne 40 miles then National Express to lay-by 200yds from hostel.
- **Directions** - Forest View is just off the A68, 4 miles from the Scottish Border, 16 miles south of Jedburgh and 10 miles north of Otterburn. The National Express bus drops off 200yds from the Hostel.

CONTACT: Colin or Joyce
7 Otterburn Green, Byrness Village, Northumberland, NE19 1TS
Tel: (01830) 520425
joycetaylor1703@hotmail.co.uk

BONNY BARN

ENGLAND

Bonny Barn, self-catering and non-smoking, was built in 2002 to accommodate cyclists using Route 68 Pennine Cycleway North which runs through Harbottle village. A mezzanine floor, with access to the upper garden, provides the sleeping area. Mattresses , sleeping bags, liners, pillows and towels are provided and 4 people can be accommodated comfortably. Contact us for provision for up to six people. There is a shower room, toilet and wash basin.

The building is centrally heated, has a kitchen area, dining table & chairs, settee & TV. The kitchen is equipped with crockery, cutlery, fridge, toaster, kettle and a two hob gas burner. Basic provisions are available, other groceries can be ordered at the time of booking. Its location in the Northumberland National Park, the Coquet Valley and the foothills of the Cheviots makes Harbottle an ideal base for walkers, cyclists, bird watchers and nature lovers.
Visit Britain approved.

DETAILS

- **Open** - All year, no restrictions
- **Number of beds** - 4 sleeping places (up to 6 by arrangement).
- **Booking** - Advance booking with deposit
- **Price per night** - 1-2 persons £50, 3 persons £60, 4 persons £70.
- **Public Transport** - Nearest train station - Morpeth 25 miles. Post bus once a day from Rothbury. Approx taxi fare from Rothbury £5.
- **Directions** - We are situated in the main street in Harbottle. Entry is next to Village Hall and by the bus stop.

CONTACT: Rosemary
Harbottle, Nr Rothbury, Northumberland, NE65 7DG
Tel: (01669) 650476
rosemary@bonnybarn.co.uk www.bonnybarn.co.uk

HOUGHTON NORTH
FARM ACCOMMODATION ENGLAND

Houghton North Farm, partly built with stones from Hadrian's Wall, has been in the Laws Family for five generations. It is situated in the beautiful Northumberland countryside right on the Heritage trail and 15 miles from the start of the Hadrian's Wall Trail. Within the region walkers can enjoy marked woodland trails, rugged moorland and hills, and some of the most beautiful deserted beaches in the UK. The newly built spacious accommodation can take a group of up to 23 and is also ideal for individuals and families. It is a 4*Hostel with Visit Britain. The bunk style rooms (some en-suite) are located around the central courtyard and include the use of a self-catering kitchen where a light breakfast is served. There is also a well appointed TV lounge with log fire and internet access, barbecue, secure cycle storage and parking. Long-term parking, baggage transfer and packed lunches are available on request. Within 10 mins walk are pubs, a restaurant and shops in Heddon-on-the-Wall.

DETAILS

- **Open** - All year, All day
- **Number of beds** - 23: 1 x 5, 4 x 4, 1 x 2
- **Booking** - Book with a non refundable deposit of £10 per person per night
- **Price per night** - From £22(adult), £15(under 15) inc breakfast. Group discounts.
- **Public Transport** - Trains at Wylam (2 miles) and Newcastle (7 miles). The 685 Newcastle-Carlisle bus stops right outside the farm. Baggage transfer is available.
- **Directions** - From Newcastle take the Heddon turn off the A69 to the B6528, farm is 1/4 mile outside of the village of Heddon. From Carlisle take Horsley junction and continue approx 3 miles beyond Horsley. Farm on the left at the top of a hill

CONTACT: Mrs Paula Laws
Houghton North Farm, Heddon-on-the-Wall, Northumberland, NE15 0EZ
Tel: (01661) 854364
wjlaws@btconnect.com www.houghtonnorthfarm.co.uk

ALBATROSS
BACKPACKERS IN!

BACKPACKERS IN !

Fly high with the award winning Albatross!
This clean and modern backpackers is located in Newcastle's City Centre.
Walking distance from sporting and musical venues, food markets, art
galleries, historical attractions and central station. So come discover
the North East, and get ready for Newcastle's highly acclaimed night
life. The Albatross provides rooms of 12, 10, 8, 6, 5, 4 or 2. The overnight
price includes; bedding; 24hr reception; fully fitted self-catering
kitchen with tea, coffee and toast; internet access; pool table;
satellite TV; 150-year old cellar; outside sitting area; first come
first serve car parking; baggage storage; laundry facilities; CCTV; and
key card system. Albatross has been awarded Outstanding Customer Service
and Best Newcomer of the Year in 2006 by North East Tourism Association.

DETAILS

■ **Open** - All year, 24 hours
■ **Number of beds** - 171: 10, 8, 6, 4 and 2 bed rooms
■ **Booking** - Recommended. Photo ID at check-in (passport or driver licence).
■ **Price per night** - From £16.50pp (dorm) to £22.50pp (2 bed room)
■ **Public Transport** - Five minutes walk from Central Train,Bus and METRO
stations. Twenty-five minutes by METRO from airport (one way ticket £2.80).
■ **Directions** - From Central train station: Cross over the road into Grainger Street,
walk towards Monument, we are on your left after passing Sports Bar. National
Express Station is just behind train station. From Airport, take METRO to Central
train station and follow above.

CONTACT: Reception
51 Grainger Street, Newcastle Upon Tyne, NE1 5JE
Tel: (0191) 2331330, Fax: (0191) 2603389
info@albatrossnewcastle.co.uk www.albatrossnewcastle.com

JOINERS SHOP
BUNKHOUSE

The Joiners Shop Bunkhouse is an attractive 17th-century building retaining much of its historical charm and character. It is situated in a quiet hamlet only 7 miles from Alnwick, the seat of the Duke of Northumberland, 5 miles from the beautiful Northumberland Coast and 10 miles from Wooler and the Cheviot Hills. The area offers opportunities for walking, climbing, mountain biking, all water sports or simply sightseeing.

The Joiners Shop Bunkhouse has full cooking facilities and a dining area along with a log fire and cosy sitting area. The 18 large pine beds are in heated dormitories of twos and threes. Indoor space is available for bikes and other equipment and there is ample parking.
Dogs welcome. NB There are dogs on site!

DETAILS

- **Open** - All year, no restrictions
- **Number of beds** - 18
- **Booking** - Advised for weekends and holidays.
- **Price per night** - £10.00 per person.
- **Public Transport** - There are train stations at Chathill (1.5 miles) limited service and Alnmouth (10 miles). There are National Express services at Alnwick (7 miles) and Berwick (24 miles). The local bus company is called ARRIVA and the nearest stop is Brownieside on the A1 (1.5 miles).
- **Directions** - GR 183 254 Seven miles north of Alnwick on the A1 to Brownieside. Turn off A1 at sign for Preston Tower, hostel is 1.5 miles on the left

CONTACT: Wal Wallace
Preston, Chathill, Northumberland, NE67 5ES
Tel: (01665) 589245 or 07745 373729
bunkhouse.wal@btinternet.com www.bunkhousenorthumberland.co.uk

Chatton Park Bunkhouse started life as a Smithy and has been converted into self-catering accommodation. It is situated on a mixed working farm which nestles around the river Till, ½ mile from Chatton village. We are 8 miles from the coast, 5miles from the Cheviot Hills, an ideal base for exploring Northumberland's vast empty beaches, heather clad hills & historic castles. Walking, watersports, climbing, fishing, golfing, cycling are all available nearby.

Accommodating 12 the bunkhouse is perfect for smaller groups, families & individuals. The 2 bedrooms are fitted with large custom made bunks and can be rented separately as secure units. Bedding can be provided at a small extra fee. The living area has a fully equipped kitchen & seating around the original fire. Wash & drying room with hot showers. Secure storage, ample parking. Room for camping. DIY livery. Dog kennels provided.

DETAILS

- **Open** - All year, flexible but no check in after 9pm
- **Number of beds** - 12: 2x6
- **Booking** - Booking recommended but not essential
- **Price per night** - £12/person. Group bookings negotiable
- **Public Transport** - Nearest train station Berwick upon Tweed. Buses to Chatton from Alnwick / Berwick.
- **Directions** - From A1 take B6348 to Chatton. 4 miles at bottom of hill on right is Chatton Park Farm

CONTACT: Jane or Duncan
Chatton Park Farm, Chatton, Alnwick, Northumberland, NE66 5RA
Tel: (01668) 215247
ord@chattonpk.fsnet.co.uk www.chattonparkfarm.co.uk

TACKROOM
BUNKHOUSE

The Tackroom Bunkhouse is situated on a mixed working farm between the seaside villages of Beadnell and Seahouses, yards from a beautiful sandy beach on the spectacular Northumberland Coast. The area is ideal for walking, watersports, climbing, cycling, diving or just sightseeing. Accommodating 12, the bunkhouse is ideal for smaller groups, individuals and couples. The two bedrooms are each fitted with 6 man sized bunk-beds and a locker for each visitor. Sleeping bags are essential. The communal area has a mini kitchen with hob, microwave, fridge, toaster etc, a dining table to seat 12 and colour TV. All crockery, cutlery and cooking utensils are supplied. Adjoining the bunkhouse is a shared shower/toilet block complete with washing machine and tumble drier. Also available is a lock-up, and off road parking. The Tackroom Bunkhouse is heated.

DETAILS

■ **Open** - Easter-October (by arrangement out of season), Flexible, but no check-in after 10pm.
■ **Number of beds** - 12: 2 x 6.
■ **Booking** - Recommended but not essential
■ **Price per night** - £10 per person
■ **Public Transport** - Nearest train station is Berwick upon Tweed. There are intermittent local buses to Seahouses and Beadnell, passing ½ mile away from the hostel.
■ **Directions** - From A1 take the B1340, follow road to Beadnell (signed Seahouses/ Beadnell). Annstead farm is approx ½ mile past Beadnell on the left.

CONTACT: Sue Mellor
Annstead Farm, Beadnell, Northumberland, NE67 5BT
Tel: (01665) 720387, Fax: (01665) 721494
susan@annstead.co.uk www.annstead.co.uk

Bluebell Farm Bunkbarn is situated on a family-owned caravan park and campsite. The Bunkbarn sleeps 14, and there is also a wooden ark which sleeps 6 and five self-catering cottages. The bunkbarn has a family room for 6 and an 8 bed dorm. The bunks are equipped with blankets and pillows. Linen and towels can be hired or bring your own sleeping bag. There is a fully equipped self-catering kitchen and a bike store. Packed lunches available by arrangement. Hot showers, electricity and gas are all included in the price. Bluebell Farm is in the centre of the village within walking distance of shops and pubs. It is ideally located for exploring Nothumberland's Heritage Coast Route to the East, the Cheviot Hills National Park to the West and the historic Scottish Borders. Many outdoor pursuits are available including:- golf, climbing, canoeing, diving, horse riding, fishing, cycling and walking. Dogs welcome by arrangement. Duke of Edinburgh groups welcome. Exclusive use available.

DETAILS

- **Open** - All year, check in by 9 pm, departure by 10 am.
- **Number of beds** - 14 : 1 x 8, 1 x 6
- **Booking** - Not essential
- **Price per night** - Adults £10, under 14s £5. Groups of 6 or over £7.50 pp. Linen and towel hire between £2 and £5 per person.
- **Public Transport** - Trains at Berwick upon Tweed. Buses from Berwick to Belford. National Express coaches stop in Belford. Local bus from Newcastle.
- **Directions** - From the A1 take B1342 into the village. Turn onto B6349 signposted for Wooler. Bluebell Farm is first main driveway on right, almost opposite the Co-op.

CONTACT: Phyl
Bluebell Farm Caravan Park, Belford, Northumberland, NE70 7QE
Tel: (01668) 213362
corillas@tiscali.co.uk. www.bluebellfarmbelford.co.uk

TWO THE COURTYARD
SELF CATERING
ENGLAND

Centuries old, Two the courtyard is conveniently situated in the heart of picturesque Old Berwick, yet is amazingly secluded, set behind high stone walls. Admire the magnificent stone fireplace as you toast yourself by the multi fuel stove. Enjoy a barbecue on the verandah or in the delightful tiny courtyard garden as you relax in the cool summer night air, heavy with the scent of honeysuckle and jasmine. Shared facilities include a well equipped kitchen, sitting room with TV and dining room. Berwick is an ideal base for exploring Northumberland, Lindisfarne and the Scottish Borders. It is also close to an amazing number of cycle routes. We have excellent secure cycle storage and drying facilities. Well behaved dogs by prior arrangement. No smoking.

DETAILS

- **Open** - All year, all day, check in 4pm-10pm
- **Number of beds** - 11: 1x3, 4x2 (1 twin ensuite, 2 double, 1 double ensuite)
- **Booking** - Booking advisable. 33% deposit, Beds held till 6pm without deposit.
- **Price per night** - £10pp (includes sleeping bag), £5 single sup. £25 made up bed.
- **Public Transport** - 10 mins walk from Berwick Station and long distance buses.
- **Directions** - Look for Church Street by the Guildhall. Enter wrought iron gate next to 'Hair at X1' and go up spiral staircase. By Car: from A698/A1 junction take A698 into Tweedmouth under railway and fork left over bridge. At mini roundabout turn right into main shopping street and look for Guildhall. From Station: Walk straight ahead then turn right then left (Railway Street). Turn right down Castlegate to town centre and look for Guildhall. From Bus (Golden Square): proceed to T junction (away from bridge) turn right into main shopping street. Look for Guildhall.

CONTACT: J Morton
1 The Courtyard, Church Street, Berwick-upon-Tweed, TD15 1EE
Tel: (01289) 308737, Mobile 07989 468008
jvm@patmosphere.uklinux.net

Maughold Venture Centre Bunkhouse is built of Manx stone, overlooking farmland with views in the distance to the sea. It offers self-catering facilities with the option of purchasing meals from the neighbouring adventure centre if required (subject to availability). All bedrooms are en-suite with full central heating. Facilities include a basic but functional games room and kitchen The number of beds in each room can be altered to suit your requirements. The local beach of Port e Vullen, 10 mins walk away, is popular with our visitors and the Bunkhouse is adjacent to the Venture Centre where you may arrange sessions of kayaking, abseiling, air rifle shooting, archery, gorge walking, dinghy sailing, power boating and team events. We have our own stop, Lewaigue Halt, on the Manx Electric Railway giving access to Douglas, Ramsay and to mountain walks and tranquil glens. Ideal for groups, families and individuals.

DETAILS

- **Open** - February to November, 24 hours
- **Number of beds** - 52   2x2 : 1x6 : 4x8 : 1x10
- **Booking** - Telephone reservation essential
- **Price per night** - £10-£15 per person
- **Public Transport** - No 3 Bus or Manx Electric Railway from Douglas or Ramsey, get off at Dreemskerry(bus - 5 mins walk) or Lewaigue Halt (railway - nearby). Taxi from Ramsey £5. Taxi from Douglas £25.
- **Directions** - GR 469922. From Douglas take the A2 coast road. When the road begins to descend into Ramsey the Venture Centre is signposted on the right hand side. Follow the signs - it is the first building on the left.

CONTACT: Simon Read
The Venture Centre, Maughold, Isle of Man, IM7 1AW
Tel: (01624) 814240
Contact@adventure-centre.co.uk www.adventure-centre.co.uk

King William's College is the only independent school in the Isle of Man and is located on Castletown Bay in the south of the island. The Isle of Man has lots to offer, including an interesting transport system, great beaches, mountainous heathland, historic sites, charming villages and numerous walks. Junior House 'formally used for junior boarding' is set in the expansive College grounds and provides a mix of accommodation options ranging from twin rooms to dormitory style accommodation. The building has recently been refurbished and all the bathroom facilities upgraded. There is a lounge, laundry room, TV room, drying room and a limited kitchen area.

Junior House is an ideal location for all the attractions in the south of the island and the facilities are well matched to those looking for outdoor activity holidays. Catering can be provided at most times although guests should check at the time of booking. Junior House is a relaxed, clean and well maintained property.

DETAILS

■ **Open** - All year (except Christmas and New Year), all day
■ **Number of beds** - 60: 1x14 : 2x12 : 1x 8: 7x2
■ **Booking** - Groups, TT races book with deposit.
■ **Price per night** - From 14.00 per person. Breakfast extra.
■ **Public Transport** - The airport is located next to the College. Ferries dock at Douglas from Liverpool, Heysham, Dublin and Belfast (approx return fare £40).
■ **Directions** - From Douglas follow signs to Castletown and the Airport. Bus stop is located opposite the entrance to King William's College.

CONTACT: Ruth Watterson
King William's College, Castletown, Isle of Man, IM9 1TP
Tel: (01624) 820470 / 820400, Fax: (01624) 820402
rooms@kwc.sch.im www.kwc.sch.im

South Wales

0 ————— miles ————— 25
0 ————— kilometres ————— 40

Aberystwyth
2
229

New Quay

Cardigan
220
218
Fishguard
216
214

Lampeter
219
222

207

Carmarthen

Haverfordwest
St Clears
208

Milford Haven 209
212

Pembroke
210

Tenby

Llanelli

206

KEY

45 - Hostel page number

45 - Page number of group
only accommodation

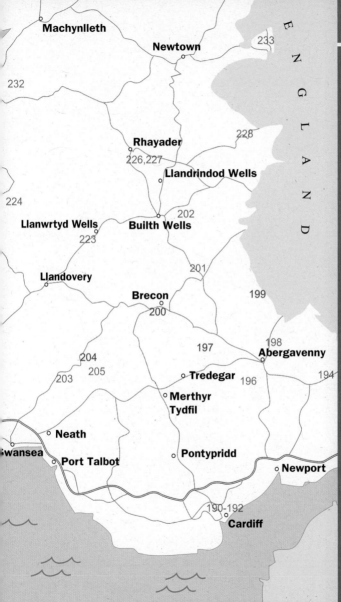

Machynlleth

Newtown

232

233

E N G L A N D

Rhayader

226,227

Llandrindod Wells

228

224

Llanwrtyd Wells

223

Builth Wells

202

Llandovery

201

Brecon

200

199

197

198

Abergavenny

Tredegar

196

194

204

205

Merthyr
Tydfil

203

Neath

Pontypridd

Swansea

Port Talbot

Newport

190-192

Cardiff

South Wales

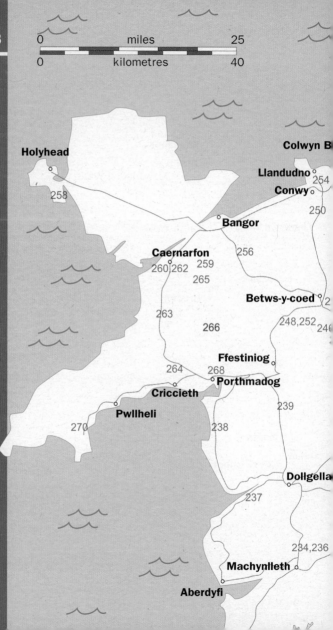

North Wales

0   miles   25
0   kilometres   40

Holyhead
258

Colwyn B
Llandudno   254
Conwy
250

Bangor
256

Caernarfon
260 262   259
265

Betws-y-coed   2

263

266   248,252   24

Ffestiniog
264   268
Porthmadog
Criccieth   239

Pwllheli
270   238

Dolgella
237

234,236

Machynlleth
Aberdyfi

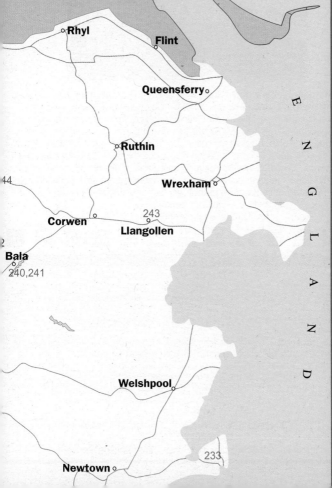

KEY

45 - **Hostel page number**

45 - **Page number of group only accommodation**

Rhyl

Flint

Queensferry

Ruthin

Wrexham

44

Corwen

243

Llangollen

Bala

240,241

Welshpool

233

Newtown

ENGLAND

North Wales

Cardiff's only central tourist hostel, only ten minutes walk from the stations and all municipal and central amenities. Enjoy a warm Welsh welcome, whilst relaxing and socialising with fellow travellers from all over the world in Europe's youngest capital city. All our friendly staff are experienced travellers; multilingual in Welsh, English and other languages; and knowledgeable about activities in Wales. Accommodation is in a combination of twin/double and group rooms. Facilities include reception/breakfast area with essentials shop; information desk; telephones and fax; comfortable lounge with digital and big screen TV; internet centre; roof garden; guest bar with pool table; launderette and car parking.
Foreign passport holders only.

DETAILS

■ **Open** - All year, Fri & Sat 24 hours. Sun - Thurs 7.30am-2.30pm
■ **Number of beds** - 70: 4x2 1x5 1x4 3x6 3x8 1x10
■ **Booking** - Booking recommended for individuals and essential (with deposit) for groups.
■ **Price per night** - From £17.70 per person, including light breakfast. Excellent weekly rates available.
■ **Public Transport** - Cardiff has train, National Express and local bus services all calling at the central bus and train station (5 to 10 minutes walk away).
■ **Directions** - From Cardiff Central Station, turn left crossing the River Taff. Follow the river embankment upstream, turning left past the Riverbank Hotel. We are on the roundabout ahead of you. Walking time from station to hostel 5-10 minutes.

CONTACT:
98 Neville Street, Riverside, Cardiff, CF11 6LS
Tel: (029) 20 345577
info@cardiffbackpacker.com www.cardiffbackpacker.com

You won't get closer to the action and the city centre than this! Uniquely situated on the River Taff in the shadow of the Millennium Stadium, Nos Da is set to become Cardiff's latest hotspot for budget tourist accommodation, atmosphere and entertainment. All rooms are en-suite and no-frills giving you hotel convenience with hostel sociability. Facilities include all the 'usual' plus 'Tafarn'- Welsh Cantina and Bar with affordable local food in a menu geared for the independent traveller, and 'Tafod'- Underground Sound Lounge, open for entertainment most nights.

DETAILS

- **Open** - All year, 24 hours
- **Number of beds** - 80: Dorms = 1x10, 1x6, 5x4, 1x2. Private rooms = 2x3, 4x2(D), 4x2(T), 8x1.
- **Booking** - Essential for groups, advisable for individuals. Book online.
- **Price per night** - Dormitory from £18.50pp, Single from £36.00, Double/Twin from £52.00, Triple from £72.00 (all rooms en-suite).
- **Public Transport** - Cardiff has train, National Express and local bus services all calling at the central bus and train station (5 minutes walk from the hostel).
- **Directions** - By Car: From the M4, take junction 32 and follow signs for city centre. Approaching the centre follow the road around the castle then straight ahead over the bridge crossing the river Taff. Take the next left into Lower Cathedral Road, then 2nd left into Despenser Street, the hostel is at the end of the street. By foot from Cardiff Central Station, turn left across the river and follow the embankment upstream, with the stadium opposite. The hostel is directly ahead.

CONTACT: Reception
53-59, Despenser Street, Riverside, Cardiff, CF11 6AG
Tel: (029) 20378866
info@nosda.co.uk www.nosda.co.uk

Cardiff University provides ideal conference and holiday accommodation in an elegant environment. Accommodation is at a number of sites all with easy access to the heart of one of Europe's most vibrant capital cities. Very close to the city centre, surrounded by bars and pubs and with limited parking, Senghennydd Hall provides en-suite single rooms with access to shared kitchen/dining rooms. A short walk from the city centre and with limited parking is Colum Hall, providing self-catering accommodation arranged in flats for eight people. Ten minutes drive from the city centre, close to the grounds of Cardiff's Castle is Talybont. Located on the banks of the river Taff, this accommodation was host to the Special Olympics and has a number of sports facilities, a large bar and up to 1200 single en-suite self-catering bedrooms and extensive free parking. Talybont is an excellent venue for groups, sporting associations and large events.

DETAILS

- **Open** - 19 June - 12 September 2008,, reception open 9am-5pm
- **Number of beds** - 1200+ bedrooms (en-suite)
- **Booking** - Telephone or email to enquire
- **Price per night** - £21pp (single en-suite) or £132.75pp per week. B&B (if available) £29.50pp. Inc VAT, bed linen and towels.
- **Public Transport** - Cardiff Central Station: trains, coaches, connections to airports. Buses from city centre.
- **Directions** - From junction 29 of M4, follow the A48(M)/A48, signpost Cardiff East and South, to the A470, signpost City Centre, into the Cathays area of the city.

CONTACT: Cardiff University Conference Office
Southgate House, PO Box 533, Cardiff, CF14 3X2
Tel: 029 2087 4702 / 4616, Fax: (029) 2087 4990
Groupaccom@cardiff.ac.uk www.cardiff.ac.uk/resid

RICKYARD
BUNKHOUSE

Rickyard Bunkhouse is nestled in idyllic countryside away from the hustle and bustle. Offa's Dyke footpath passes the entrance to the Rickyard. Within 25 mins of the Wye valley, Symonds Yat and the Forest of Dean. Most outdoor pursuits are available,canoeing,rafting, potholing, cycle paths, rock climbing, golf to name a few. Fishing is also available; the river Trothy contains brown trout and eels; kingfishers and otters have been seen to enjoy the peace and tranquillity of the Trothy. The magnificent buzzard can be seen to soar high above the valley where the Trothy nestles. The bunkhouse accommodates 24 easily and has excellent cooking facilities. Separate dining /relaxing area with TV. The bunkhouse is split into 3 areas. Male and female showers and toilets with electric showers. Background heat can be provided but will incur a small charge. Popular for parties and reunions and groups of friends due to secluded location. Secure area for camping where children can play in safety. Ample parking. Packed lunches available and luggage transfer arranged. Breakfast next door at the Hendre farmhouse if needed. Bedding available if required.

DETAILS

- **Open** - All year, all day
- **Number of beds** - 24: + camping
- **Booking** - Deposit required, no credit cards. Notice not always required.
- **Price per night** - £12pp. Private en-suite room for 4 persons £15pp. Can be booked for sole use. Tents £4pp.
- **Public Transport** - Trains at Abergavenny (11m). Buses Monmouth (3m).
- **Directions** - Next to the Hendre Farm House on the same side of the road.

CONTACT: Graham Edwards
Wonastow, Monmouth, NP254DJ
Tel: (01600) 740128
rickyard@campingandbunks.fsnet.co.uk www.rickyardbunkhouse.co.uk

MIDDLE NINFA
BUNKHOUSE

Middle Ninfa Farm, situated in the Brecon Beacons on the edge of the newly designated Blaenavon World Heritage Site, offers bunkhouse accommodation, cottage accommodation, camping and hands-on training in creative working with willow. The farm has fine views over the Usk Valley, of the Skirrid and rural Monmouthshire. The Bunkhouse provides comfortable self-catering accommodation for up to 6 people. The rustic charm of the old stone building has been retained whilst ensuring modern comforts. The ground floor has lounge/dining area with double divan and TV, well-equipped kitchen and toilet/ shower room. Upstairs (Mezzanine Floor) there are 4 single beds, accessed by a spiral staircase. Guests should bring food, sleeping bags, towels & pillowcases. Home grown fruit, veg and local produce available on the farm. Walking and Cycling Welcome and Green Dragon Level 2 environmental award.

DETAILS

■ **Open** - All year, all day
■ **Number of beds** - 6: 1x4, 1x2
■ **Booking** - Book by phone or email
■ **Price per night** - Bunkhouse Sun to Thur £10pp or £50 sole use. Fri,Sat and Bank Holidays £12pp or £60 sole use. Cottage £220-£300 per week. Camping £3pp.
■ **Public Transport** - The nearest bus is at Llanfoist (1.5 miles) The train station is at Abergavenny (3.5 miles) Taxis from the station cost approximately £7.00
■ **Directions** - Approx. 2 miles from A465 (Hereford/Neath), A40 (Brecon/Monmouth and M50) and A4042 (Newport, M4). See website for map. The farm is reached by a steep winding road from Llanfoist, crossing the Monmouthshire and Brecon Canal.

CONTACT: Richard and Rohan Lewis
Middle Ninfa Farm, Llanellen, Abergavenny, NP7 9LE
Tel: (01873) 854662
richard@middleninfa.co.uk www.middleninfa.co.uk

Wern Watkin Bunkhouse is located in the Brecon Beacons National Park, high up on Mynnedd Llangattock. It is also known as YHA Llangattock Mountain. There is direct access on foot to the mountainside and a flat mountain road to a National Cycle Route. The Bunkhouse is a converted stone barn with bunks for 30 people in 7 mainly en-suite bedrooms. The massive dining room and seating area opens out onto ancient woodlands. There is under-floor heating throughout, excellent drying facilities and ample hot water. The location is ideal for caving, rock climbing, canoeing, abseiling, orienteering, pony trekking and mountain biking. Outdoor pursuit training can be arranged from local qualified instructors. The bunkhouse is within easy walking distance of Llangattock cave complex (one of Europe's most elaborate cave systems) as well as climbing crags and open moorland. A short drive away are the rest of Brecon Beacons, the scenic Wye and Usk river valleys and a wealth of industrial heritage at the World Heritage site of Blaenavon. Catering can be provided for groups.

GROUPS ONLY

DETAILS

- **Open** - All year, all day
- **Number of beds** - 30: 4x6, 1x4, 2x2. All rooms but one en-suite
- **Booking** - Availability shown online. 10% deposit, balance two weeks in advance.
- **Price per night** - Sole use £450 week nights, £555 weekend nights. Smaller groups by negotiation £16pp weeknights, £18.50 pp weekend.
- **Public Transport** - Trains Abergavenny (8miles). Nearest buses Crickhowell.
- **Directions** - Access can be either from Crickhowell or Brynmawr on small mountain roads. Detailed instructions will be sent with your booking.

CONTACT: Andrew Fryer
Wern Watkin, Hillside, Llangattock, Crickhowell, NP8 1LG
Tel: (01873) 812307
enquiries@wernwatkin.co.uk www.wernwatkin.co.uk

SMITHY'S
BUNKHOUSE

Located on a working hill farm, Smithy's Bunkhouse lies in the Black Mountains within the Brecon Beacons National Park, two and a half miles from the historic market town of Abergavenny. Designed to accommodate 24 persons in two dormitories of 12 bunks, additional space is available above the common room if required. The bunkhouse is equipped with showers, toilets, fully equipped kitchen, drying area, coin operated washer and dryer and a common room with a wood burning stove. It is heated during the winter by night storage heaters, hot water and electricity are supplied at no extra cost, some firewood is provided and extra may be purchased. A 16th-century coaching inn is located at the top of the farm drive which serves bar snacks, restaurant meals and traditional ales. The area is ideal for walking, climbing, caving, mountain biking, canoeing, water sports, pony trekking.

DETAILS

- **Open** - All year, 24 hours by arrangement
- **Number of beds** - 24 : 2 x 12
- **Booking** - Booking is advised. £150 deposit required for groups. Cheques payable to Smithy's Bunkhouse.
- **Price per night** - £12pp for individuals & small groups. £10pp for groups of 7+.
- **Public Transport** - Nearest train station Abergavenny (2 miles). Taxi fare from station approximately £5. No local buses.
- **Directions** - GR 304 178. Pantygelli village is located two and a half miles north of Abergavenny on the old Hereford Road. Access to the bunkhouse is down the farm drive opposite the Crown Inn.

CONTACT: Neil or Katy Smith
Lower House Farm, Pantygelli,Abergavenny, Monmouthshire, NP7 7HR
Tel: (01873) 853432
info@smithysbunkhouse.com www.smithysbunkhouse.com

This old stone barn continues the tradition of 900 years when Llanthony Priory provided shelter and accommodation. Surrounded by the Black Mountains in the Brecon Beacons National Park, this spectacular setting is a superb base for walking, riding, pony trekking and other mountain activities.

Sixteen bunks are split into three separate areas for sleeping; there is a fully equipped kitchen, hot water for showers, heating throughout and a wood burning stove in the eating area. Small or large groups are welcome, but there is a minimum charge at weekends. Two pubs offer real beer and bar food.

Just 50 minutes from the M4 Severn Bridge and 1 hour from the M5/M50 Junction, this must be one of the easiest bunkbarns to reach from the motorways - and yet you feel you are miles from anywhere.

DETAILS

- **Open** - All year, 24 hours no restrictions
- **Number of beds** - 16: 1 x 8 : 1 x 4 : 1 x 6
- **Booking** - Booking and deposit required.
- **Price per night** - £10.00 per person. Minimum charge of £220 at weekends (2 nights).
- **Public Transport** - Abergavenny railway station 12 miles.
- **Directions** - GR SO 288 278 Map on website. Turn west off A465 Abergavenny to Hereford road at Llanvihangel Crucorney (5 miles north of Abergavenny). Llanthony is 6 miles along country lane - follow signs to Priory. On cycle route 42.

CONTACT:
Court Farm, Llanthony, Abergavenny, Monmouthshire, NP7 7NN
Tel: (01873) 890359
courtfarm@llanthony.co.uk www.llanthony.co.uk

CANAL BARN
BUNKHOUSE

Nestling between the river Usk and the Canal, Canal Barn Bunkhouse has a superb setting and yet is near Brecon town centre. The Bunkhouse is at the centre of activity in the Brecon Beacons National Park with easy access to the numerous exciting outdoor activities available in this beautiful part of Wales. Brecon town has a range of pubs, restaurants, takeaways and entertainments to satisfy most tastes and pockets, and all nearby in a safe walking distance.

Sleeping up to 24 people, the Bunkhouse offers award winning environmentally friendly, competitively priced, group accommodation of exceptional quality that is accessible by disabled people. Specifically designed as a base for your outdoor activities club, the Bunkhouse is equipped to a very high standard indeed and is an excellent venue for team building and residential training courses, or the place for an action packed get together with friends and family.

DETAILS

■ **Open** - All year, all day
■ **Number of beds** - 24 (in 6 rooms)
■ **Booking** - Booking essential (minimum group of 6 people)
■ **Price per night** - From £12.50
■ **Public Transport** - Train/bus to Merthyr Tydfil or Abergavenny, then bus to Brecon.
■ **Directions** - GR 052 279. On the canal towpath close to Brecon town centre. Vehicular access is via the canal bridge next to the Morrison Petrol Station on the nearby Abergavenny to Brecon road (B4601).

CONTACT: Ralph or Liz
Ty Camlas, Canal Bank, Brecon, Powys, LD3 7HH
Tel: (01874) 625361
ihg@canal-barn.co.uk www.canal-barn.co.uk

Across the stream from Trericket Corn Mill this stone bunkhouse in an old cider orchard overlooks the River Wye. It is particularly suitable for small groups and individuals with two rooms sleeping four people each and an additional en-suite bunkroom for two in the mill. The bunkhouse is clean and cosy; heating, hot water and showers are all inclusive. Limited self-catering facilities are provided in a covered outdoor kitchen. Alternatively breakfasts and packed lunches can be provided and good pub meals are available locally. There are heated drying and common rooms in the mill and camping is also available.

Trericket Mill is situated on the Wye Valley Walk and National Cycle Route 8. An ideal stop-over for walkers, cyclists and for others wishing to spend time in the beautiful countryside of Mid Wales. Canoeing, pony trekking, gliding, mountain bikes, rope centre and white water rafting all available locally.

DETAILS

- **Open** - All year, 24 hour access
- **Number of beds** - 10: 2 x 4, 1 x 2 en-suite, plus 6 veggie B&B beds
- **Booking** - Advanced booking advised.
- **Price per night** - From £12 per person
- **Public Transport** - Train stations at Builth Wells (10 miles) Hereford (30 miles) Merthyr Tydfil (30 miles). Daily bus service - ask to be dropped at Trericket Mill. National Express coaches drop off at Hereford and Brecon (13 miles). For transport enquiries call 0870 6082608.
- **Directions** - GR SO 112 414. We are set back from the A470 Brecon to Builth Wells road between the villages of Llyswen and Erwood.

CONTACT: Alistair/Nicky Legge
Erwood, Builth Wells, Powys, LD2 3TQ
Tel: (01982) 560312
mail@trericket.co.uk www.trericket.co.uk

MAESBRYNCOCH
BARN

Maesbryncoch Barn is set in a peaceful spot near Builth Wells with lovely views of Mid Wales Hills. Ideal for families and small groups to get away from it all. The open-plan living, sleeping and kitchen area has 6 fold out beds (pillow and pillowcase provided), heater, large dining table, cooking facilites, fridge/freezer and sink unit. There's a fully equipped kitchen, separate washroom with shower (free hot water) and WCs. There is also storage for bikes and a pony paddock.

The local area is excellent for paragliding, walking, mountain biking, riding, canoeing and fishing. Less than 2 miles from the Wye Valley, 3 miles from Royal Welsh Showground and 3½ miles from Builth Wells with shops, pubs, a theatre, cinema, leisure centre and golf course. Nearest pub serving food is 2½ miles away in Hundred House village. We can provide breakfast and supper with a little notice. Bring your own sleeping bags or order a bedding and towel pack for your stay. Visit Wales rated 2* bunkhouse. Member of ABO. Sorry, no dogs.

DETAILS

- **Open** - Open all year, all day
- **Number of beds** - 6: 1x6
- **Booking** - By email or phone
- **Price per night** - £9 per person, £45 for sole use. Bedding & towel pack £5 pp.
- **Public Transport** - Nearest trains at Builth Road (4½ miles). Daily buses to Builth from Newtown, Brecon, Cardiff, Abergavenny, Aberystwyth. Pick up from Builth /Builth Road may be possible or local taxi. More info: 0870 6082608, www.traveline.org.uk
- **Directions** - Just to the south of the A481, 3½ miles from Builth Wells, half way between Llanelwedd and Hundred House. Grid reference SO079527.

CONTACT: Louise and Tim
Maesbryncoch, Llanfaredd, Builth Wells, Powys, LD2 3TE
Tel: (01982) 551116 or 07709 202355
louise.mbc@virgin.net www.maesbryncochbarn.co.uk

Exciting, untamed, & beautiful - do you see yourself in Wales? Ko Samui, Goa, London, Dublin, Merlins Ystradgynlais - what never heard of us? You will be describing us to your friends as a 'must go' place. Merlins offers basic but comfortable rooms the majority of which have en-suite facilities. Merlins has a warm and welcoming atmosphere and we pride ourselves on our Welsh hospitality. We have a bar and café. We are Wales Tourist board accredited, they say 'very comfortable hostel accommodation presented to a very good overall standard and very worthy of the 3 star quality rating awarded'. Being on the very edge of the Brecon Beacons National Park the area has lots of castles and historic sites to visit, is steeped in folklore and is famous for it's natural beauty. Merlins is well placed to offer a range of 'in your face' high adrenalin adventure activities such as canyoning, caving, climbing, abseiling, coasteering, hill walking, kayaking, canoeing, quad biking, paintballing, adventure days, and nearby Swansea has excellent nightlife.

DETAILS

- **Open** - All year, 24 hours
- **Number of beds** - 40: 1 x 13 : 1 x double : 2 x 2 : 1 x 5 : 4 x 4
- **Booking** - Booking essential
- **Price per night** - £11pp Monday to Thursday. £15pp Friday to Sunday.
- **Public Transport** - Hourly train services from London Paddington to Neath & Swansea, buses connect. Regular ferry between Swansea and Cork.
- **Directions** - M4 Junc.45. North on A4067 for 10 miles, right for Ystradgynlais, left at mini roundabout, over bridge, left after pedestrian crossing, 50 mtrs down on right.

CONTACT: Connie
44-46 Commercial Street, Ystradgynlais, Swansea, SA9 1JH
Tel: (01639) 845670
info@callofthewild.co.uk www.backpackerwales.com

DULWICH COLLEGE
FIELD CENTRE

Dulwich College Field Centre is situated in the small hamlet of Glyntawe on the southern edge of the Brecon Beacons. This conversion of an old primary school sleeps up to 40 people. The ground floor has 5 six-bed dorms, a large fully fitted kitchen, dining room, 7 toilets and showers, drying room and wet entrance with boot store. On the first floor are a large common room (with TV, DVD, SKY & games), 2 ensuite rooms (one with an additional set of bunks), a twin room and a 2 bedroomed self-contained apartment sleeping 4 with its own bathroom, lounge and kitchen. Within walking distance are many attractions and opportunities for outdoor pursuits such as walking, mountain biking, fishing, caving and gorge walking. We're within easy reach of the Central Beacons and the waterfall area of Ystradfellte. The Centre is disabled friendly and has won the level 2 award in the Green Dragon Environmental Scheme.

DETAILS

■ **Open** - All year, flexible
■ **Number of beds** - 40
■ **Booking** - Phone or email booking required.
■ **Price per night** - Bunk rooms:- £11pp self-catering. En-suites £13pp self-catering (includes all bedding, heating & hot water)
■ **Public Transport** - Trains at Aberdare, Neath and Swansea. Stage Coach buses between Brecon and Swansea - the Dan yr Ogof show caves stop is 5 mins walk.
■ **Directions** - From Brecon take A40 west. Just before Senni Bridge take the A4067 south for 8 miles. Just after the Tafarn Y Garreg pub turn left opposite the phone box (Heol Callwen road). First building on right (black gates).

CONTACT: Gary
Heol Callwen, Glyntawe, Penycae, Swansea, SA9 1GR
Tel: (01639) 730892
fieldcentre@dulwich.org.uk http://fieldcentre.dulwich.org.uk/

Clyngwyn Bunkhouse is situated in the Brecon Beacons, in the heart of waterfall country, very near to the caves & waterfalls of Ystradfellte and close to the famous Sgwd Yr Eira waterfalls where you can walk behind the falling water. The location has ideal terrain for mountain biking, gorge walking, canyoning, caving, abseiling, climbing, quad biking, photography and painting. Clyngwyn Bunkhouse is ideal for groups of friends or family. It sleeps up to 15 with camping for 5 people available to larger groups. There is a fully equipped kitchen, central heating and a drying area which ensure a cosy stay. There is a relaxation area with TV, DVD and CD player and outside there is a fire-pit and BBQ which make a great place to relax in the evenings enjoying the mountain views. There is also 4 acres of land ideal for ball games and team building exercises and a separate function room for hire. The local villages of Ystradfellte and Pontneddfechan (2½ miles away) have pubs with restaurants and are accessible via a local mini bus taxi service. Dogs by arrangement.

DETAILS

- **Open** - All year, all day
- **Number of beds** - 15: 1x11/9, 1x4
- **Booking** - Booking essential. Credit/Debit cards not accepted
- **Price per night** - Whole bunkhouse, sole use : Fri - Sun £164, Mon - Thur £136, Bank Holidays £178. All prices per night.
- **Public Transport** - Trains Neath or Merthyr (11 miles). Mini bus can be arranged.
- **Directions** - From A465 leave at Glenneath drive-through and take signs for Pontneddfechan. Then 2.5 miles up Ystradfellte road, turn right down small track.

CONTACT: Julie Hurst
Clyngwyn Farm, Ystradfellte Rd, Pontneddfechan, Powys, SA11 5US
Tel: (01639) 722930
enquiries@bunkhouse-south-wales.co.uk www.bunkhouse-south-wales.co.uk

HARDINGSDOWN
BUNKHOUSE

Hardingsdown Bunkhouse is a tastefully restored stone barn situated on an organic farm. It provides comfortable self-catering accommodation for families or groups. The ground floor consists of a fully equipped kitchen, 2 shower/toilet rooms, a living room with 2 single sofa-beds and comfy chairs. Off the living room is a bedroom with a bunkbed sleeping 2 people. A spiral staircase leads upstairs where there are 3 bedrooms sleeping 5, 3 and 2 in bunks and single beds. A separate drying room is available for outdoor gear and a lock-up for storing bikes, surfboards, canoes etc. There is ample parking and a patio area which catches the evening sun. The Gower has national nature reserves, outstanding coastal scenery, family beaches, castles and ancient monuments. Llangennith beach is one of the best surfing beaches in the south west and Mewslade Bay and Fall Bay are used by climbers. Walkers and bikers can use the local network of footpaths and bridleways. Shops and pubs nearby.

DETAILS

- **Open** - All year, 24 hours
- **Number of beds** - 14: 1x5, 1x3, 3x2
- **Booking** - Non-returnable deposit of 30%, balance 1 month before arrival.
- **Price per night** - Sole use £180, £1100 per week. Smaller groups sharing the bunkhouse with other users, £15 per person.
- **Public Transport** - Regular bus (No16) from Swansea 0870 6082608.
- **Directions** - Turn left off the B4295 ½ mile after Burry Green (by bus shelter and post box). Follow lane till it changes into a rough track and turn right into Lower Hardingsdown Farm. Bunkhouse is on left of farmyard.

CONTACT: Allison or Andrew Tyrrell
Lower Hardingsdown Farm,Llangennith, Gower,Swansea, SA3 1HT
Tel: (01792) 386222
bunkhousegower@tiscali.co.uk www.bunkhousegower.co.uk

Gilfach Wen Barn, has been converted to provide competitively priced self-catering accommodation for individuals, extended families or groups on a working farm adjacent to Brechfa Forest. Designed to achieve 4 star grading, the barn conversion is too new to have yet been graded. It sleeps upto 28 in 7 bedrooms and has a large kitchen/dining room, lounge and drying room. There is a downstairs bedroom and shower room for disabled visitors. The facilities are purpose designed to be walker, cyclist and equestrian friendly for those taking advantage of the benefits of being adjacent to Brechfa Forest - the largest man made forest in Europe. Gilfach Wen Barn is a perfect venue for a holiday or weekend away – if you do not want to drive you need never leave the valley. The barn is fully equipped and the village shop and pub are within walking distance (1mile). This is a stunningly beautiful area and is far less commercialised than a national park. Within a short drive there are numerous sites of interest and fun things to do for all the family.

DETAILS

- **Open** - Open all year, opening 20th July, all day
- **Number of beds** - 28: 3x6, 1x5, 2x2, 1x1 (9 double beds, 10 single beds)
- **Booking** - Booking essential, but will accept telephone bookings 24 hours in advance. Booking only confirmed if 50% deposit received.
- **Price per night** - £15 per person. Sole use is £325 per night.
- **Public Transport** - Trains and coaches at Carmarthen. Daily bus from Carmarthen to Brechfa passes gate. Bus stop at Horeb crossroads but may drop at gate,
- **Directions** - GR SN 513 292 On the B4310 between Horeb and Brechfa.

CONTACT: Jillie
Gilfach Wen, Brechfa, Carmarthenshire, SA32 7QL
Tel: 07970 629726
GilfachWenBarn@aol.com www.holisticfarm.co.uk/barn

PANTYRATHRO
INTERNATIONAL HOSTEL

Llansteffan is a beautiful quaint village set at the tip of the Towi River and Carmarthen Bay. The sandy beaches nestled below the castle offer swimming and relaxation. The virtually traffic free country lanes make this area ideal for cycling. For the walker Carmarthenshire offers coastal walks and country walks. Carmarthen (Wales' oldest city) and ancestral home to Merlin of King Arthur's Legends, offers most social and cultural activities. The Pantyrathro International Hostel provides dorm and double room accommodation and also 3 new ensuite units of 6, 8 and 12 beds. Facilities include self-catering kitchen, dining area, TV lounge and showers. Our two Mexican bars offer pool, darts, TV and weekly drink specials, food (eat-in or take-out). Horse riding, cycle hire and excursions for trekking, canoeing and surfing offered. Take a day trip or relax on the beaches or have a drink in our bars - something for everyone.

DETAILS

- **Open** - March to Jan, 24 hours
- **Number of beds** - 51: 1 x 12, 1 x 8, 2 x 6, 4 x 4, 1 x 3
- **Booking** - Booking recommended. 50% depost required in advance for groups.
- **Price per night** - £13pp dorm, £14pp ensuite. Group discounts.
- **Public Transport** - Carmarthen has both coach and train stations servicing South Wales, SW England and London. Local bus runs 6 times a day to Llansteffan. Ask driver to let you off at Pantyrathro.
- **Directions** - Pantyrathro is 6 miles from Carmarthen on the B4312, midway between Llangain and Llansteffan. Two miles from Llangain you will see the hostel signposted, turn right and follow signs to top of lane.

CONTACT: Ken Knuckles
Pantyrathro Country Inn, Llansteffan, Carmarthen, SA33 5AJ
Tel: (01267) 241014, Fax: 241014
kenknuckles@hotmail.com www.backpackershostelwales.co.uk

Millennium hostel is a refurbished Victorian school situated in an attractive village on the upper reaches of the Cleddau River with almost direct access to river and woodland areas. The hostel is centrally heated thoughout, it has a modern kitchen/dining area, a good-sized common room and access to a large hall for activities (hire separate). There are 2 showers, 3 WCs and all rooms have wash hand basins. The kitchen area is equipped with a large oven, 3 four-ring hobs, 2 microwaves, 2 large toasters, 2 fridges and a freezer. There is a good drying room, a large car park, cycle shelter and a patio with picnic tables. The hostel has a 15-seater mini-bus, which can be hired by the day. Community shop in village open 7 days a week. Pub and tearoom within walking distance. There is 24 hour contact by freephone with the Warden who lives in the village.

DETAILS

- **Open** - All year for groups. Easter to 31st Oct for individuals/ families, from 5pm.
- **Number of beds** - 23. 1x3, 3x4, 1x8. All can be used as family rooms.
- **Booking** - Required with deposit of 50%, balance payable on arrival. No deposit required if booking less than 7 days in advance.
- **Price per night** - Adult £12, under 18 £8, under 3 years free. Sole use by group £200 per night (groups must bring their own sleeping bags).
- **Public Transport** - Coachs/trains at Kilgetty (8m). Get 381 bus (Tenby to Pembroke Dock) at Kilgetty, ask for Cresswell Quay, 2½m (40 min walk) from hostel.
- **Directions** - From A40 St Clears to Haverfordwest take A4075 signed Tenby and Oakwood Leisure Park. Just past turning to Oakwood, turn right and follow signs to Lawrenny. Bear right in front of church. Car park is on left behind Village Hall.

CONTACT: Barry or Marijke
Lawrenny, Pembrokeshire, SA68 0PN
Tel: (01646) 651270 / 651866
lawrenny.hostel@xifos.co.uk www.lawrenny-village.co.uk

The Stackpole Centre provides fully accessible holiday and conference accommodation, only a mile from Broadhaven and Barafundle beaches in the Pembrokeshire National Coastal Park. The Stackpole estate of countryside and coast includes a nature reserve, ancient settlements, a stately home and an eco-centre providing environmental and outdoor education for all ages.

The accommodation has been developed from a range of stone farm buildings. It comprises three large houses and five cottages, which sleep between 5 and 19 people in single and twin rooms. Facilities include a leisure pool, sauna, jacuzzi, theatre and covered arena. Contacts are available for activities such as canoeing, rock climbing, abseiling, cycling, horseriding, music and drama.

DETAILS

■ **Open** - All year, all day, Reception 9am - 8 pm
■ **Number of beds** - Kingfisher House 17/19: 2x2, 13x1. Swan House 14: 2x2, 10x1. Heron House 16: in ten bedrooms. Swift Cottage:7. Swallow Cottage 6: 3x2, two more cottages of 6: 3x2, 1 cottage 4 : 2x2
■ **Booking** - Bookings are made through reception.
■ **Price per night** - Minimum of two nights stay. Please contact bookings team for a quote. There are low and high season tariffs.
■ **Public Transport** - Trains Pembroke (5 miles). Bus from Pembroke Silcox 387 Coastal Cruiser from Pembroke.
■ **Directions** - On the B4319 from Pembroke to Stackpole and Bosherton (various entry points onto estate).

CONTACT: Stackpole Reception
Old Home Farm Yard, Stackpole, nr Pembroke, Pembrokeshire, SA71 5DQ
Tel: (01646) 661425
stackpole.receptionc@nationaltrust.org.uk www.nationaltrust.org.uk

UPPER NEESTON
LODGES

Upper Neeston Lodges are energy-efficient barn conversions on a family run sheep farm. Close to the Milford Haven Waterway in the Pembrokshire Coast Park they are ideal for divers, climbers and walkers. There are two independent units, one accommodating 10 people and one accommodating 8. Shared between the units are a laundry/drying room, wash-down area, secure storage areas and ample parking. THE COWSHED is single storey with disabled access. It has a large sitting room and kitchen/dining area, and two bedrooms, each with a large en-suite shower room and sleeping 6 and 4 in bunks. THE BARN is two storey with an upstairs sitting room and kitchen/dining area. The bedrooms are downstairs sleeping 6 and 2 in bunks each with en-suite shower room. Each unit has a TV, CD player and wood burning stove, both have access to garden/patio areas. Graded as a 5 Star bunkhouse by the WTB.

DETAILS

- **Open** - All year, check in from 4pm. Check out before10.30am
- **Number of beds** - Cowshed 10:1x6,1x4 Barn 8:1x6,1x2
- **Booking** - Provisional booking taken by phone and confirmed by deposit.
- **Price per night** - School holidays & weekends £15.00pp. Other Dates £12.50pp (includes bed linen). Minimum of 6 people (this guarantees exclusive use of a lodge). Minimum of 2 nights on weekends (3 nights on Bank Holidays).
- **Public Transport** - Trains and coaches at Milford Haven. Buses at Herbrandston (approx 1/4 mile). Puffin coastal shuttle passes the farm. www.traveline-cymru.org.uk
- **Directions** - Follow A4076 through Milford Haven to roundabout by Docks. Take first exit (signed Hakin). Follow for 2 miles, look for first farm on left (next to layby).

CONTACT: Sean or Mandy Tilling
Upper Neeston Farm, Dale Road, Herbrandston, Milford Haven, SA73 3RY
Tel: (01646) 690750
mail@upperneeston.co.uk www.upperneeston.co.uk

CAERHAFOD
LODGE

Ideally situated between the famous cathedral city of St Davids and the Irish ferry port of Fishguard, the Lodge overlooks the spectacular Pembrokeshire coastline. It is within easy walking distance of the well known Sloop Inn at Porthgain and the internationally renowned Coastal Path.   The Celtic Trail cycle route passes the bottom of our drive making it an ideal stopover for cyclists. The Lodge is a good base for all outdoor activities. Boat trips around Ramsey Island or to Grassholm to see the gannets can be arranged, as well as surfboard, wetsuit and cycle hire. The lodge is centrally heated and sleeps 23 in 5 separate rooms (4,4,4,5,6) all en-suite with great showers! There is a modern fully equipped kitchen/diner with patio and picnic tables, glorious sunsets. On site washing/drying room and secure storage area. Dogs welcome by prior arrangement. Smoking outdoors. Wales Tourist Board 4 star. Bike hire.

DETAILS

- **Open** - All year, 24 hours
- **Number of beds** - 23:   3x4 : 1x5 : 1x6.
- **Booking** - Advised in high season 30% deposit.
- **Price per night** - Adult £14 Under 16 £11.50. Group rates.
- **Public Transport** - Trains at Fishguard (9m) and Haverfordwest (15m). Fishguard/Rosslare ferry. National Express Haverfordwest. 411 Bus Haverfordwest-St Davids-Fishguard 50yds from Lodge. Seasonal coastal shuttle service for walkers.
- **Directions** - GR Landranger 157, SM 827 317. A40 from Haverfordwest, left at Letterston (B4331) to Mathry. Left onto A487 to St Davids, right in Croesgoch for Llanrhian, at crossroads right for Trefin. After ½ mile turn into our drive.

CONTACT: Sion or Carolyn Rees.
Llanrhian, St Davids, Haverfordwest, Pembrokeshire, SA62 5BD
Tel: (01348) 837859
Caerhafod@aol.com www.caerhafod.co.uk

OLD SCHOOL HOSTEL
FORMERLY YHA TREFIN

Escape to this wonderful, wild and rugged corner of the Pembrokeshire Coast National Park. We are in the centre of Trefin, an attractive village just a quarter of a mile from the famous coastal path and only 15 minutes from the cathedral city of St Davids and the popular beach at Whitesands Bay. The village has a pub and an award winning café/gallery. Stunning wild beaches and small harbour villages can be reached in a few minutes by car, or visited as part of a days circular walk. Our friendly characterful hostel (WTB 3 Star hostel) offers comfortable accommodation at prices that are hard to beat. Shared rooms are £12 per person and, outside school holidays, we also offer singles at £20 and doubles/twins for only £14 per person. Family rooms sleeping up to 5 are available from £42. We also provide breakfast, if required, from £2. Our electricity is supplied from renewable energy, we offer 'eco' discounts and plant a tree for every booking. Help create a forest for the future – come and stay!

DETAILS

- **Open** - All year, check in from 5pm. All day access.
- **Number of beds** - 20: 1x6, 3x5, 1x2
- **Booking** - Advance booking recommended
- **Price per night** - £12 shared, private rooms from £14 per person, family rooms from £42, exclusive use of hostel £200 per night
- **Public Transport** - Train/National Express to Haverfordwest then Richards Brothers bus 411 via St Davids to Trefin. For times phone Traveline 0870 608 2 608
- **Directions** - From the A40 turn left onto the B4331 at Letterston then left onto the A487. After 2.5 miles turn right just after the Square and Compass pub for Trefin.

CONTACT: Sue or Chris
Ffordd-yr-Afon, Trefin, Haverfordwest, Pembrokeshire, SA62 5AU
Tel: (01348) 831 800
oldschoolhostel@btconnect.com www.theoldschoolhostel.co.uk

Hostel
Yr Hen
Ysgol

The Old School Hostel

HAMILTON
BACKPACKERS

Hamilton Backpackers Lodge is an excellent overnight stop on the stunning Pembrokeshire Coast Path. It is also an ideal overnight stay five minutes from the ferries to Rosslare in Ireland. Pembrokeshire has a wealth of natural beauty and local history and many beautiful secluded beaches. The Backpackers Lodge is a very comfortable and friendly hostel with small dormitories and double rooms, all centrally heated. There is a dining room and TV lounge with Sky. The garden at the back of the hostel has a hammock, barbecue and picnic tables. We provide free tea, coffee and light breakfast. There is parking close by and the hostel is in the centre of town near to a number of pubs serving good meals. There is no curfew. Smoking is permitted only in the garden patio. To view web page see : www.hamiltonbackpackers.com

DETAILS

- **Open** - All year, 24 hours
- **Number of beds** - 16: 1 x 6, 2 x 3, 2 x 2
- **Booking** - Booking advised to confirm beds. 50% deposit required from groups.
- **Price per night** - £14 (bunk), £18 (double) per person.
- **Public Transport** - Fishguard ferry port has a train station and ferries to Rosslare in Ireland. The port is 1 mile from the hostel (approx taxi fare £3). National Express coaches call at Haverfordwest (15 miles). Local buses in Pembrokeshire phone Richard Bros (01239) 613756.
- **Directions** - From Haverfordwest (A40) to Fishguard Square, across first right by tourist office, 50 yds on left. From Cardigan A487 (North Wales Road) up hill and first left. From harbour 1 mile to Fishguard Square, left, first right, 50 yards on left.

CONTACT: Steve Roberts
21/23 Hamilton Street, Fishguard, Pembrokeshire, SA65 9HL
Tel: (01348) 874797 / 07813 687570
hamiltonbackpackers@yahoo.co.uk www.hamiltonbackpackers.co.uk

The Long Barn is a traditional stone barn providing comfortable and warm bunkhouse accommodation. It is situated on a working organic farm in beautiful countryside, with views over the Teifi Valley. The stunning Ceredigion Coast and the Cambrian Mountains are both an easy drive away and the busy small town of Llandysul (1.5 miles away) has all essential supplies.

The barn's location is ideal for exploring, studying or simply admiring the Welsh countryside. Activities enjoyed by guests in the surrounding area include: horse riding, fishing, swimming, climbing, abseiling, canoeing, farm walks and cycling. The barn is open all year, having adequate heating with a lovely warm Rayburn, log fire, roof insulation and double glazing throughout.

DETAILS

- **Open** - All year, all day
- **Number of beds** - 34
- **Booking** - Essential, deposit required
- **Price per night** - £8.50pp (adult), £6.50pp (under 18s). Discount of 10% for groups of 20 or more.
- **Public Transport** - Carmarthen (16 miles) has a train station and National Express service. Taxi fare from Carmarthen is approximately £20. Llandysul (1.5 miles away) has a local bus service, phone (0870) 6082608 for details.
- **Directions** - OS map 146, GR 437 417. In Llandysul, at the top of the main street, take right hand lane. Turn sharp right down hill. After 100 yds turn sharp left. Another ½ mile turn first right. Continue for 1 mile Long Barn is on your right.

CONTACT: Tom or Eva
Penrhiw, Capel Dewi, Llandysul, Ceredigion, SA44 4PG
Tel: (01559) 363200, Fax: (01559) 363200
cowcher@thelongbarn.co.uk www.thelongbarn.co.uk

TYCANOL FARM
CAMPING BARN

Tycanol Farm offers accommodation for four in a camping barn close to the beautiful Pembrokeshire coast. For larger groups there is a camp site for tents and caravans which overlooks the whole of Newport Bay. Showers are available for the barn and camping and the hot water is free. There are no meals provided on the site but the camping barn has self-catering facilities and there are pubs and restaurants within a 10 minute walk. Laundry facilities are available on the site and there is also access to a drying room. There are many activities to enjoy in the surrounding area. Pony trekking and a golf club are within a mile of the site. The area is also ideal for canoeing and sailing. The site is a five minute walk to the coastal path and ten minutes to Newport itself. There is also a nature trail which contains badger setts. Free barbecue every night at 6.30pm. Everybody greeted with a warm welcome.
PLEASE CONTACT THIS HOSTEL BY PHONE OR POST.

DETAILS

- **Open** - All year, 24 hours
- **Number of beds** - 4 in the barn plus camping.
- **Booking** - Booking not always necessary.
- **Price per night** - £12pp per night (camping barn), £7pp per night (camping).
- **Public Transport** - Nearest train station is at Fishguard (7 miles away). Nearest National Express coaches are at Haverfordwest (18 miles away). Local buses pass the farm drive every hour; call (01239) 613756.
- **Directions** - Tycanol Farm is near beach a mile outside of Newport, Pembrokeshire on the A487 towards Fishguard, turn right at milk-stand signpost.

CONTACT: Hugh Harries
Tycanol Farm, Newport, Pembrokeshire, SA42 0ST
Tel: (01239) 820264
sam@backpackerspress.com

The hostel is a basic but nice old stone building on a small working farm in the hills near the West Wales coast. Our closest beach is about 7 miles away. The hostel has two floors, the top floor splitting into two rooms of 8 or two family rooms. The sleeping is basic on comfortable camp beds. There is a fully equipped kitchen, nice sized lounge, log burning stove and TV. There are 2 toilet shower rooms and a small drying room. We are close to one of the 7 top Welsh mountain bike areas (Brechfa Forest). Also as Adventure Beyond we offer a number of packages for stag and hen groups, schools, etc for team building or just a good laugh. Activities include canoeing,kayaking, rafting and raft building, climbing, fishing, farm fun, assault course, clay shooting, zorb ball, hill walking and orienteering, navigation courses, coasteering and surfing,

DETAILS

- **Open** - All year, all day
- **Number of beds** - 10: 2x8, 1x2 (Family rooms on request)
- **Booking** - Booking is essential, deposit required if booking more then 1 week.
- **Price per night** - £10pp (bring your own bedding)
- **Public Transport** - Train and bus stations at Carmarthen. Bus stop at Croeslan.
- **Directions** - From Carmarthen follow the A485, At Windy Corner Garage take left turn A4459 to Pencader, After Pencader take the next left (at top of hill) to Llandysul, Follow the road over the river on the A486 to the village of Croeslan. Take the left turn to Maesllyn, a very small road. Follow the road down a large hill and up the other side, At the village of Coed-y-Bryn there will be a dead end road in front of you. Go down to the yard and you are there.

CONTACT: Jethro, Glenis or Stuart
Nant Y Pobty Farm, Coed Y Bryn, Llandysul, Ceradigion, SA44 5LQ
Tel: (01239) 858852, Mob 07787123761
fun@AdventureBeyond.co.uk www.adventurebeyond.co.uk

Stonecroft Lodge, our self-catering guest house, is situated in Llanwrtyd Wells, 'The Smallest Town in Britain '. Surrounded by the green fields, mountains and glorious countryside of Mid-Wales, Llanwrtyd is renowned Red Kite country and is the centre for mountain biking, walking, pony trekking etc. The town hosts many annual events such as the Man V Horse Marathon, World Bog Snorkelling Championships and the Mid-Wales Beer Festival.

The Hostel offers a warm welcome and a comfortable stay. We are Wales Tourist Board Star Graded and have private or shared rooms with fully made up beds. There is a fully equipped kitchen, TV, video, free laundry and drying facilities, central heating, large riverside garden and ample parking. The Hostel adjoins our Good Beer Guide pub, Stonecroft Inn (where great food is available), and is truly your 'home away from home ', offering the best of everything for your stay.

DETAILS

- **Open** - All year, all day - phone on arrival
- **Number of beds** - 27: 1 x 1 : 3 x 4 : 1 x 6 : 4 x (dbl + 1 sgl)
- **Booking** - Welcome, 50% deposit.
- **Price per night** - £15. Discounts for 3+ nights. Phone for exclusive-use rates.
- **Public Transport** - Llanwrtyd Wells Station on the Heart of Wales line is a few minutes walk from the hostel.
- **Directions** - GR 878 468. From Llanwrtyd town centre (A483) take Dolecoed Road towards Abergwesyn. Hostel is 100 yds on left. Check in at Stonecroft Inn.

CONTACT: Jane Brown
Dolecoed Road, Llanwrtyd Wells, Powys, LD5 4RA
Tel: (01591) 610327, Fax: (01591) 610304
party@stonecroft.co.uk www.stonecroft.co.uk

TY'N CORNEL
TYNCORNEL HOSTEL

Ty'n Cornel Hostel is an isolated old farmhouse in the hills, with a cosy open fire. Favoured by walkers, cyclists, bird-watchers and lovers of solitude it is in the beautiful Doethie valley on the Cambrian Way long distance footpath.

There are comfortable wooden bunk beds and good self-catering facilities. You can enjoy the wild open moorlands and lakes of the Elenydd uplands.

Other attractions include the Cors Caron National Nature Reserve, red kite feeding station, the Welsh Gold Centre at Tregaron, Teifi Pools, Elan Valley reservoirs, Dolaucothi Roman gold mines, Strata Florida Abbey and Llanerchaeron country house (National Trust).

DETAILS

- **Open** - All year, 24 hours, Reception 5pm -11pm & 7am -10am
- **Number of beds** - 16: 2x8
- **Booking** - Booking advisable; essential mid Nov-mid March. Bookings at least 1 week in advance.
- **Price per night** - £10pp, (£7.50 under 18s), block bookings negotiable.
- **Public Transport** - Trains: Aberyswyth 28 m; Llanwrtyd Wells 16m. Coach: x40 (Cardiff – Aberyswyth) Lampeter 15 m. Bus: 585 (Lampeter – Tregaron) Llanddewi-Brefi 7m.
- **Directions** - Road from Llanddewi-Brefi, near Tregaron: follow hostel signs SE 7m (last mile track) Bridle path N. up Doethie valley on the Cambrian Way (Llandovery 15 m) or byway 2m NW from Soar y Mynydd chapel.

CONTACT: YHA booking office or www.yha.org.uk
Llanddewi Brefi, Tregaron, Ceredigion, SY25 6PH
Tel: (01629) 592 707, Fax: 0870 7706081
tyncornel@yha.org.uk www.elenydd-hostels.co.uk

Greenfields is a category II listed building, just across the road from the famous Rebecca Riots toll house, in the historic market town of Rhayader. Rhayader is the gateway to the Welsh lake district, which has walking and cycling trails, lots of canoeing opportunities (bring your own canoe) and nature reserves which are within easy walking distance of the town. Other attractions nearby include the 19th century engineering phenomena of the Elan Valley dams, and the red kite breeding grounds and feeding station. Greenfields was built in 1768 and has private rooms, family rooms and small dorms. The beds come complete with linen and duvets and a full English breakfast is available. There is a small kitchen for guests' use and free tea and coffee. Rhayader has lots of pubs, all serving good meals at reasonable prices. There is a lovely pool and leisure centre, children's play areas, laundry and shops all within 100 yards of the hostel. Secure parking is available.

DETAILS

- **Open** - All year, 24 hours
- **Number of beds** - 22: 5 x (dble + single), 2x4, 1x3, 1x2 (bunks)
- **Booking** - Advised but not compulsory.
- **Price per night** - £13pp, £15pp en-suite room. Children under 14 half price. Organiser free for groups of over 10. Breakfast £4.50.
- **Public Transport** - Trains at Llandrindod Wells. Buses about hourly to Rhayader.
- **Directions** - From A470 turn right at direction sign onto Caehebert Lane (1 street before town clock). Big stone house on the corner of South Street. From A44 turn left at clock, take first left, then first driveway on left.

CONTACT: Lyn
South Street, Rhayader, Powys, LD6 5BH
Tel: (01597) 811 101, Mobile 07865 046604
greenfields06@yahoo.co.uk

Neuadd Bunkhouse is a recently converted 16th-century stone barn beautifully positioned in quiet, secluded countryside with delightful views, its own stream, trout pools and woodland. The barn is situated just 2 miles from the small market town of Rhayader - the gateway to the Elan Valley reservoirs, known as The Lakeland of Wales. The centrally heated barn sleeps 16 in 3 en-suite rooms and includes a fully equipped kitchen/dining room, drying room and facilities for wheelchair users. Rooms are also available in the main house. Situated in kite country, half way between the coast and Offa's Dyke (English border), we offer a comfortable base to explore the magnificent Elan Valley, Upper Wye and Cambrian Mountains. The nearby area offers a wide range of countryside activities including cycling, mountain biking, fishing, pony trekking, canoeing and of course bird watching and walking.

DETAILS

- **Open** - All year, all day access
- **Number of beds** - 16: 2 x 6, 1 x 4. B&B main house 3 x 2.
- **Booking** - Booking preferred (with deposit).
- **Price per night** - £14 per person.
- **Public Transport** - The nearest train station is Llandrindod Wells -12 miles. There are intermittent local buses to Rhayader.Taxi from Rhayader is approx £4.
- **Directions** - OS Explorer 200/OS147 GR 994698 Take the A44 east bound from Rhayader town centre (clock). Within ½ mile turn left on unclassified road signposted Abbey Cwm-hir. Beili Neuadd is on the right and is signposted from town.

CONTACT: Joe and Sara King or Gillian Marks
Beili Neuadd, Rhayader, Powys, LD6 5NS
Tel: (01597) 810211 or 0774 232 6835
rhayaderbreaks@yahoo.co.uk www.midwalesfarmstay.co.uk

FFRYDD HOUSE
INDEPENDENT HOSTEL

Ffrydd House offers eco-friendly, self-catering accommodation for up to 6 guests in Knighton – home of the Offa's Dyke Path and Glyndwr's Way National Trails. Knighton is a small, busy market town typical of the mix of Welsh and English heritage found in the Marches. The hostel is opposite an award winning Indian Restaurant/take-away and close to pubs, restaurants and a small supermarket. It has 3 comfortable bedrooms (2 double and twin) with ready made beds. Towels can be hired (£1). There are 2 bathrooms with a shower and a bath. Self-catering is available in a large, beamed farmhouse kitchen. There is an aga, dishwasher, plenty of crockery, pans and a large pine table and chairs. The hostel also has a dining-lounge with TV, an upstairs library area with relaxing view and a south-facing terrace and garden ideal for al-fresco dining. There is a drying room, laundry facilities, under cover secure cycle storage and plenty of parking. WTB 5 star hostel. No smoking

DETAILS

■ **Open** - All year, all day. Arrival from 3pm, leave by 10am.
■ **Number of beds** - 6: 2 x double, 1x twin
■ **Booking** - Book by phone or email. Entire payment in advance.
■ **Price per night** - Double room £35, Twin room £25.
■ **Public Transport** - Trains at Knighton. More frequent trains at Ludlow with Whittle Bus no. 740 to Knighton (1hr). Buses from Presteigne and Kington.
■ **Directions** - The hostel is in the centre of Knighton. The A4113 from Ludlow brings you directly onto Bridge Street. Ffrydd House is on your left (just past a filling station on the right). The driveway is to the right of the house.

CONTACT: Alice and Gary
Ffrydd House, 13 Bridge St, Knighton, Powys, LD7 1BT
Tel: (01547) 520374, Mobile 07968 136381
enquiries@ogtraining.co.uk www.border-holidays.co.uk

Maes-y-Mor is located in the Cardiganshire coastal town of Aberystwyth. It is a new luxury hostel in a detached house with 9 bedrooms (1 en-suite), 2 bathrooms, a kitchen/diner and launderette. All bedrooms have colour TV and tea/coffee making facilities and are furnished to a high standard. Beds are of a superior quality to ensure a good night's sleep, linen, towel and soap are provided. Halls and landings are themed in Welsh history pictures. There is a car parking area at rear and a secure shed for bikes. Aberystwyth is an ideal base for both North and South Wales. Visit Devil's Bridge with its dramatic waterfalls or the Vale of Rheidol narrow gauge railway. There is the National Library of Wales, the Castle and the Harbour. Aberystwyth is a University town so there is plenty of night life. We offer a personal and helpful service.

Croeso Cymraeg Cynnes i bawb / Warm Welsh Welcome to all.

DETAILS

- **Open** - All year, 8am to 10pm
- **Number of beds** - 20: 8x 2, 1 x 4 (en-suite)
- **Booking** - Booking advisable
- **Price per night** - £18 per person, en-suite £20 per person. Single £20.
- **Public Transport** - Bus and Train Stations are within approximately 400 mts.
- **Directions** - From Bus and Train Stations follow Terrace Road in a straight line towards beach. Turn right at Tourist Board Shop, you will find us approx 30 mts along next to the cinema.

CONTACT: Gordon or Mererid
25 Bath Street, Aberystwyth, Ceredigion, SY23 2NN
Tel: (01970) 639270 or 0770 2184463
maesymor@hotmail.co.uk www.maesymor.co.uk

PLAS DOLAU

Plas Dolau is set in quiet countryside just 3 miles from the popular coastal town of Aberystwyth. Ideal for exploring West Wales, walking, cycling, riding, fishing and golf etc. The holiday centre includes a warm country mansion (WTB 4 star hostel) with mainly dormitory style accommodation and an adjoining Scandinavian style farmhouse (WTB 2 star guesthouse) set on a 22 acre smallholding. Plas Dolau includes meeting rooms, dining rooms, games room, outdoors areas and walks. The centre can accommodate groups of up to 45 people. Various options for accommodation, provision of food, cooking facilities, etc are available. We are ideally suited for youth groups, field courses, retreats, house parties and many other groups or individuals. Phone to discuss your requirements.

DETAILS

- **Open** - All year, 24 hours
- **Number of beds** - 45: + cots etc. Plus 16 in farmhouse.
- **Booking** - Recommended.
- **Price per night** - Ranges from £15 (including basic breakfast) to £26 (private room, en-suite with full breakfast). From £500 per night for the whole mansion.
- **Public Transport** - Nearest train station is in Aberystwyth. Taxi from the station will cost around £5. National Express coaches and local buses (525 and 526) will set down at the end of the hostel drive.
- **Directions** - GR 623 813, OS map 135. On the A44, 3 miles from Aberystwyth, 1 mile from Llanbadarn railway bridge, 0.6 miles from turning to Bow Street. Sign on roadside says 'Y Gelli', B+B. Reception in 'Y Gelli'.

CONTACT:
Lovesgrove, Aberystwyth, Ceredigion, SY23 3HP
Tel: (01970) 617834
pat.twigg@virgin.net www.dolau-holidays.co.uk

MAESNANT
CENTRE

Maesnant is set in the remote hillsides of the Plynlimon mountain, an ideal location for hillwalking and mountain biking. The Centre is designed for use by youth groups, but family and other groups are welcome. Inside the centre there are 3 bunk rooms, two wash rooms (each with shower, wcs etc), kitchen and a large common room with dining facilities. Accommodation in the Centre is limited to 16 persons, though camping is possible in the 12 acres of grounds. Maesnant is hired out on a self-catering basis. Groups under 16 years of age must include 2 adults

There are many attractions in the area; Devils Bridge waterfalls and steam powered railway, Llywernog Mine Museum, Bwlch Nant Yr Arian Forest Centre and the Powergen Rheidol Hydro Electric Power Scheme visitor centre.

DETAILS

■ **Open** - March to November, no restrictions
■ **Number of beds** - 16: 2 x 6 : 1 x 4
■ **Booking** - Telephone booking essential. Deposit (£30) required 4 weeks in advance.
■ **Price per night** - £5 pp
■ **Public Transport** - Nearest mainline railway station Aberystwyth, bus services to Ponterwyd.
■ **Directions** - A44 from Aberystwyth to Ponterwyd, take scenic route to Nan y Moch via mountain road, (east end of village by 30mph sign) after 6 cattle grids and before 7th take a right turn, Maesnant is 1.5 miles at the end of the road.

CONTACT: Julie Bellchambers
Maesnant, Ponterwyd, Aberystwyth, Ceredigion, SY23 3AG
Tel: 07747 017371
info@maesnant.org.uk www.maesnant.org.uk

Broughton Bunkhouse offers comfortable accommodation in 17th-century barn with a wealth of exposed beams and full of character.

The bunkhouse is clean and cosy, central heating, hot water and showers are all inclusive. There is a fully-equipped kitchen with cookers, fridge-freezer, dishwasher and all the utensils you will need. Clothes washing and drying facilities are also provided.We are just outside Bishops Castle in South Shropshire, an excellent area for walking on the nearby Stiperstones and Long Mynd, cycling around Clun or just enjoying the real ale brewed in two of Bishop Castle's own pubs.

DETAILS

- **Open** - All year, 24 hours
- **Number of beds** - 12 : 2 x 6
- **Booking** - Check availability and arrange check-in. Deposit required for advance bookings.
- **Price per night** - From £10pp. Can be hired for sole use by groups per night or per week. Please telephone for prices.
- **Public Transport** - Train Station at Craven Arms (12 miles). Taxi or bus service to Bishops Castle or pick up from hostel for £10 fee. National Coach stop in Shrewsbury. Local bus service to Bishops Castle, free pick-up to hostel from Bishops Castle.
- **Directions** - GR 313 906. From Bishops Castle take B4385 (signed Montgomery). Lower Broughton Farm is 2 miles out of town on the right (on the B4385).

CONTACT: Tom or Kate
Lower Broughton Farm, Nr Bishops Castle, Montgomery, Powys SY15 6SZ
Tel: (01588) 638393, Fax: (01588) 638393
broughtonfarm@micro-plus-web.net www.virtual-shropshire.co.uk

BRAICH GOCH
BUNKHOUSE & INN

The Braich Goch is a 16th-century coaching inn situated 3 miles from Cadair Idris. There are stunning views of the Dulas valley and Dyfi Forest. The Braich has been specifically set up with outdoor enthusiasts in mind. Facilities include drying room, secure bike storage and large well equipped self-catering kitchen. There are 6 bedrooms, 4 en-suite and a further two bathrooms.

The location is ideal for walking, mountain biking, cycling, climbing and canoeing at all levels as well as bird watching or simply chilling out. Dyfi Forest mountain bike trails on doorstep. The Braich is also a pub with pool table, darts and other games to keep you entertained in the evening! Also available are activity packages with qualified instructors suitable for all levels. In the area are King Arthur's Labyrinth and Corris Craft Centre, Centre for Alternative Technology, Coed-y-Brenin Forest Park and the coast. WTB 4 star. Walkers & Cyclists Welcome Awards. EMAIL VIA CONTACT FACILITY ON WEBSITE.

DETAILS

- **Open** - All year, all hours by arrangement
- **Number of beds** - 26: 5 x 4 : 1 x 6
- **Booking** - Essential for groups. 20% deposit, balance 2 weeks before arrival.
- **Price per night** - From £16pp
- **Public Transport** - Nearest train station to Corris is Machynlleth. Bus stop outside the 'Braich Goch' Inn. Taxis can be hired from Machynlleth.
- **Directions** - GR 754 075 On A487 between Machynlleth and Dolgellau at Corris turning. 2.5 miles north of Centre for Alternative Technology.

CONTACT: Ann or Andy
Corris, Machynlleth, Powys SY20 9RD
Tel: (01654) 761229 mobile 07881 626734
AnnBottrill@aol.com www.braichgoch.co.uk

CORRIS
HOSTEL

Nestled in the foothills of Cadair Idris, this award winning hostel enjoys splendid views over the Dyfi Valley. Corris Hostel is renowned as a spiritual haven with its caring, easy going atmosphere, friendly staff, cosy wood fires and collection of books, games and artefacts. Outdoors the evolving landscaped gardens provide a serene, relaxing environment.   Environmental awareness is promoted through the hostel's vegetarian focus, recycling, composting, gardens and energy efficiency.

Visitors can find more about Green lifestyle at the nearby Centre for Alternative Technology (celebrated worldwide as Europe's leading Eco-Centre). Down river are national Biosphere nature reserves and miles of golden beaches at Aberdyfi. Wide range of countryside and environmental activities with workshops run by local people.

DETAILS

- **Open** - All year, all day access.
- **Number of beds** - 42/44
- **Booking** - Phone to check.
- **Price per night** - Adult £14.00, child £12.00, Breakfast £3.
- **Public Transport** - Buses 30, X32, 34 and Trawscambria 701 pass Machynlleth train station on the Cambrian Coast line with connection to Aberystwyth and Birmingham.
- **Directions** - GR 753 080. We are in the mountain village of Corris 6 miles north of Machynlleth. At Braich Goch turn off A487 into Corris. At Slaters Arms pub turn left, hostel is 150m uphill beyond a small carpark.

CONTACT: Anne, Michael or Steve
Old School, Corris, Machynlleth, Powys, SY20 9TQ
Tel: (01654) 761686
mail@corrishostel.co.uk www.corrishostel.co.uk

Caban Cader Idris is a listed building in a secluded wooded valley within walking distance of Cader Idris and the Mawddach Estuary in Snowdonia National Park. It is in an ideal setting for field work and outdoor pursuits with wonderful unspoilt mountain, valley and estuary walks from the doorstep. Local activities include climbing, hill walking, pony trekking, biking, canoeing, rafting and fishing. The area is also ideal for the study of geology, geography, local history, industrial archaeology and ornithology (RSPB woods adjoin grounds). Nearby are slate mines, dry ski slope, narrow gauge railways and beaches. There is a large kitchen/dining room, two dorms sleeping 6 and 10, a lounge (with 3 beds), toilets, hot showers and a drying room. It is heated and has a payphone, car park and fire safety certificate. Camping by arrangement. This self-catering bunkhouse is ideal for groups but also open to individuals.

DETAILS

■ **Open** - All year, no restrictions
■ **Number of beds** - 19:
■ **Booking** - Booking is essential. Always phone before arrival. £20 per night deposit. Last minute enquiries welcome from individuals or groups.
■ **Price per night** - Sole use:- £100 midweek, £125 Fri, Sat, Bank Holidays and New Year. Reduced rates for whole week bookings. Individuals £8 pp when available.
■ **Public Transport** - Nearest train station is Morfa Mawddach (4 miles). Nearest bus stop is Abergwynant (¼ mile). For local bus info call (01341) 422614.
■ **Directions** - GR 682 169. From Dolgellau take the A493 to Fairbourne. 1 mile after Penmaenpool turn left just before Abergwynant Bridge. Bunkhouse 300yds on left

CONTACT: Dafydd Rhys
Islawrdref, Dolgellau, Gwynedd, LL40 1TS
Tel: (01766) 762588, Mobile 07887954301
dafydd.rhys@virgin.net

CROWN LODGE
GROUP ACCOMMODATION

Crown Lodge, in Snowdonia National Park, sleeps 19 and is ideal for groups who require twin and single bedrooms. It is owned by Coleg Harlech WEA and is often used for educational purposes. It offers good basic no-frills accommodation (VisitWales 2 star) with ample parking and views over the miles of sandy beach at Tremadog Bay. There is a kitchen for self catering and meals can be provided with prior notice. All bedding is provided but bring your own towels. The area is a haven for anyone who enjoys walking, climbing, sailing, fishing, pony trekking or cycling.

Crown Lodge is within ¼ mile of Harlech town centre with its pubs, cafes, small shops, Harlech Castle and Theatr Ardudwy. The prestigious Royal St David's links golf course, considered to be the most difficult par 69 in the world, is nearby.

DETAILS

- **Open** - All year, key provided
- **Number of beds** - 19: 8 x 2, 3 x 1
- **Booking** - Booking is essential, non-refundable deposit of £60 required, full payment due 6 weeks prior to start date.
- **Price per night** - Sole use of property £340 - £1765 / week – shorter periods available on request
- **Public Transport** - Harlech train station ¼ mile, limited bus service passes the property.
- **Directions** - Please apply for directions when booking.

CONTACT: Valmai Owen
Ffordd Isaf, Harlech, Gwynedd, LL46 2PR
Tel: (01766) 781927
accom@fc.harlech.ac.uk www.harlech-holidays.com

Cabin 32 is in a picturesque holiday village of log cabins, overlooking the Rhinog Range of mountains with Cader Idris to the south and Snowdon to the north. The holiday village is ideally situated for touring North and Mid Wales. There are long sandy beaches a short drive away at the small seaside town of Barmouth. Horse riding with panoramic views, lake and river fishing, walking, and mountain biking are all nearby. Mountain bikes can be hired from the holiday village office and fishing permits are available in the next village. Coed y Brenin Forest Park is 10 mins drive away, with the finest mountain biking in the UK, visitors centre, walking trails and riverside picnic area. The cabin has spectacular views of the mountains. It sleeps 4 in two bedrooms and has full self-catering facilities and central heating. The lounge has a colour TV, video and DVD Player. The dining area, in the conservatory overlooks the mature lawned garden and patio which is ideal for BBQ's. There is a shower room with toilet and a reserved parking space for one car. Bring your own bed linen, pillows, duvets, towels and cleaning materials.

DETAILS

- **Open** - 1st Dec – 31st Sept,, office 9.30–5pm (later arrivals by arrangement)
- **Number of beds** - 4: 1 double bedroom, 1 room with bunk beds
- **Booking** - Booking is essential. Full balance must be paid 1 week before arrival.
- **Price per night** - Sole Use £40 low season, £50 high season. Apply for discounts.
- **Public Transport** - Trains at Portmadog and Dolgelleu (both about 20 miles away)
- **Directions** - On the A470 between Dolgellau and Trawsfynydd. Turn right at Bronaber to get to the Holiday Village.

CONTACT: Samantha
Trawsfynndd Holidays, Bronaber, Trawsfynndd, Gwynedd, LL41 4UR
Tel: (01706) 642856
sammyjcs@hotmail.co.uk

BALA
BUNK HOUSE

The coach house is a converted 200-year-old Welsh stone building. It carries WTB two star approval and is set back from the road in over an acre of picturesque grounds with a river and stream. Modernised to provide accommodation for outdoor activity groups, it is light, airy and comfortable with night storage heating and drying facilities. There is a large lounge/dining area and bunk rooms for 2, 4 and 8 plus annexe for 6. Separate ladies' and gentlemen's toilets have washing areas and hot showers. Fully equipped self-catering kitchen. The Little Cottage, a newly converted self-contained bunkroom sleeping 6, with kitchenette, shower and toilet/washing area, is ideal for smaller groups & families. Sheets & pillowcases are provided - bring a sleeping bag. There is a splendid view of the Berwyn Hills; together with the Aran and Arenig hills they provide superb walking. Bala Lake and the National White Water Centre are brilliant for water sports. Good pubs, restaurants and shops in Bala.

DETAILS

- **Open** - All year, no restrictions
- **Number of beds** - 26 : 1x2 : 1x4 : 1x6 : 1x8. 1x6 self-contained
- **Booking** - Book if possible, ring or write with 20% deposit. Weekends are busy.
- **Price per night** - Single night £15 pp, two or more nights £14 pp.
- **Public Transport** - Trains at Wrexham (30 miles). National Express at Corwen (10 miles). Local buses call at Bala (1.6 miles from hostel). Call hostel for a taxi.
- **Directions** - GR 950 372. From England take M6, M54, A5 through Llangollen then A494 for Bala. We are on the A494 1.5 miles before Bala.

CONTACT: Guy and Jane Williams
Tomen Y Castell, Llanfor, Bala, Gwynedd, LL23 7HD
Tel: (01678) 520738, Fax: (01678) 520738
thehappyunion@btinternet.com www.balabunkhouse.co.uk

For Outdoor Adventures within the Snowdonia National Park, Bala Backpackers is nice for the price of <£1/hour! It is clean and safe with a caring atmosphere in a homely hostel, with 27 comfortable SINGLE BEDS in an old 1800s character building, located in a quiet, sunny chapel square, in the bustling market town of Bala, Mid North Wales.

Bala boasts a five-mile-long Lake, a white-water River, ever popular for raft rides, and nestles beneath three 900 metre Peaks.

The hostel is equipped with Dining Room, Dripping Room and Guest Kitchen. Catering is available from the owner. A Leisure Centre, with fun pool, is at the lakeside, 5 mins walk away. Plan your activities or just soak up the atmosphere (not literally!) by day or evening, in Town, 100m away, Lake, River or Hills.

DETAILS

■ **Open** - All year. Winter midweek by prior arrangement, reception 5pm-10pm, 8am-10am. 12pm Lock-Out

■ **Number of beds** - 27: 3x4 : 3x5 Plus 3 new Private Twin Rooms, £45 per Room.

■ **Booking** - On-line or by phone or email.

■ **Price per night** - £12 pp, £13 Sat, £10 Mon, £70 weekly. Includes sheetbag and bedding.

■ **Public Transport** - Trains at Wrexham 30 miles. Buses daily from Wrexham and Barmouth (Bus 94). Ferry Terminal: Holyhead (60 miles) to Ireland.

■ **Directions** - GR 926 358. Bala is on A494, off the A5 between Llangollen and Betws-y-Coed. From A494 in Bala town, towards Dolgellau, turn left at the end of Bala High St for Plassey St Car Park. Tegid Street one minute walk.

CONTACT: Stella Shaw
32 Tegid Street, BALA, LL23 7EL
Tel: (01678) 521700
info@Bala-Backpackers.co.uk www.Bala-Backpackers.co.uk

CORNERSTONE QUEST
ADVENTURE CENTRE

The Cornerstone Quest Adventure Centre is at the foot of Arenig, one of the highest mountains in Wales. Being seven miles from Bala and 25 miles from Porthmadog, the centre is ideally located for a variety of local pursuits to suit everyone's tastes. The Centre is developing a conservation area on the shores of Llyn Celyn. All this is set within the natural beauty of the Snowdonia National Park. We have two houses on site which can be booked separately or jointly. There is a real homely atmosphere at Cornerstone Quest with great facilities for self-catering. Each house is self-contained with lounge/dining area, kitchen, shower, toilets. Bed linen is provided. There is a shared meeting room, games room and 29 acres of land to explore. Restricted facilities for people with disabilities.

DETAILS

■ **Open** - All year, all day

■ **Number of beds** - 30: 2x6 : 3x4 : 3x2

■ **Booking** - Booking essential, 25% deposit. Final payment 4 weeks prior to visit.

■ **Price per night** - Farmhouse £216 (sleeps 18). Celyn House £176 (sleeps 16). Guide prices (lower prices at different seasons).

■ **Public Transport** - Nearest Train Station; Wrexham (30miles). Own transport essential.

■ **Directions** - From Bala take the A4212 Trawsfynydd road, after ½ mile fork left signposted Rhyduchaf and Llidiardau. Five miles, two cattle grids later pass Bryn Ifan Cottage, turn first right. Gwern-y-Genau is ¼ mile on the left, about half way along the railway cutting.

CONTACT:
Gwern-y-Genau, Arenig, Bala, Gwynedd LL23 7BP
Tel: (0121) 643 1984
admin@cornerstone.uk.com www.cornerstonequest.co.uk

Opening in May 2008, Llangollen's independent hostel is a fully refurbished town house, with plenty of charm and character. It is in the centre of town, the perfect spot to explore the magnificent Vale of Llangollen, which offers walking, climbing, water sports, fishing, paragliding, mountain biking and many other activities. Other attractions include Valle Crucis Abbey, Telford's aqueduct, a steam railway and the spectacularly positioned Dinas Bran Castle. Llangollen is also home to many arts and music festivals, including the Fringe music festival and the annual International Eisteddfod, and there is a great choice of restaurants and traditional pubs close by - some with open fires! The hostel provides comfortable and clean accommodation with cosy twin/double rooms, great value 6 bed dorms and family rooms. The rooms are spacious, beds are comfy and the showers superb. Prepare your food in the fully equipped self-catering kitchen and dining room, or sit and relax in our cosy lounge – helping yourself to our book exchange, internet, and as much tea and coffee as you like.

DETAILS

- **Open** - All year (opening April 2008), all day
- **Number of beds** - 32:
- **Booking** - Book by phone or email
- **Price per night** - From £14 per person
- **Public Transport** - Daily National Express from London. Trains Ruabon (5 miles).
- **Directions** - From the A5 heading west, the hostel is located 50 yards past the main set of traffic lights on the right. Parking is at the rear of the hostel on Market Street – at the main traffic lights, turn right then first left.

CONTACT:
Isallt, Berwyn Street, Llangollen, LL20 8NB
Tel: (01978) 862970, Mob 07786 157776
enquires@llangollenhostel.co.uk www.llangollenhostel.co.uk

TYDDYN BYCHAN

WALES

Tyddyn Bychan is an 18th-century traditional Welsh farmhouse, set in two and a half acres of private grounds surrounded on all sides by farmland with a large parking area well away from the road. Situated in an excellent location for fieldwork in Hiraethog and Snowdonia, climbing, fishing and numerous watersports including whitewater rafting, and many local walks.

The main bunkhouse sleeps 18 in two en-suite rooms. All the bunks are handmade and of a very high standard. There is also a well equipped kitchen/dining room. The smaller bunkhouse sleeps 12 in two en-suite rooms and has its own kitchen and conservatory. All bedding, heating and electricity are included. We can provide delicious pre-booked, homemade food in the farmhouse and make up packed lunches. The bunkhouses are also very well equipped for self-catering.

DETAILS

- **Open** - All year, all day
- **Number of beds** - 30:- 1x10 1x8 2x6
- **Booking** - Booking is advisable
- **Price per night** - £10pp including bedding.
- **Public Transport** - Nearest train station is at Betws-y-Coed. Nearest National Express service at Llandudno. Phone (01492) 575412 for details.
- **Directions** - GR 931 504. Turn off A5 at Cerrig y drudion. Take B4501 out of village for Llyn Brenig, take the turning on left for Cefn Brith. After about 2 miles you will see a phone box on left, chapel on right and the road widens for a layby. The gate for Tyddyn is on the left directly opposite junction on the right.

CONTACT: Lynda
Cefn Brith, Cerrig y drudion, LL21 9TS
Tel: (01490) 420680
lynda@tyddynbychan.co.uk www.tyddynbychan.co.uk

Hendre Isaf is a 400-year-old converted farm building of stone and slate construction situated on the Ysbyty Estate. The 8,000 hectare estate takes in 51 Hill Farms, 31 cottages, forested valleys and high open moorland known as the Migneint. The Basecamp, set in a peaceful part of Snowdonia 6 miles from Betws-y-Coed, is available for private hire by groups and by negotiation is free for volunteers undertaking conservation work for the National Trust. Local attractions include the dry ski slope and Plas y Brenin National Mountain Centre at Capel Curig, shops, leisure centre and swimming pool at Llanrwst, seaside resorts of Rhyl, Prestatyn and Llandudno. The centre may be able to accommodate one person with special mobility needs - telephone for details of access. No pets permitted.

DETAILS

■ **Open** - All year, 24 hours
■ **Number of beds** - 17 in two dormitories on two floors
■ **Booking** - Early booking recommended (March to October is very busy). A non returnable deposit of £50 paid with booking (cheques payable to the National Trust).
■ **Price per night** - £10 per person (minimum of 8 people).
■ **Public Transport** - Trains at Betws-y-Coed (6 miles), Llandudno Junction (20 miles) and Llanrwst (10 miles); National Express bus station at Llandudno. Some local buses to Betws-y-coed, but we advise bringing your own transport.
■ **Directions** - We are situated 6 miles SE of Betws-y-Coed near the junction of the A5 and the B4407 (signposted Ysbyty Ifan and Ffestiniog). GR855511 (OS sheet 116).

CONTACT: Elfyn Jones
National Trust N.W. Wales Office, Dinas, Betws-y-Coed, Gwynedd, LL24 0HF
Tel: (01248) 600954, Fax: (01248) 600954
elfyn.jones@nationaltrust.org.uk

THE EAGLES

WALES

The Eagles is a traditional inn offering real ales, and a very friendly atmosphere. Wales Tourist Board 4 star graded. The private accommodation (no sharing with strangers) consists of 6 rooms sleeping 4 and 2 rooms sleeping 2. All rooms are centrally heated and with tea and coffee making facilities; duvets, pillows and sheets are supplied. There are two separate showers, a bathroom and two washrooms/toilets. A fully equipped guest kitchen, secure bike storage and drying room are available. The Eagles is situated on the edge of the peaceful village of Penmachno, in a secluded valley 4 miles south of Betws-y-Coed, within the heart of the Snowdonia National Park. The new Penmachno Mountain Bike Trail is half a mile away. Snowdon itself is about 15 miles away. Surrounded by mountain scenery, this is ideal accommodation for groups or individuals walking, climbing, cycling or canoeing - also perfect for families - self-catering cottages are also available.

DETAILS

- **Open** - All year, totally flexible
- **Number of beds** - 28: 6 x 4 : 2 x 2.
- **Booking** - Recommended, essential for groups
- **Price per night** - £15pp. Groups of 10 plus £13.50pp. Whole bunkhouse £300.
- **Public Transport** - Betws-y-Coed Station 3.5miles. Bus 64 from Betws-y-Coed to Penmachno. From Ireland or London and points between London to Holyhead main line change at Llandudno Junction for Betws-y-coed.
- **Directions** - From A5, 2 miles east of Betws-y-Coed, at Conwy Falls Café, turn onto B4406 to Penmachno, cross bridge, The Eagles is in front of you.

CONTACT: Gerry or Linda McMorrow
Penmachno, Betws-y-Coed, Conwy, LL24 0UG
Tel: (01690) 760177
inn@eaglespenmachno.co.uk www.eaglespenmachno.co.uk

WOODLANDS
OUTDOOR CENTRE

Woodlands Outdoor Centre is a large Victorian property specially adapted to provide self-catering accommodation for groups of up to 30. It has seven dormitories varying in size from one to ten beds, complete with duvets and linen. The centre is centrally heated and has a common room, games room, large self-catering kitchen, drying room, hot showers and bike sheds.

Nestling in the heart of the mountains and set on the banks of the river Llugwy, Betws-y-Coed has shops for essentials, tourist shops and hotels who cater for non-residents. The area is popular for trekking, canoeing, mountain biking, orienteering and rock climbing and is also convenient for travelling to the coast (20 miles away). The centre welcomes adults and youths as individuals or groups. It is run by a registered charity 'The Barn Outdoor Pursuits Association' whose aim is to encourage young people to share and enjoy the outdoors.

DETAILS

- **Open** - All year, all day
- **Number of beds** - 30: 1x10, 1x8, 1x4, 1x3, 2x2, 1x1
- **Booking** - Phone, email, book online or write.
- **Price per night** - Youth £3.50-£4.50, Youth Leaders £7.75-£8.70, Adults £9.00-£10.00. Exclusive use: youth activities £108-£134, Adult only groups £234-£260. Further reductions for members and youth groups from Staffordshire (see website).
- **Public Transport** - Trains at Betws-y-Coed. Arriva bus from Llandudno,Bangor etc
- **Directions** - In Betws-y-Coed on the A5 towards Capel Curig take the first turning left after the pelican crossing. At the top of the hill turn left onto Vicarage Road.

CONTACT: Booking Office
Vicarage Road, Betws-y-Coed, Conwy, LL24 0AD
Tel: 0870 787 3326, Fax: 0870 787 3326
enquiries@woodlandscentre.co.uk www.woodlandscentre.co.uk

LLEDR
HOUSE

Nestled alongside the River Lledr in the heart of Snowdonia National Park, this former Quarry Manager's house is popular with travellers, walkers, cyclists and families. There is a large self-catering kitchen, dining room and television lounge, all centrally heated. All bedding is provided in single, twin and family rooms plus a nine-bed dorm. We also offer a luxury self-contained cedarlog cabin, sleeping 5, in the grounds. Lledr House has a private riverside garden, bicycle shed and plenty of parking. It is surrounded by woodland walks and cycle trails. Betws-y-Coed (4 miles) and stunning Llyn Elsi are popular tourist sites. Within walking distance of a pub, one mile from a SPAR shop (open daily until 9pm), and 25 minutes drive to Mount Snowdon.

DETAILS

- **Open** - All year (except Christmas week), check in from 5pm till 10.30pm.
- **Number of beds** - 31: 1x9, 2x4,1x6, 3x2, 2x1
- **Booking** - Bookings by phone or email held till 6pm. First nights deposit for larger groups.
- **Price per night** - £11.50 per person, £9 for children under 16. Sole use of hostel £255.
- **Public Transport** - Pont-y-Pant Station on the Conwy Valley Line is ¾ mile away. On Sunday there are 2 buses a day instead of the train.
- **Directions** - On the A5 from Llangollen to Bangor turn left just before Betws-y-coed onto the A470 (signposted Dolgellau). The hostel is 4 miles, just after the large playing field. Walking from Pont-y-Pant station, turn left and left again after stone road bridge.

CONTACT: Brian or Melanie Quilter
Pont-y-Pant, Dolwyddelan, North Wales, LL25 0DQ
Tel: (01690) 750 202. Mobile 07915-397-705 or 07915-397-660
Lledrhouse@aol.com www.ukyh.com

CONWY VALLEY
BACKPACKERS BARN

Conwy Valley Backpackers is situated on a peaceful working farm that has organic status, in the heart of the beautiful Conwy Valley with excellent access to Snowdonia. Centrally heated with fully equipped self-catering kitchen, log fires, hot showers and a fire alarm system. We have three separate dorms sleeping 4, 6 and 10, two of which have their own toilet facility. We can also provide secure bike / canoe storage, grazing for horses & tourist information.

Beside the barn is a small stream and guests may picnic and BBQ on the river bank. An ideal space for restoration, relaxation and retreat. Continental breakfast (£3.50) / packed lunch (£5) / and buffet suppers (£10) are available by arrangement. Local activities range from fishing and hiking to white water rafting and mountain biking,and there are some great pubs and eating places within walking distance. Groups are welcome. Dogs only by prior arrangement.

DETAILS

- **Open** - All year, all day
- **Number of beds -** 20: 1 x 4 : 1 x 6 : 1 x 10
- **Booking** - Not essential but recommended
- **Price per night -** From £12.50pp. Sole use from £200. £1.50pp duvet hire.
- **Public Transport -** Train stations and coaches at Llandudno Junction and Conwy. Local bus 19 or 19a runs every 20 minutes from Conwy and Llandudno Junction, ask driver to drop you at Pyllau Gloewon farm gate.
- **Directions -** GR 769 697. Six miles south of Conwy on the B5106, look for Backpackers sign just before entering Talybont.

CONTACT: Claudia or Helen
Pyllau Gloewon Farm, Tal-y-bont, Conwy, Gwynedd, LL32 8YX
Tel: (01492) 660504
claudia.bryan@btconnect.com www.conwyvalleybarn.com

BRYN TIRION FARM
BUNKHOUSE

Bryn Tirion is a traditional hillside farm set in the shadow of the imposing tower of Dolwyddelan Castle, with magnificent views over the upper reaches of the Lledr Valley. The farm has a campsite, bed and breakfast accommodation and bunkhouse. The bunkhouse occupies the first floor of a traditional farm building and is a non smoking area. It consists of one room with a fully equipped kitchen area and 4 bunks (sleeps 8). A second unit of 2 bunks (sleeps 4) on the ground floor has its own kitchen. Both units have mattresses, pillows, sheets and duvets. The toilet block (shared with the campsite) has hot showers, basins with hot & cold water, and shaving points. Situated at the foot of the mountain of Moel Siabod, Bryn Tirion is an ideal base for walking in the Snowdonia National Park. The farm is convenient for travelling to the popular village of Betws-y-Coed (6 miles), Llechwedd Slate Mines & Ffestiniog Railway at Blaenau Ffestiniog (5 miles), the Italianate village of Portmeirion (10 miles), Porthmadog (11 miles) and Bodnant Gardens (18 miles). The tranquil village of Dolwyddelan is a short stroll away with many paths to explore.

DETAILS

- **Open** - All year, by arrangement
- **Number of beds** - 8: 1x8 and 4: 1x4
- **Booking** - Recommended (with deposit). CONTACT BY PHONE OR POST.
- **Price per night** - From £12.50pp, Camping £3pp, B&B from £27.50pp.
- **Public Transport** - Dolwyddelan train station ¾ mile away.
- **Directions** - On the A470, ¾ mile on the Ffestiniog side of Dolwyddelan at the foot of the prominent castle, and 6 miles from Betws-y-Coed.

CONTACT: Mrs Caroline Price
Bryn Tirion Farm, Dolwyddelan, Nr Betws-y-Coed, Sir Conwy, LL25 OJD
Tel: (01690) 750366
sam@backpackerspress.com

LLANDUDNO
HOSTEL

James and Melissa would like to invite you to their charming Victorian 4 star WTB hostel. We are a friendly hostel where individuals, families and groups (including schools) are welcome all year. Some of the guests comments "friendliest hostel we've ever stayed in", "Wow isn't it clean", "these bathrooms are fabulous as good as any hotel". Come and try us, we love to meet new people and look forward to getting to know you. Set in the heart of the Victorian seaside resort town of Llandudno, an ideal place to shop or explore the many varied local attractions. Excellent blue flag beaches, dry slope skiing, toboggan run, ten pin bowling, Bronze Age copper mine, traditional pier and many museums, fishing trips etc. Llandudno is within easy travelling distance to Snowdon, Bodnant Gardens and local castles. We are able to book local attractions for groups and secure some discounts.

DETAILS

■ **Open** - All year. Telephone in winter prior to arrival, All day
■ **Number of beds** - 46: 2x8 : 2x6 : 4x2 : 1x4 : 1 x family
■ **Booking** - Essential April to July
■ **Price per night** - From £17 per person, £40 per private twin room, £44 per private twin en-suite. Group and family rates on request.
■ **Public Transport** - Trains at Llandudno. Turn right as you exit station, cross road, turn left down Vaughan Street (towards the beach), left into Charlton Street.
■ **Directions** - From the A55 take A470 and follow signs to Llandudno town centre, straight through all roundabouts, after Asda turn 3rd left into Vaughan Street (signed train station), then 1st right into Charlton Street. Hostel is No 14.

CONTACT: James
14 Charlton Street, Llandudno, LL30 2AA
Tel: (01492) 877430
info@Llandudnohostel.co.uk www.llandudnohostel.co.uk

CABAN CYSGU
GERLAN

Caban-Cysgu offers comfortable, purpose-built accommodation at the foot of the Carneddau in the Welsh-speaking village of Gerlan. Being a community-run bunkhouse, a warm welcome is guaranteed. This is an ideal location for walking in Snowdonia, and provides an obvious base for the '14 3000ft Peaks' long-distance challenge. Cyclists are welcome too, the hostel being within a mile of Sustrans route 'Lôn Las Ogwen'.

Rock-climbing at Idwal is close at hand, as well as the Carneddau crags. The nearby Afon Ogwen provides a popular venue for canoeists. For more leisurely pursuits, try visiting Coed Meurig, Penrhyn Castle or the Greenwood Centre. Shops, pubs and cafés in Bethesda are within walking distance.

DETAILS

■ **Open** - All year, all day
■ **Number of beds** - 16 : 1x5, 1x2, 1x1, 1x8
■ **Booking** - Not essential, but recommended (with 20% non-returnable deposit).
■ **Price per night** - From £12.50 - £15 (with concessions for group bookings and children).
■ **Public Transport** - Bangor train station is 6 miles. Catch a bus from Bangor bus station to Gerlan (66), or Bethesda (fare £1.40). Taxi from Bangor approx. £10.00.
■ **Directions** - GR 632665. Travelling South on the A5, turn left in the centre of Bethesda just before Spar. Bear right, go up the hill over 2 cross-roads. Caban-Cysgu is the old school on the left, about ½ mile from the A5.

CONTACT: Dewi Emyln, Manager
Ffordd Gerlan, Gerlan, Bethesda, Bangor, LL5 3TL
Tel: (01248) 605573
dewi@cabancysgu-gerlan.co.uk www.cabancysgu-gerlan.co.uk

Wonderfully situated in 7 acres of an Area of Outstanding Natural Beauty, 300m from a beach at south end of Holy Island, Anglesey. Nearby Holyhead has rail links and ferries to Ireland. The centre is an excellent base for so much in the outdoors and is immediately adjacent to the Anglesey Coastal Path. There is spectacular geology, a range of habitats and species of marine life, birds and plants. There are prehistoric remains and good walking on a varied and accessible coast. Kayakers have classic sea tours, overfalls, playwaves, surf and rockhopping. Climbers have Gogarth nearby and Rhoscolyn offers all grades in an attractive setting. Divers can beach launch for wrecks and scenic marine life. Birdwatching is excellent. There are two self-contained units and camping with toilets and showers. We encourage careful energy use, composting & recycling. Walking distance to Pub.

DETAILS

- **Open** - All year, 24 hour access
- **Number of beds** - 20: 2x2, 1x4, 2x6. 16: 1x3, 2x4,1x5.
- **Booking** - Essential
- **Price per night** - £14.80
- **Public Transport** - Trains at Holyhead (10km) (London direct 4.5 hrs) or Valley (5km). National Exp Valley (6km). Bus 23/25 Holyhead Rhoscolyn (1km) or 4 & 44 Holyhead-Four Mile Bridge (3km). Ferry: Holyhead - Dublin or Dun Laoghaire.
- **Directions** - GR SH 278 752. From A5 traffic lights at Y Fali/Valley take B4545 Trearddur. In 2km at Four Mile Bridge fork left at sign Rhoscolyn 2miles. After 2km sharp left at camping symbols. In 800m fork right at large white gatepost.

CONTACT: Jacqui or Andy
Cerrig-yr-Adar, Rhoscolyn, Holyhead, Anglesey, LL65 2NQ
Tel: (01407) 860469
centre@outdooralternative.org www.outdooralternative.org

Waltons' Farmhouse lies in a secluded valley, 3 miles north of Snowdon. The converted stone farmhouse and buildings are set amidst a mountain sheep farm, 1/3 of a mile from the village of Brynrefail and 2 miles from Llanberis. Ten minutes walk from the house is a nature reserve which contains some excellent bouldering (Fachwen boulders) as well as ideal beginners faces (Lion Rocks). Below this area is Lake Padarn, which stretches half way up the Llanberis Pass. This is the home of some of the most famous walking and climbing areas in Britain and there are plenty of outdoor activities nearby. The beautiful location and unspoilt surroundings provide peace with accessibility. The Waltons have provided accommodation for over 30 years, and have a reputation for a warm and friendly atmosphere. The centrally heated dormitory style wool loft has 5 single beds. A hearty breakfast, with freshly laid eggs is cooked for you on the Aga in the farmhouse kitchen and visitors are welcome to drink tea and coffee in the sun lounge which has with views down the valley. Packed lunches, complete with home made cake can be provided by arrangement.

DETAILS

- **Open** - All year round, except Christmas Day and Boxing Day, all day
- **Number of beds** - 5:
- **Booking** - Booking essential
- **Price per night** - £12.50 per person (no credit cards) Minimum of two people.
- **Public Transport** - There are daily buses to Brynrefail from Llanberis, Caernarfon & Bangor.
- **Directions** - Ring for full directions. 400m from village of Brynrefail.

CONTACT: Hugh and Judith Walton
Rhydau Duon, Brynrefail, Caernarfon, Gwynedd, LL55 3NT
Tel: (01286) 870744
hugh@waltonsbunkhouse.co.uk www.waltonsbunkhouse.co.uk

TOTTERS
OVER THE ROAD (O.T.R)

Totters "Over the Road" is quite literally over the road from Totters. Totters O.T.R is the perfect alternative for small groups who are looking for complete privacy of their own home. The house comprises an open plan living and kitchen/dining area on the ground floor. This in turn goes upstairs to 2 bedrooms (one king size double and one twin). A further flight of stairs leads to a large double/twin bedroom with en-suite bathroom (see photos opposite) Unlike most self catering lets O.T.R asks for a minimum rental period of only 2 days, giving people that extra flexibility to their travel plans. Step out of the front door and you are just 10 seconds from the promenade over the Menai Straits. Amazing for sunsets and star gazing! Known localy as "the South of France"

DETAILS

- **Open** - All year, all day
- **Number of beds** - 6: 3 x 2
- **Booking** - Booking is essential.
- **Price per night** - £20pp (based on 6 people), £25pp (based on 4 people). Weekly rates available.
- **Public Transport** - Bangor train station is 7 miles from the hostel. Catch a bus from outside the station to Caernarfon. National Express coaches drop off in Caernarfon 200m from the hostel.
- **Directions** - Coming by road:- follow signs for town centre, turn right 200m after the big Celtic Royal Hotel, keep going and Totters Hostel is the last house on the left. Ring doorbell at Hostel.

CONTACT: Bob/Henryette
Plas Porth Yr Aur, 2 High Street, Caernarfon, Gwynedd, LL55 1RN
Tel: (01286) 672963, Mob 07979 830470
totters.hostel@googlemail.com www.totters.co.uk

Totters is situated in the heart of the historic castle town of Caernarfon. Sheltered by the castle town wall, we are only 30 metres from the shores of the Menai Straits and get to see some fantastic sunsets. The town not only offers the visitor a huge selection of pubs and restaurants to choose from, but also acts as the perfect base for trips into the Snowdonia National Park. There is very good public transport in and out of the National Park. The hostel is a 200-year-old, five floored town house, which is fully heated with all the comforts of home. We have a common room with TV and games, drying room, book exchange, dining room and a secure left luggage facility. The bedrooms sleep either 4 or 6 and can be arranged as mixed or single sex dorms.

We also have what we call our 'Penthouse' a huge double en-suite with views over the Straits. This can be arranged as a family room

     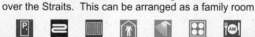

DETAILS

- **Open** - All year, all day access. Book in by 10pm.
- **Number of beds** - 30 : 4 x 6, 1 x4, 1 x 2 (en-suite)
- **Booking** - Booking is essential for groups in June, July, August and September.
- **Price per night** - £15 per person. Discounts for groups.
- **Public Transport** - Bangor train station is 7 miles from the hostel. Catch a bus from outside the station to Caernarfon. National Express coaches drop off in Caernarfon 200m from the hostel.
- **Directions** - Coming by road:- follow signs for town centre, turn right 200m after the big Celtic Royal hotel, keep going and Totters is the last house on the left.

CONTACT: Bob/Henryette
Plas Porth Yr Aur, 2 High Street, Caernarfon, Gwynedd, LL55 1RN
Tel: (01286) 672963, Mob 07979 830470
totters.hostel@googlemail.com www.totters.co.uk

Pentre Bach provides alpine style bunkhouse accommodation, outdoor activities and a campsite. The camping barn has two floors. The ground floor has tables with benches and a cooking area with gas burners, a microwave, fridge and freezer. Upstairs are alpine sleeping platforms with mattresses for 16. Toilets with washing facilities and showers, shared with the campsite, are just across the yard. Based between Waunfawr and Betws Garmon, Pentre Bach is surrounded by the superb scenery of Moel Eilio and Mynydd Mawr and has views towards Mount Snowdon. There are great walks from the barn or take a short car journey to the Nantlle ridge and the main footpaths up Snowdon (Ranger and Rhyd Ddu). Bach Ventures provide a variety of outdoor activities, whether you wish to be guided around the hills, try kayaking, climbing, or have an adventure gorge-scrambling.

DETAILS
- **Open** - All year, enquiries 9am until 10pm. Arrival after 4pm.
- **Number of beds** - 16: 1x16
- **Booking** - One night's deposit, balance payable on arrival. Short notice bookings accepted by phone or email.
- **Price per night** - £8.00 per person (inc gas / electric / showers). Sole use bookings negotiable according to group size.
- **Public Transport** - Train station at Bangor. S4 bus from Caernarfon to Beddgelert stops at the bottom of the drive on request.
- **Directions** - GR 531 579. At Pentre Bach just south of Waunfawr on the Caernarfon to Beddgelert road (A4085). Look for Camping Barn sign.

CONTACT: Karen Neil
Pentre Bach, Waunfawr, Caernarfon, Gwynedd, LL54 7AJ
Tel: (01286) 650643
info@bachventures.co.uk www.bachventures.co.uk

STONE BARN

The Stone Barn and Studio are converted farm buildings at Tyddyn Morthwyl Farm and Caravan Park near Criccieth on the fringe of Snowdonia. The farm provides a good centre for climbing and walking in Snowdonia and the Lleyn Peninsula. Tremadog Rocks (an all year rock climbing venue) is only 7 miles away. Canoeing and wind surfing nearby.

The Barn has an alpine style sleeping platform. Hot showers and toilets are shared with the caravan park. There is a wood burning stove for heating and clothes drying (wood provided free) and a kitchen area with fridge and water.

There is also The Studio, a small stone building with two single beds and washbasin, and a static caravan to let.

Several pubs in the locality serve good bar meals.

DETAILS

- **Open** - All year, flexible
- **Number of beds** - 12
- **Booking** - 48 hrs advanced booking required, with one night's fee as deposit.
- **Price per night** - £7 per person in the Stone Barn including wood (discount for groups). £8 per night the Studio.
- **Public Transport** - Criccieth has a train station and National Express coach service. The hostel is 1.25 miles from Criccieth and a taxi service is available.
- **Directions** - 1.25 miles from Criccieth on B4411 Caernarfon road.

CONTACT: Mrs Trumper
Tyddyn Morthwyl, Criccieth, Gwynedd, LL52 0NF
Tel: (01766) 522115
trumper@yrhenstabal.freeserve147.co.uk

YR HELFA
BUNKHOUSE

Yr Helfa is a traditional bunkhouse situated in the heart of the Snowdonia National Park. This former farmhouse has been carefully restored and will sleep up to 18 people in 3 comfortable rooms. It has underfloor heating, 3 shower rooms with toilet and sink and a coal fire in lounge. All bedding is supplied. Yr Helfa nestles directly at the foot of Moel Gynghorion with panoramic views from the Llanberis path around to Bwlch Masgwn (Telegraph Pass). It is in a mountain environment with direct access to a number of routes up Snowdon and yet only 20 minutes walk (1 miles) from Llanberis. The area is ideal for climbing, walking, fell running, horse riding and mountain biking. Award winning attractions include The Slate Museum, Electric Mountain, Dolbadarn Castle, Llanberis waterfall, Lake Railway and Snowdon summit railway. Llanberis has several restaurants and plenty of pubs for a night out.

DETAILS

- **Open** - All year, all day
- **Number of beds** - 18: 3x6
- **Booking** - Availability and booking form on website. Book by post, 30% deposit.
- **Price per night** - Whole Bunkhouse - £150 per night, 7 nights £1,000. Shared occupancy - Smaller groups £12 per person per night, each room sleeps six.
- **Public Transport** - Trains at Bangor (10 miles). Buses from Llanberis to Caernarfon and Bangor every half hour.
- **Directions** - The bunkhouse is on the road to the beginning of the Llanberis Snowdon track. Carry on past the track and it is the first gate on your right. Park in the parking area then walk ten minutes down another track.

CONTACT: Jane O'Donnell
Grove House, 18 High Street, Llanberis, Gwynedd, LL55 4EN
Tel: 0790 0087692
yrhelfa@hotmail.co.uk www.snowdonbunkhouse.co.uk

CRAFLWYN
BASECAMP

The historic Craflwyn Estate dates back to 1200 AD. Having been part of a monastery, a family residence and a Victorian hunting lodge, it is now a fully resourced conference and activity centre. The bunkhouse, located in the old stables, accommodates 12 people and can be divided into 2 self-contained units of 7 and 5 beds which can be hired individually. There is a dining/lounge area and a large kitchen. Craflwyn is set in a stunning location at the foot of Snowdon, in the Nantgwynant valley, with dramatic views and a magical atmosphere. The village of Beddgelert can be reached on foot via a riverside footpath. The village has pubs, bistros, cafés, shops and an information centre. Snowdon and the legendary Dinas Emrys are both on the doorstep and a wide range of beaches, historic houses, gardens and archaeological sites are all within easy reach.
The hall offers en-suite accommodation and sleeps 14 people.

DETAILS

- **Open** - All year, all day. Office hours 9am-5pm Mon-Fri.
- **Number of beds** - 12: (2 self-contained units of 7 and 5 beds)
- **Booking** - 33% non-returnable deposit to secure the booking. Full payment due 10 weeks in advance.
- **Price per night** - Check website for latest prices. Two night minimum stay. Bank holidays 15% extra.
- **Public Transport** - Trains at Bangor and Porthmadog. Local buses stop nearby.
- **Directions** - Craflwyn Hall is approximately ¾ mile outside Beddgelert on the A498 towards Capel Curig.

CONTACT: Eirian Jones
The National Trust, Craflwyn, Beddgelert, Gwynedd, LL55 4NG
Tel: (01766) 510120
eirian.jones@nationaltrust.org.uk www.craflwyn.org

SNOWDON
LODGE

Snowdon Lodge is a grade 2 listed building in which Lawrence of Arabia was born in 1888. The hostel provides the ultimate in clean, comfortable and secure accommodation for individuals and groups. Choice of dormitories or private rooms. Heating and personal lockers in every bedroom. Licensed bar, large dining room, fully equipped kitchen, lounge/TV room with real log fires and a private car park leading to extensive woodland walks.

Ideally positioned just 6 miles from Snowdon, yet only 2 miles from beautiful sandy beaches, and only a few minutes walk from the train station, National Express coaches, and many pubs and restaurants. Within a mile are the Ffestiniog and Welsh Highland railways, the famous Tremadog rocks for climbers, and virtually every other outdoor activity one could wish for. Guided outdoor activities arranged on request. Snowdon Lodge is the perfect base from which to explore Snowdonia and the Lleyn Peninsula.

DETAILS

- **Open** - All year. Booking is essential in winter months, no restrictions
- **Number of beds** - 48: dorms (4-10), twins and doubles.
- **Booking** - Essential. Deposit for first night payable by credit card.
- **Price per night** - From £16.50 including light breakfast and linen.
- **Public Transport** - Half mile from Porthmadog train station and 250 yards from National Express coach stop.
- **Directions** - Half a mile from Porthmadog on Caernarfon road (A487).

CONTACT: Carl or Anja
Lawrence House, Tremadog, Nr Porthmadog, Snowdonia, LL49 9PS
Tel: (01766) 515354
info@snowdonlodge.co.uk www.snowdonlodge.co.uk

SGUBOR UNNOS
BUNKHOUSE

Croeso Welcome Sgubor Unnos provides luxury bunkhouse accommodation on a Welsh speaking, traditionally run, family farm in the village of Llangian, one mile from Abersoch, famous for it's watersports and surfing beaches, Hell's Mouth and Porth Ceiriad. Centrally located, it is the ideal centre for outdoor activities including walking the newly opened Llyn Coast Path, surfing, cycling, golf, fishing and sailing. The farm also offers hovercraft cruising, a new experience in outdoor activities. Situated a few miles from Llangian at the tip of the Peninsula lies Bardsey Island where 20,000 saints are buried!! Why not pay them a visit? Trips around the island for it's wildlife and heritage can be arranged and sometimes accommodation on the island itself. The modern bunkhouse offers 3 bedrooms ideal for individuals or groups. Fully equipped kitchen/lounge, disabled facilities, covered BBQ area, secure storage, private parking, traditional village shop, post office and phone 500m away.

DETAILS

- **Open** - All year, all day
- **Number of beds** - 14: 2 x 4 : 1 x 6
- **Booking** - Not essential but recommended.
- **Price per night** - £15 (adult), £7 (under 10 years), including a light breakfast. Discount for more than 2 nights.
- **Public Transport** - Nearest train station is Pwllheli (7 miles). Good local bus and taxi service to Llangian. Public transport details on web site.
- **Directions** - GR 296 288 On entering Abersoch from Pwllheli, take the right hand turning up the hill signed to Llangian (Follow Brown signs). On left on leaving village.

CONTACT: Phil or Meinir
Fferm Tanrallt Farm, Llangian, Abersoch, Gwynedd, LL53 7LN
Tel: (01758) 713527
tanrallt@btconnect.com www.tanrallt.com

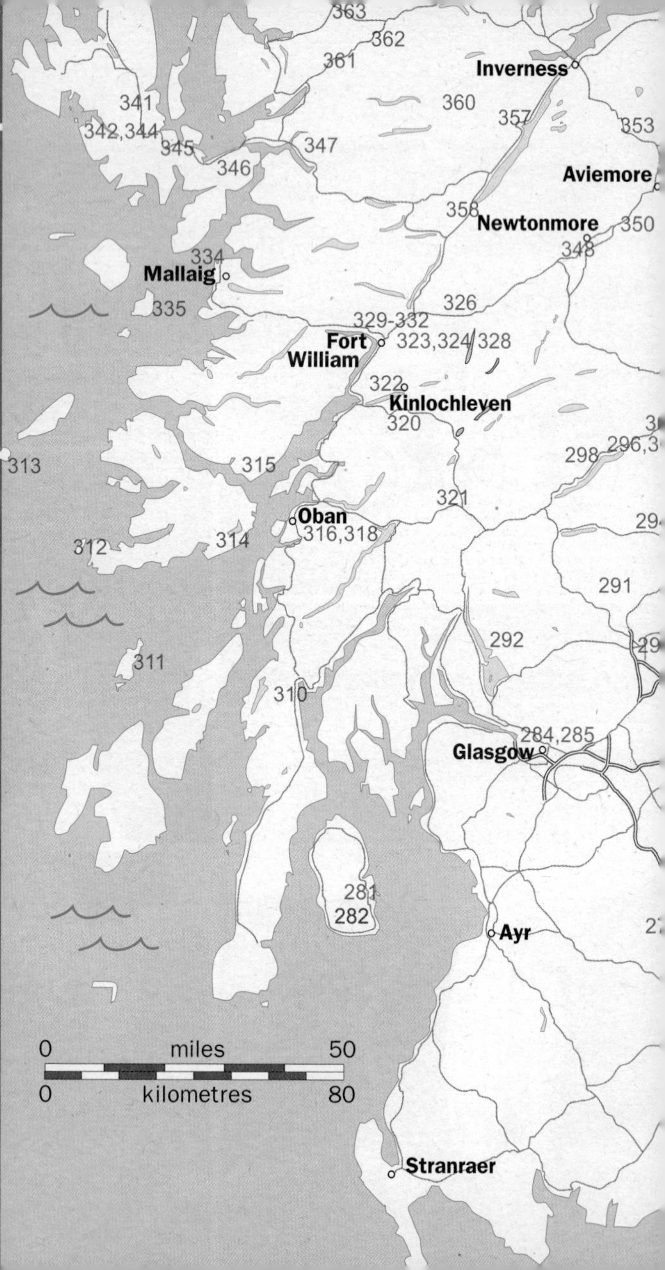

South Scotland

363
362
361
360
357
353

Inverness

341
342,344
345
346
347

Aviemore

358
Newtonmore
348
350

334
Mallaig
335

326
329-332
323,324 328

Fort William

322
Kinlochleven
320

313

315

298 296,3

321

Oban
316,318

29

291

312
314

29

311

292

310

284,285
Glasgow

29

281
282

Ayr

2

0   miles   50
0   kilometres   80

Stranraer

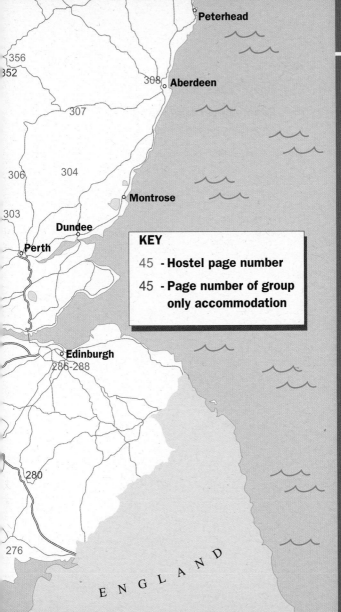

South Scotland

Peterhead

356
352

308 Aberdeen

307

306   304

303

Montrose

Dundee

Perth

KEY

45 - Hostel page number

45 - Page number of group
only accommodation

Edinburgh
286-288

280

276

E N G L A N D

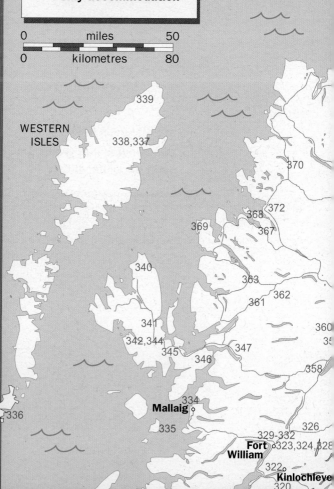

KEY

45 - **Hostel page number**

45 - **Page number of group only accommodation**

| 0 | miles | 50 |
| 0 | kilometres | 80 |

WESTERN ISLES

339

338,337

370

368 372

369 367

340

363

361 362

360

341

35

342,344

345 347

358

346

334

Mallaig

336

335

329-332

326

Fort William 323,324,328

322

Kinlochleven

320

ORKNEY
ISLANDS

376

373 Kirkwall
Stromness o
374

Thurso o   o John O'Groats

377

Lerwick o

SHETLAND ISLANDS

366

365

364

Fraserburgh

354
Peterhead

353
356
352
Inverness o

Aviemore o 351

348
350
Newtonmore

308
Aberdeen o

307

306
304

Montrose o
300

MARTHROWN
SCOTLAND OF MABIE BUNKHOUSE

Marthrown is set in the heart of Mabie Forest, about 6 miles south of Dumfries. It has a traditional sauna, a wood burning spring water hot tub, a large BBQ, garden areas and plenty of room for groups. The forest itself has newly developed mountain bike routes, ranging in length and difficulty. Bike hire is nearby as is the 7 Stanes mountain bike trails.

Although we are a self-catering hostel meals are available to order. Marthrown is suitable for all age groups. Facilities include secure dry store for bikes and equipment and a large dining area suitable for meetings. For something a little different why not try staying in the Roundhouse or the Tipi. For more info see our web site below.

DETAILS

- **Open** - All year, 24 hours
- **Number of beds** - 24: 1x8: 2x6: 1x4. plus Roundhouse and Tipi
- **Booking** - Telephone a few days in advance.
- **Price per night** - £15pp (duvet £3.00). Sole use booking available on request.
- **Public Transport** - From Dumfries (White Sands) take the Stagecoach bus service 372 to Mabie Forest. It is best to arrive in daylight. 1.5 mile walk from road.
- **Directions** - From Dumfries take A710 (west) to Mabie Forest passing through the village of Islesteps. Turn right signposted Mabie Forest and Mabie House Hotel. Follow tarmac road over speed bumps to the end of the Hotel and Forest Rangers Office, through courtyard and onto forest track, Marthown is signposted and is exactly one mile into the forest.

CONTACT: Mike or Pam Hazlehurst
Mabie Forest, Dumfries, DG2 8HB
Tel: (01387) 247900
mike@marthrown.com www.marthrown.com

LOTUS LODGE
HOSTEL

Nestled in the Lowther Hills, Lotus Lodge is a remote getaway in Wanlockhead, the highest village in Scotland, but is only one hour from Carlisle, Glasgow and Edinburgh. A large traditional village house the accommodation is fully modernised, comfortable and cosy. The relaxing guest lounge and large kitchen both have wood burning stoves and there is a selection of bunk, family and twin rooms to choose from. Whole house and group bookings available all year – ideal for groups or family get-togethers. Wanlockhead is directly on the Southern Upland Way long distance walking trail and Lands End to John O'Groats cycle route. The Lead Mining Museum offers a historical mining experience (and gold panning!) while the village pub offers good value meals. Lotus Lodge is a great base for exploring the stunning surrounding area and many other attractions of Southern/Central Scotland. Only 15mins from the M74 it is also a convenient and interesting stopover on trips North or South.

DETAILS

- **Open** - All year, all day, no lock-out time and no curfew.
- **Number of beds** - 28:
- **Booking** - Essential only from Oct to Mar. Payment on arrival.
- **Price per night** - All prices include continental breakfast & bed linen. Bunk: £16pp. Twin: £18.50pp. Family: £18.50pp adult, £11.50pp child (min £60 per room).
- **Public Transport** - Trains at Sanquhar. Bus no.30 (6 daily except Sun) from Sanquhar or Lanark to Wanlockhead – ask for hostel..
- **Directions** - Entering Wanlockhead follow hostel signs. By Car: 45mins Glasgow/1hr Carlisle – M74, 1¼ hrs Edinburgh – A702

CONTACT: Lisa Montgomery
Lotus Lodge, Wanlockhead, Dumfries & Galloway, ML12 6UT
Tel: (01659) 74544
lotuslodge@tiscali.co.uk www.lotuslodge.co.uk

WELL ROAD CENTRE

SCOTLAND GROUP ACCOMMODATION

The Well Road Centre is a large Victorian house set in its own grounds in the charming spa town of Moffat. The centre is ideal for youth groups, adult groups, conferences, residential workshops, sports events, multiple family gatherings and outdoor activity clubs. All rooms are fully carpeted and centrally heated. There are two spacious meeting rooms, a large bright self-catering kitchen fully equipped for 65, games hall for indoor sports, table tennis room and snooker room. The are 13 bedrooms of various sizes, two of them with en-suite facilities. Two separate toilet/shower areas for mixed groups. Bring your own sleeping bags or duvets. Ample parking for cars, minibuses and equipment trailers and the nearby park can be used for football matches. Moffat is in the Southern Uplands, an hour from Edinburgh and Glasgow. Ideal area for golfers, bird watchers, walkers and cyclists. All groups have sole use.

DETAILS

- **Open** - All year, all day
- **Number of beds** - 65: in 13 rooms (2 en-suite)
- **Booking** - Check availability and send £100 deposit to secure booking.
- **Price per night** - £10pp (based on 2 nights), £8.30pp (based on 3 nights). £7.50pp (based on 4 nights), £5.71pp (based on 1 week). Fuel extra. Minimum group size is 25. Smaller groups are welcome but must pay for 25.
- **Public Transport** - Trains at Lockerbie(16m). Citylink bus to Glasgow/Edinburgh.
- **Directions** - From A74 take Moffat turning and enter the High Street (town square). Turning to the right around the shops on the south side of the square, follow Holm St to the T-junction. Turn left into Burnside, following up and right into Well Rd.

CONTACT: Ben Larmour
Huntly Lodge, Well Road, Moffat, DG10 9JT
Tel: (01683) 221040
Ben8363@aol.com www.wellroadcentre.co.uk

Aldersyde Bunkhouse is a purpose built bunkhouse on the beautiful Island of Arran (Scotland in miniature). Lamlash is a haven for golfers, there are 3x18 hole 1x12 hole and 3x9 hole golf courses all very reasonably priced. Arran - lovely coastal and forestry walks and Goatfell at 874 metres. Both loch and sea fishing are available with boats for hire or organised trips. Bird life is plentiful and varied. We are a short sail from the Holy Island which has been bought by Same Ling as a retreat, visitors are welcomed. The 'Waverley', the only remaining sea going paddle steamer in the world, calls at Arran twice weekly during the summer for trips on the Clyde. Arran offers a unique geology formation and is well used by universities. Brodick Castle and gardens are well worth a visit. There are standing stones at various sites, the most popular are at Machrie Moor. Crafts are part of island life and are varied, with visitor participation welcomed. A distillery and brewery are also very interesting. Food is available to suit all tastes, while the bunkhouse has limited self-catering with a new kitchen. Wheelchair friendly - electric wheelchair available.

DETAILS

- **Open** - All year, all day
- **Number of beds** - 21: 1 x 11 : 1 x 7
- **Booking** - Advisable
- **Price per night** - £10pp - group reduction and for length of stay
- **Public Transport** - Bus meets the Ferry at Ardrossan.
- **Directions** - Due south from the Ferry at Ardrossan. The Hostel is in Lamlash behind the Aldersyde Hotel.

CONTACT:
Lamlash, Arran, KA27 8LS
Tel: (01770) 600959
jpricelamlash@hotmail.com www.aldersydebunkhouse.co.uk

KILMORY LODGE
BUNKHOUSE

This brand new bunkhouse in a tranquil, rural setting is ideal for your group accommodation. The Isle of Arran is one of the most accessible Scottish islands; it's only a one hour ferry trip from the mainland. It offers the visitor hill-walking, mountaineering, golf, fishing, cycling, pony trekking, a bewildering choice of extreme sports and everything else you would expect of Scotland's premier tourist venue. The bunkhouse is affordable, modern, comfortable and able to sleep up to 23. We supply all the bed linen, so no need to bring anything except your towels and of course, your food! We have a great, contemporary kitchen with all you'll need. Attached to the bunkhouse is the village hall which can provide extra rooms and an auditorium at extra cost. Ideal for educational groups, music workshop groups, clubs or any group needing extra facilities. We look forward to welcoming your family, club, group, school or any combination of these except stag parties! Phone or email with your queries.

   GROUPS ONLY

DETAILS

- **Open** - All year, 24 hours
- **Number of beds** - 23: 2 x 8, 1 x 4 (en-suite) 1 x 3 (en-suite)
- **Booking** - Book ahead, 40% deposit. £100 security deposit on arrival.
- **Price per night** - Sole use 15 people or less £230 per night. £15pp over 15 people (ie. £230 plus £15pp over the 15)
- **Public Transport** - Buses stop on demand directly outside the Hall and Bunkhouse. These buses meet all the ferries that arrive and depart from the main ferry terminal at Brodick.
- **Directions** - Bunkhouse attached to Kilmory Public Hall located in village centre.

CONTACT:
Kilmory, Isle of Arran,KA27 8PQ
Tel: (01770) 870345, Fax: (01770) 870345
kilmory.lodge@btinternet.com www.kilmoryhall.com

Cairncross House is in an excellent location within walking distance of the trendy West End and City Centre and is close to public transport. The West End is great for pubs and restaurants and has lots of good value places to eat. Nearby you will find some of Glasgow's top visitor attractions: Art Gallery and Museum, Transport Museum, University of Glasgow and its Visitor Centre, Hunterian Museum and Art Gallery. The City Centre offers great shopping, clubs and pubs. The Hostel is part of the University of Glasgow's student residence and offers great value for money. Modern, well equipped with bed linen, wash basin in room, cooking facilities, showers, free laundry facilities and common room.

DETAILS

- **Open** - June to September, 8.00 am - 10.00 pm
- **Number of beds** - 242
- **Booking** - Advised but not essential, Booking address: Residential Services, University of Glasgow, 73 Great George Street, Glasgow, G12 8RR
- **Price per night** - £16.80 (inc. VAT) per person
- **Public Transport** - Buchanan Street Bus Station, Central Station and Queen Street Station are all 2 miles away. The nearest underground station is Kelvinhall (half mile) From George Square take buses 6 or 16, ask for Kelvinhaugh/Radnor St.
- **Directions** - From George St take St Vincent St, which becomes Argyle St after 1 mile. Through traffic lights take third left into Kelvinhaugh St, Cairncross House is on the right. From M8 J19 take A814 to Finnieston. Turn right into Finnieston St, continue to traffic lights and turn left into Argyle St. Kelvinhaugh St is third on the left.

CONTACT:
20 Kelvinhaugh Place, Glasgow, G3 8NH
Tel: 0141 330 4116/2318 or 0141 221 9334
vacationaccom@gla.ac.uk

'Glasgow's Only City Centre Hostel' providing budget en-suite accommodation in Glasgow City Centre, only 2 minutes walk from Central Station.
Ideally suited for international visitors to discover the city's cultural heritage and vibrant nightlife or convenient for guests to stay over after a concert or night out clubbing. We welcome groups of all sizes throughout the year and make an ideal choice for sports teams, concertgoers and school/college parties. Facilities include the 'Osmosis' bar, games room, chill-out lounges with Big-screen TV and SKY, 24hr reception, internet access, self-catering kitchen, guest laundry and free bike and luggage storage. There are TV's in all the twin and double rooms and FREE Wi Fi.

DETAILS

- **Open** - All year, all day
- **Number of beds** - 364: Singles, 2, 4, 8 and 14 person all en-suite
- **Booking** - Individuals with credit card. Groups - 20% deposit required. Book on-line at www.euro-hostels.co.uk
- **Price per night** - From £13.95 B&B pp en-suite. Discount for mid-week bookings and long stays. Groups:1 free for every 20.
- **Public Transport** - Central Railway Station (2 mins), Queen Street Railway Station (7 mins), Buchanan Bus Station (10 mins), Glasgow Airport 8 miles.
- **Directions** - From the bus station turn right into North Hanover St and right into West George St (past Queen St Rail Station), turn left into Buchanan St and right down Argyle Street (left if arriving from Central Rail Station). Go down Jamaica St and the hostel is on the corner joining Clyde St.

CONTACT: Reception
318 Clyde Street, Glasgow, G1 4NR
Tel: (0141) 222 2828, Fax: (0141) 222 2829
info@euro-hostels.co.uk www.euro-hostels.co.uk

WESTEND
HOSTEL

The Westend Hostel is a lively hostel with a relaxed atmosphere, located in Edinburgh's historic West End, directly opposite Haymarket Train Station and within 5 minutes walking distance of Princes Street, the sights, Edinburgh Castle and nightlife. The hostel is due to be refurbished in early 2008, it is bright, clean and spacious, and offers modern standards at a budget price.

We provide free fresh linen and duvets, free hot showers (24 hours), free continental breakfast, free tea and coffee facilities, room cleaning on daily basis, 24 hour access, secure entry, laundry and tour booking facility. The popular communal lounge, with digital TV, pool table and free internet access is an ideal place to meet fellow backpackers. Self-catering kitchen and a choice of restaurants catering for all tastes nearby. We specialise in group bookings.

DETAILS

- **Open** - All year, 24 hours
- **Number of beds** - 95:
- **Booking** - Advisable, phone with credit card.
- **Price per night** - From £10pp - £25pp in dorm, £40 for a double room and £45 for a triple and £60 family room. All prices include breakfast.
- **Public Transport** - Waverley train station is 10 mins walk. If approaching from Glasgow or the north get off at Haymarket station which is opposite the hostel. If coming from Edinburgh Airport, the Air Link Bus drops off in front of Hostel.
- **Directions** - Directly opposite Haymaket Train Station. Car parking is available in the streets surrounding the hostel or at station car park.

CONTACT: Reception
3 Clifton Terrace, Edinburgh, EH12 5DR
Tel: (0131) 313 1031, Fax: (0131) 313 1131
info@edinburghcitycentrehostels.co.uk www.edinburghcitycentrehostels.co.uk

GLOBETROTTER INN
EDINBURGH
SCOTLAND

Cheap accommodation in Edinburgh. Backpacking on a budget? Globetrotter Inns provides cheap accommodation for backpackers, students and independent travellers that's gloBEtroTTER than anywhere else. The overnight prices include sparkling clean linen, all taxes and continental breakfast. Luxury comfortable bunks are available in twin, double, quad and 6/8 bed rooms.

Facilities include steaming hot showers, immaculate clean bathrooms, self-catering kitchen, in-house supermarket, gym, laundry, internet, cinema, TV and hot tubs. The bar is open 24 hours and in hot whether you can spill out into the garden for a BBQ. Other facilities include CCTV, Smart cards, 24 hour reception, travel desk and a regular shuttle bus to and from the city.

DETAILS

- **Open** - All year, all day
- **Number of beds** - 382 : 16x8, 29x6, 10x4, 9 x twin en-suite, 11 x double en-suite
- **Booking** - Book online, by phone, fax or email.
- **Price per night** - From £15pp (6/8 bed room), £18pp (6/4 bed en-suite), £23pp (double/twin en-suite). Surcharge Fri and Sat
- **Public Transport** - 10 minutes from Edinburgh Waverley station. 15 minutes from Edinburgh International Airport. Our shuttle bus will collect you from outside Waterloo Place bus stop. Airport pick-ups can be arranged for a minimum of 3 people at £5 per person. Our shuttle bus runs from 6am to 11pm throughout Edinburgh.
- **Directions** - Located on the south shore of the Firth of Forth with some of the best views in the city.

CONTACT: Reception
46 Marine Drive, Edinburgh, EH4 5EP
Tel: (0131) 336 1030, Fax: (0131) 336 0945
edinburgh@globetrotterinns.com www.globetrotterinns.com

Looking for a hostel in Edinburgh? Do the smart thing and choose SmartCityHostels the newest Edinburgh hostel. We're a purpose-built five-star city centre hostel, great for anyone visiting Edinburgh, whether for the Festivals, Hogmanay or just backpacking on a budget. Our location is right in the heart of Edinburgh's Old Town - one minute from the Royal Mile and only a few minutes from Edinburgh Castle, the Scottish Parliament, many more of Edinburgh's visitor attractions, and night-life. All our rooms are en suite with the biggest and most comfortable hostel beds in Edinburgh. Fantastic showers, towels and bedlinen included in the price. Our Smart City Café serves food and drinks all day every day with Wi-Fi access throughout the café.
If you are looking for cheap hostel accommodation in Edinburgh then do the smart thing and make your hostel in Edinburgh Smart City Hostels.

DETAILS

- **Open** - All year, 24 hours
- **Number of beds** - 620
- **Booking** - Not essential, but recommended in summer
- **Price per night** - From £13.50 per person per night. Group rates available on request.
- **Public Transport** - Airport transfer and Waverley train station 5 minutes walk; St Andrews Bus Station 5-10 minutes walk.
- **Directions** - From Waverley bridge turn left into Market Street, then turn right into Jeffrey Street. At first set of traffic lights at the Royal Mile turn right. Blackfriars Street is first left and smartcityhostels is on your right.

CONTACT: Reservations
50 Blackfriars Street, Edinburgh, EH1 1NE
Tel: (0870) 892 3000, Fax: (0131) 524 1988
info@smartcityhostels.com www.smartcityhostels.com

WILLY WALLACE
HOSTEL

The Willy Wallace Hostel is the only independent backpackers accommodation in Stirling. This historic town, midway between Glasgow and Edinburgh, has an important medieval castle which has guarded the "Gateway to the Highlands" since ancient times. Willy Wallace is a friendly well-run hostel in an attractive Victorian building right in the town centre and next to the train and bus stations. It offers discount accommodation for families, groups and touring backpackers visiting historic Scotland. The hostel is well-known for its friendly staff, large comfortable common room and clean well equipped kitchen. The bedrooms are warm, bright and spacious. There are twin and double rooms, family rooms and dormitories. The specially built bunks are adult size and robust. The mattresses are comfortable and all bed linen is provided. Relax and make friends in the grand common room where tea and coffee are free. Or keep in touch with your friends using our Internet facilities.

Come and stay at Willy Wallace Hostel in the heart of historic Scotland.

DETAILS

- **Open** - All year, all day - no curfew
- **Number of beds** - 64: 1x18, 1x12, 1x10, 1x8, 3x4(family), 1x 2(bunks), 1x2 (dble)
- **Booking** - Book online or by phone
- **Price per night** - £14 per person (dorm), Family rooms from £35. Doubles from £35. Twin in bunks £30.
- **Public Transport** - Near to Stirling train and bus stations.
- **Directions** - From train station walk to the top of Station Road and turn right onto Murray Place. Hostel is at the end of Murray Place above Oxfam.

CONTACT: Reception
Willy Wallace Hostel, 77 Murray Place, Stirling, FK8 1AU
Tel: (01786) 446773
contact@willywallacehostel.com www.willywallacehostel.com

Trossachs Backpackers has been purpose-built on its own 8 acre site, set amidst beautiful scenery (on Sustrans route 7c) just outside the bustling tourist town of Callander. The Hostel, which is the only one in the Trossachs area, opened in August 1997 and is finished to a very high standard, hence its nickname 'Poshtel' The rooms are all en-suite and are either 8,4 or single. The 4 bed family rooms have their own private kitchen/dining facilities and can be used as twin rooms on request. There is a spacious dining/common room, well equipped kitchen, a laundry and drying room. A large meeting/recreation room is also available and may be booked separately for conferences, parties, etc. We have an on-site Cycling Centre, which also sells basic provisions. Other activities available locally include Hill Walking, Pony Trekking, Canoe Hire/ Instruction, Fishing and Sailing.

DETAILS

- **Open** - All year, Nov to Feb advanced bookings only, receptiion 8am - 11pm
- **Number of beds** - 30
- **Booking** - Booking advised at all times. Groups must book with deposit.
- **Price per night** - £15 to £25 including linen & continental breakfast. Group and family discounts on request.
- **Public Transport** - Nearest train station is at Stirling (15 miles). Nearest Citylink coach stop is at Callander (1.5 miles). Pick up from Callander can usually be arranged.
- **Directions** - GR 606 072. The hostel is situated one mile up Invertrossachs Rd from its junction with the A81 (Glasgow Rd) in Callander.

CONTACT: Mark or Janet
Invertrossachs Road, Callander, Perthshire, FK17 8HW
Tel: (01877) 331200, Fax: (01877) 331200
mark@scottish-hostel.co.uk www.scottish-hostel.co.uk

LEDARD FARM
BOTHIES

Ledard Farm is a working hill farm and the centre for the Scottish Sheepdog School. It faces the Queen Elizabeth State Forest (25,000h), Ben Lomond and Loch Ard. Highland Adventure outdoor activity centre is also sited on the farm and offers clay pigeon shooting, fishing, sailing, canoeing, mountain bikes, quad biking and hill walking. Ledard Farm has beautiful views across Loch Ard. The main path to the twin summits of Ben Venue passes through the farm and there are numerous forest paths for walking and cycling all within easy reach.

Four Ledard Bothies each sleep 2 people and one sleeps 4. They are fully heated and also have fans. Guests can use their own sleeping bags or hire them for £5 (beds have quilt, sheet and pillow slip). The toilets and showers are in an adjacent building as are the self catering facilities. There is ample secure parking. Cars can be left safely when walking climbing or cycling in the area.

DETAILS

- **Open** - Apr–Oct (inc), all day (arrive between 1600 and 2000, depart before 1100)
- **Number of beds** - 12: 1 x 4, 4 x 2
- **Booking** - Booking essential – deposit for groups only.
- **Price per night** - £15 per person. £5 to hire sleeping bag.
- **Public Transport** - Bus services to Aberfoyle from Stirling (adjacent to train station) or Glasgow (Buchanan Street Bus Station). We will pick you up from Aberfoyle or you can get a local taxi.
- **Directions** - Located in the middle of the Loch Lomond and The Trossachs National Park. From Aberfoyle take B829 in the direction of Kinlochard and Inversnaid for 5 miles (8kms). The farm is on the right 300m after Forest Hills Hotel.

CONTACT: Ferg or Fra
Ledard Farm, Kinlochard, Stirling, Stirlingshire, FK8 3TL
Tel: (01877) 387219
ferg@ceilidh-band.demon.co.uk   www.highland-adventure.co.uk

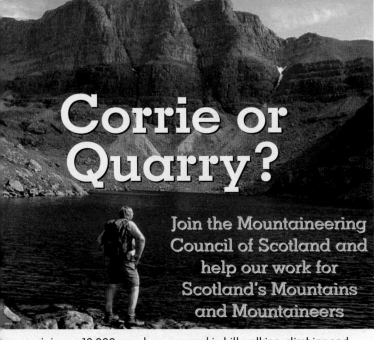

COMRIE
CROFT

Situated in a 200-year-old farmstead, Comrie Croft offers an attractive, great value escape amongst the Scottish hills. Just over one hour's drive from Edinburgh or Glasgow, the Croft is ideal for individuals, families or groups. There are endless things to see and do. Explore the mountains, have a go at adventure sports like quad-biking or white-water rafting, hold a team-building meeting or seminar, tour Scotland's Oldest Distillery, discover Loch Lomond National Park at Loch Earn, swim or fish in our own loch, walk on the estate, hire a bike, find ruined castles, or simply read a book on the sofa. Among the facilities are a choice of standard or en-suite private rooms, a cosy living room with books, games and movies and full self-catering facilities. We also have a shop, bike hire, indoor and outdoor games facilities, conference facilities, and our own 300 acre estate offering walks, bike routes and a beautiful loch.

DETAILS

- **Open** - All year, all day
- **Number of beds** - 56 + 14 (2 units)
- **Booking** - Recommended
- **Price per night** - £15pp - £17pp en-suite. Group and family discounts.
- **Public Transport** - Train stations: Dunblane, Stirling, or Perth. Our own bus stop is served by no. 15 from Perth (approx. every hour). Summer only Citylink service to Oban and Fort William. From Stirling or Dunblane take no. 47 to Crieff then change to no. 15 for Comrie. Ask for Comrie Croft.
- **Directions** - Signposted from the A85 between Crieff (5 miles) and Comrie (2 miles).

CONTACT:
Braincroft, By Crieff/Comrie, Perthshire, PH7 4JZ
Tel: (01764) 670140
info@comriecroft.com   www.comriecroft.com

DUNOLLY
SCOTLAND ADVENTURE OUTDOORS

Dunolly House comprises two units, the first is a 48-bed Victorian house, the other is a smaller 15-bed cottage. All rooms are fully carpeted and centrally heated with modern pine beds (linen and duvets provided). The complex can be taken together or as separate units for groups and individuals with catering to suit.

We have a fantastic range of activities on site which can be booked by groups and individuals. They include river rafting, duckying, kayaking, gorge ascent, archery, mountain biking, high ropes challenge and climbing wall. We have our own qualified instructors and we are licensed to run activities for children under the regulations of the Adventure Activities Licensing Authority.

Come and enjoy !!

DETAILS

- **Open** - All year, 24 hours
- **Number of beds** - 63
- **Booking** - Booking is normally necessary
- **Price per night** - From £11.00
- **Public Transport** - Nearest train station is in Pitlochry (14 miles away). Citylink coaches stop at Ballinluig (11 miles away) and Pitlochry. Local buses to Aberfeldy.
- **Directions** - Turn off the A9 Road at Ballinluig. Travel for 5 miles. Turn right at the T junction. Travel 6 miles until Aberfeldy. Continue through the main street and we are the last house on the right as you exit Aberfeldy.

CONTACT: Booking Office
Taybridge Drive, Aberfeldy, Perthshire, PH15 2BP
Tel: (01887) 820298
info@dunollyadventures.co.uk www.dunollyadventures.co.uk

CULDEES
BUNKHOUSE

Culdees offers an independent hostel and B&B accommodation in the heart of a caring community which aims to live at one with the natural environment. Whether you're a motorist, a cyclist or a Munro bagger, you'll find it a homely place for just a night or for all your holiday. The bunkhouse has a well equipped kitchen with dining area for 16 people. Four bedded bunk rooms with digital locks, individual reading lights, duvets, fresh linen, towels, and an extra pillow. The Bed and Breakfast accommodation in the house has two family rooms and one double room. Also available to guests is a living room with television area and a wide range of movies. Large music room with baby-grand and other instruments. Big open barn, ideal for barbecues, gatherings, great when it's raining! Drying room with washer and dryer. Lockable bike shed. Toys, play area, plenty of space for outdoor games. Goat milk and eggs when available. Tourist Board 3 star recommended. Gold Award for Green Tourism.

DETAILS

- **Open** - All year, 24 hours
- **Number of beds** - Bunkhouse 16: 4x4, B&B 10: 2x4, 1x2
- **Booking** - Book with credit card.
- **Price per night** - £15pp (bunkhouse), £24.50 Bed and Breakfast
- **Public Transport** - Train Pitlochry 25 miles. Coach Aberfeldy 9miles. Local bus four days a week and the school bus will drop at hostel track. Collection from Aberfeldy's bus stop if stuck.
- **Directions** - GR 716 447 From A827 Killin to Aberfeldy road turn left at the hotel in Fearnan. At top of hill turn left (Dalchiaran) signposted Culdees.

CONTACT: Maryse
Culdees, Boreland Farm, Fearnan, nr Aberfeldy, Perthshire, PH15 2PG
Tel: (01887) 830519, Mobile 07904 954116, Fax: (01887) 830664
contact@culdeesbunkhouse.co.uk www.culdeesbunkhouse.co.uk

THE BUNKHOUSE
GLASSIE FARM

We are situated 1,000 feet above sea level on a south facing mountainside. The steading has been converted into two high standard units. They are perfect for relaxing after a busy day out on the local hills and lochs. Fantastic location for group gatherings, stag and hen parties, outdoor activity weekends or just a place to re-charge and take in the amazing views. There are 2 totally separate units which can be hired individually or as a whole. These units both have fully equipped kitchens and a dining area / seating area. We have tables and chairs and B-B-Q`s for outside eating, an upright fridge freezer and plenty of parking space. Bunks come with fitted sheets / pillow with case and duvet hire is optional. Activities in area include; W/W/Rafting, Clay Shooting, Paintball, Quad Bikes and many other pursuits which are listed on my website

DETAILS

- **Open** - All year, 24 hours
- **Number of beds** - 34: Original Unit 20:1x6, 2x5,1x4. Newer Unit 14; 2x4,1x6.
- **Booking** - Groups ONLY for Fri / Sat Weekends. Individuals / groups for Sun to Thur nights. Book on-line and deposits required.
- **Price per night** - Whole units are from £12.75pp on weekdays to £15pppn at weekends. Individuals / small groups are £14pp. Check website for Special Deals.
- **Public Transport** - Trains at Pitlochry (12 miles), bus at Aberfeldy (2.5 miles)
- **Directions** - From the x-roads in Aberfeldy, follow the B846 over Wades Bridge. Turn right at the Aileen Craggan Hotel (signed Strathtay). After 800 mtrs turn left (at yellow sign on RH side) signed to Bunkhouse, and follow track for 1.5 miles. See website for printable directions.

CONTACT: Julian Rickard
The Bunkhouse, Glassie Farm, Aberfeldy, Perthshire, PH15 2JN
Tel: (01887) 820265
julian@thebunkhouse.wanadoo.co.uk www.thebunkhouse.co.uk

ADVENTURERS
ESCAPE

Wade House and the Bunkhouse are at the foot of a south facing slope with beautiful walks and climbs in Tayside (Weem) Forest Park. Built in the 1700s Wade House is a listed building where General Wade stayed while building his roads. The adjoining old barn has been converted to a 4* luxury bunkhouse, with underfloor heating and log fired stoves. There are also two self-contained cottages.

Home of the National Kayak School, ideal for whitewater kayaking and sea kayaking. Superb mountain biking also on cycle route #7 and Rob Roy Way. Instruction available for rock climbing, ice climbing, hill walking, mountaineering, whitewater rafting and canyoning. Bar meals next door at Weem Hotel. Midge free and sheltered sunny front garden and courtyard.

DETAILS

- **Open** - All year, flexible but generally all day
- **Number of beds** - Wade House 9 : 1x5, 1x4. Bunkhouse 27: 3x4/5, 1x2/3, 1x8/9, Two new units: 4 + 6
- **Booking** - Advisable, book by phone or email
- **Price per night** - From £13 per person. Long stay rates available.
- **Public Transport** - Buses from Aberfeldy connect to trains at Pitlochry & Perth.
- **Directions** - North from traffic lights in Aberfeldy, over General Wade's bridge over the River Tay for 1km, the Adventurer's Escape is next to the Weem Hotel on the B846.

CONTACT: Stuart Wagstaff
Weem, Aberfeldy, PH15 2LD
Tel: (01887) 820498 or 07774 644 660
info@adventurers-escape.co.uk www.adventurers-escape.co.uk

Wester Caputh Hostel, an intimate relaxed place, sits by the River Tay in beautiful rural Perthshire. Near to Dunkeld, at the heart of Scotland, it is just over an hour's travel from Edinburgh and Glasgow. There are quiet roads for cycling and excellent woodland and river walks. Close to the hostel are prehistoric, Pictish and Roman sites. The river offers some of the best rafting, canoeing and fishing in the country. Dunkeld is an unspoilt town of antiquity with places to eat and drink and plenty to see and do. We offer very comfortable bunk-bedded accommodation. The hostel kitchen is equipped for serious cooking. The living room has many instruments, games and books. Enjoy music and good conversation - or simply the deep peace of green Perthshire.

DETAILS

- **Open** - All year, all day
- **Number of beds** - 17: 2x2, 1x3, 1x4, 1x6
- **Booking** - Booking advisable
- **Price per night** - From £15 pp
- **Public Transport** - Train station at Birnam (5 miles). Hourly Stagecoach bus from Perth (Mill St), ask for Caputh Village. Infrequent buses from Dunkeld. Local taxis available.
- **Directions** - From north: From A9 take A923 to Dunkeld. After Dunkeld bridge turn right onto A984 to Caputh (4.5 miles). After church on right turn right (B9099) then 1st right at foot of hill. A few hundred yards on right (long white building). From south: From A9 take B9099 through Luncarty and Murthly. Cross river into Caputh. Turn left at foot of hill (signed Dunkeld). A few hundred yards on right (long white building).

CONTACT: Catherine Boot
Caputh, By Dunkeld, Perthshire, PH1 4JH
Tel: (01738) 710449
sam@backpackerspress.com www.westercaputh.co.uk

PROSEN HOSTEL

SCOTLAND

Glenprosen is the most intimate of the Angus Glens on the southernmost edge of the Cairngorm National Park. Two Munros, the Mayar and Driesh, link Glenprosen to the Cairngorms plateau. The Minister's Path leads over to Glen Clova, whilst a new footbridge and path along the prettiest stretch of the river Prosen connects to Glenisla and the Cateran Trail in Perthshire. Prosen Hostel was recently converted from an old school to provide accommodation for those using the upgraded East Cairngorms footpath network. Converted to the latest and greenest specification, the living room has a wood burning stove, internet connection, and raised area for admiring the view (& red squirrels) through the school's huge windows. A drying room and laundry facilities complete the cosy welcome. It sleeps a total of 18 in 3 bunkrooms, sleeping 4, 4 &6 and a family room sleeping 4. The nearby village hall is available to rent for ceilidhs, music sessions, parties and celebrations. STB 4 star. Green Tourism Bronze Award.

DETAILS

- **Open** - All year, all day
- **Number of beds** - 18:1x6, 3x4
- **Booking** - Book by phone or email
- **Price per night** - £18 pp, £14pp if whole hostel is taken. Minimum periods apply for Christmas and New year
- **Public Transport** - Trains Dundee; buses Kirriemuir (regular to Dundee & Forfar)
- **Directions** - From Kirriemuir follow B955 signed to Prosen, Clova and Cairngorms National Park. At Dykehead fork left. Carry on for 7 miles until public road ends at telephone kiosk. Turn acute right and follow tarmac 200m uphill to hostel.

CONTACT: Hector or Robert
Prosen Hostel, Balnaboth, Kirriemuir, Angus,DD8 4SA.
Tel: (01575) 540238/302
hectormaclean@compuserve.com www.prosenhostel.co.uk

GULABIN
LODGE

Gulabin Lodge is beautifully situated in the heart of Glenshee at the foot of Beinn Gulabin offering the nearest accommodation to the Glenshee ski slopes. We offer nordic, alpine, telemark skiing and snowboarding and have a dry ski slope where lessons are available. Gulabin is an ideal base for climbing, walking or mountain biking, whether you are a beginner or an expert. Other activities available include rock climbing, gorge walking, abseiling, archery, rifle shooting, orienteering, canyoning, kayaking. Nine-hole golf course, 85m aerial runway and pony trekking nearby. Five minutes walk from the hostel are the Spittal of Glenshee Hotel and Dalmunzie Hotel both with friendly bars and excellent meals. The lodge offers comfortable accommodation for individuals, families and groups with two cosy lounges with log fires. Free hot showers. All rooms have wash basins and linen. Packages for groups. Ski, Snowboard & Nordic hire equipment, and Mountain bike hire with guided trips available.

DETAILS

- **Open** - All year, 24 hours, arrive by 9pm
- **Number of beds** - 33 :- 8 rooms available
- **Booking** - Booking advisable with 50% deposit
- **Price per night** - From £15pp (bed only). From £17.50pp B&B, Family rooms from £45. Full board available. Sole use available.
- **Public Transport** - Train and bus stations at:- Pitlochry (22 miles), Blairgowrie (20 miles), Glasgow (100 miles), Edinburgh (70 miles). Post bus calls half a mile away.
- **Directions** - Gulabin Lodge is on the A93 road at Spittal of Glenshee - 20 miles north of Blairgowrie and 19 miles south of Braemar. Transport can be arranged.

CONTACT: Darren and Tereza
Spittal of Glenshee, By Blairgowrie, PH10 7QE
Tel: (01250) 885255 Mobile: 07799847014
info@gulabinlodge.co.uk www.cairnwellmountainsports.co.uk

Exceptional accommodation in the Scottish highlands for families, friends, couples and groups. Guests from all over the world have been delighted by this refreshingly stylish base in Royal Deeside, in the dramatic surroundings of the Cairngorm Park. The owners Alan and Cathy Low are committed to meeting the highest standards. Cathy is a professional storyteller and both speak French and German and teach English. For details of English programmes, please visit www.schoolhouse-english.eu. There's a large lounge with giant sofas and open fire, a bright dining room and a choice of family, double or twin rooms. The beds are superkingsize and all rooms have excellent ensuite showers. There's a large garden with BBQ hire, outdoor eating facilities and car park. Schoolhouse can provide excellent accommodation for groups of up to 24 in 3 ensuite dorms with up to 8 bunks in each. Bed linen and towels are supplied and breakfast is included. In-house catering can be provided, delicious meals and lunches being freshly prepared often using ingredients straight from the garden.

DETAILS

- **Open** - All year, all day
- **Number of beds** - 18: 24 possible (3 rooms for up to 8 people)
- **Booking** - Booking essential for groups
- **Price per night** - From £18 per person, includes breakfast.
- **Public Transport** - From Aberdeen Bus Station (bus enquiries (01224) 212266).
- **Directions** - From Aberdeen follow the A93 to Ballater (43 miles). From Inverness follow Grantown-on-Spey then A939 to Ballater (70 miles). From Perth follow A93 to Blairgowrie, then continue to Ballater (65 miles).

CONTACT: Alan or Cathy Low
Anderson Road, Ballater, Aberdeenshire AB35 5QW
Tel: (013397) 56333
info@school-house.eu www.school-house.eu

Craibstone Estate is a 750 acre country estate situated on the edge of the granite city of Aberdeen. It offers excellent accommodation to individuals, families, groups and conferences in an attractive area of woodland and hills. The accommodation is in two adjacent halls with extra facilities in nearby buildings. Bedding and linen is provided in all the rooms. Sutton Hall was built in 1995 to high standards and contains 60 en-suite bedrooms (single) with communal self-catering kitchens. The building also houses a self service laundry. Hunter Hall was built in 1954 and has 14 singles with wash hand basins and communal bathrooms and self-catering kitchen. The building also has a TV lounge, snooker room, meeting room and a lounge bar with a dance floor, pool table, plasma TV and darts. Other facilities on site include a shop & café, multi-gym, sauna & steam room, golf course, putting green, floodlit astroturf, walled garden (ideal for BBQs) and woodland walks. Pets welcome.

DETAILS

- **Open** - 17/03/08 to 11/04/08 and 23/06/08 to 26/09/08, 24 hour access.
- **Number of beds** - Sutton 60: 60x1 Hunter 14: 14 x1
- **Booking** - Advisable, groups require deposit.
- **Price per night** - Sutton: £15 per person. Hunter: £12 per person
- **Public Transport** - From Guild Street Bus Station (opposite Aberdeen train station) take Bus No 307 to Inverurie (quarter to and quarter past the hour). Get off at Craibstone roundabout. Only a short taxiride from Airport.
- **Directions** - Craibstone is on the north west of Aberdeen City just off the A96 Inverness road. At airport roundabout, turn left and follow the signs to Craibstone.

CONTACT:
Scottish Agricultural College, Facilities Office, Bucksburn, Aberdeen, AB21 9TR
Tel: (01224) 711012, Fax: (01224) 711298
gwen.bruce@sac.co.uk www.sac.ac.uk/holidayletsaberdeen

SEASIDE HOUSE

Seaside house has a lochside position in the small Scottish village of Ardrishaig. The large garden runs down to the shore making an ideal location for watersports such as canoeing, windsurfing and sailing. The house is split into two self contained flats and these are available for weekly hire. Each flat has its own kitchen, bathroom, dinning room, sitting room and sleeps 6 people in 3 rooms of twin beds. There is sky TV, wireless internet and the bothy in the garden has a laundry and drying area. The ground floor flat has disabled access and is being converted for use by wheelchair users. Ardrishaig is on the shores of Loch Fyne, one of the most beautiful lochs on the West Coast of Scotland - the home of crystal clear lochs, lush green vegetation and exceptionally warm weather in summer! Ardrishaig is 40 miles south of Oban close by the Crinan Canal and 9 miles from Kilmartin. Seaside House has plenty of parking.

DETAILS

- **Open** - All year, all day, key provided.
- **Number of beds** - Top flat 6: 3x2, Bottom flat 6: 3x2
- **Booking** - Book in advance
- **Price per night** - Weekly lets only. Sole use of each 6 bed flat £600 per week (electricity included).
- **Public Transport** - Citylink coaches from Glasgow and Campbeltown, West Coast Motors bus to Tarbert, Lochgilphead and Oban. Caledonian Macbrayne ferries to Portavadie, Gigha and the Isle of Islay.
- **Directions** - Ardrishaig is on the A83 between Tarbert and Lochgilphead. Seaside House is on Lochgilphead side of Ardishaig on the A83 (Glenburn road)

CONTACT: via Corran House
Glenburn Road, Ardrishaig, Argyll, PA30 8EU
Tel: (01631) 56 6040, Fax: (01631) 56 6854
enquiries@corranhouseoban.co.uk www.corranhouseoban.co.uk

COLONSAY
KEEPER'S LODGE
SCOTLAND

The Lodge is located on a peaceful and idyllic Inner Hebridean island to the south of Mull which boasts magnificent sandy beaches, ancient forests and beautiful lochs. The place is teeming with wildlife which includes dolphins, seals, otters and many rare species of bird. There are ancient standing stones and a 14th-century priory with exceptional carved Celtic tombstones, and the famous Colonsay House gardens and café are open to visitors to enjoy twice a week. We offer for hire mountain bikes to tour the area and tennis racquets to use on the free court. The pub, café, shop and village hall, where there are regular Ceilidhs, are all within three miles. Fresh lobster, crab and langoustines can be bought from the fishing boats in the harbour and don't forget the best oysters in the world are grown on Colonsay. The lodge is a refurbished former gamekeeper's house and bothies. It is centrally heated and has 3 large twin, 3 small twin and 1 family room. It has a huge dining/cooking/sitting area and a separate sitting room with a log fire. Bed linen provided.

DETAILS

- **Open** - All year, 24 hours
- **Number of beds** - 16   6 x 2 : 1 x 4.
- **Booking** - Required 24 hours in advance.
- **Price per night** - £16pp twin, £12pp bothy, £14pp 4 bed dorms.
- **Public Transport** - Train and coach in Oban. Ferry to Colonsay takes 2.5 hours.
- **Directions** - Ferry departs Oban 5 times a week April to October, Sun, Mon, Wed, Thurs, Fri (rest of year Mon, Wed, Fri). From Kennacraig and Port Askaig, Islay on Weds. Transport for hostellers can be arranged if required.

CONTACT: Rhona Robinson
Colonsay Estate Cottages, Isle of Colonsay, Argyll, PA61 7YP
Tel: (01951) 200312
colonsaycottages@dial.pipex.com www.colonsay.org.uk

IONA
HOSTEL

Tucked into the rocky outcrops at the north end of the island, Iona Hostel has spectacular views to Staffa and the Treshnish Isles, and beyond Rhum to the Black Cuillins of Skye. The hostel is situated on the working croft of Lagandorain (the hollow of the otter). This land has been worked for countless generations, creating the familiar Hebridean patchwork of wildflower meadow, crops and grazing land, home to an amazing variety of plants and birds.

We offer quiet sanctuary for those that seek it, while being in easy reach of island activities. Iona Hostel is new, well-reviewed and recommended. Whether travelling on your own, with friends, or as part of one of our many visiting groups, Iona Hostel offers you a warm welcome - with the best views and duck eggs this side of heaven. 4 star STB. Green Tourism Gold Award. We regret no dogs are allowed.

DETAILS

- **Open** - All year, Closed 11am-1pm for cleaning - no curfew
- **Number of beds** - 21: 1 x 2 : 2 x 4 : 1 x 5 : 1 x 6.
- **Booking** - Is strongly advised 50% deposit.
- **Price per night** - £17.50 adult £12.00 under 10s (bedding included).
- **Public Transport** - Caledonian Macbrayne ferry service from Oban or Mull (08705 650000). For buses on Mull (01546) 604695. Taxi service on Iona 0781 032 5990.
- **Directions** - You cannot bring your car onto Iona, but there is free parking in Fionnphort on Mull at the Columba Centre. Iona Hostel is the last building at the north end of the island, 2 km from the pier and up beyond the abbey.

CONTACT:
Iona Hostel, Iona, Argyll, PA76 6SW
Tel: (01681) 700781
info@ionahostel.co.uk www.ionahostel.co.uk

Tiree is an idyllic Hebridean Island, perfect for outdoor pursuits, wildlife enthusiasts, and those yet to experience the total tranquility of stunning white beaches and crystal clear seas.

A warm welcome and excellent facilities await you at Millhouse. Bikes are for hire to explore the island, visit the thatched cottage and lighthouse museums, find the standing stones, wonder at the machair flowers or watch the seals. Watersports take place on adjacent Loch Bhasapol, and the secluded Cornaig beach is a ten minute walk away.

There is a resident RSPB warden on the island and a bird hide near the hostel. For walkers, Millhouse is on the Tiree Pilgrimage route linking the ancient chapels and monuments around the island. STB 4* Hostel

DETAILS

- **Open** - All year, all day. Quiet after 11.30pm. Check out 10am
- **Number of beds** - 16/18 : 2 x 2/3 : 2 x 6 plus 3 family rooms : 12 beds: 3 x 4
- **Booking** - Advisable, Please check vacancies before boarding the ferry
- **Price per night** - Twin £13.50-£16.50pp. Dorms £13.50pp. Family £42-£54 per room.
- **Public Transport** - Caledonian MacBrayne ferry from Oban to Tiree or BA flight from Glasgow. Local Ring and Ride bus (01879) 220419.
- **Directions** - From Ferry turn right at T junction, then left at next fork. Continue for 4 miles to Millhouse Hostel

CONTACT: Judith Boyd
Cornaigmore, Isle of Tiree, Argyll, PA77 6XA
Tel: (01879) 220435
tireemillhouse@yahoo.co.uk www.tireemillhouse.co.uk

SHIELING
HOLIDAYS

We're right on the sea, with views to Ben Nevis. There are regular sightings of seals and otters, and sometimes of porpoises, dolphins and eagles.

Stroll to the ferry, pub, shops, and miniature steam railway. Walk to Torosay and Duart Castles. Catch the bus for Tobermory; for Iona (where Columba brought Christianity to Scotland) and for Staffa (home of puffins, and inspiration for Mendelssohn's overture 'Fingal's Cave').

Your accommodation is in Shielings, unique carpeted cottage tents, made by us on Mull, which are clean, bright and spacious, and have real beds for 2, 4, or 6. There are super showers, and communal Shielings with woodburner, TV, payphone and launderette. Our campsite is rated '5 stars, exceptional, World Class' by the Scottish Tourist Board.

DETAILS

- **Open** - April to October, 24 hours (Reception 0800 - 2000)
- **Number of beds** - 18: 6 x 2 : 1 x 6.
- **Booking** - Booking advisable. Phone bookings held to 6pm
- **Price per night** - £11.50 pp, Under 15's £8.50 pp, bedding £2.50pp
- **Public Transport** - From Glasgow, rail (08457 484950) or bus (08705 505050) at 12.00, ferry (01680 812343) at 16.00 from Oban, arrive Mull 16.40; back by 11.00 ferry, arrive Glasgow 15.45. Please check times before travel.
- **Directions** - GR 724 369 From ferry, left on the A849 to Iona. After 400 metres, left opposite church past old pier to reception - 800 metres in all.

CONTACT: David Gracie
Craignure, Isle of Mull, Argyll, PA65 6AY
Tel: (01680) 812496
info@shielingholidays.co.uk www.shielingholidays.co.uk

Lochaline on the shores of the Sound of Mull has two bars, a café and a shop. There are lovely coastal, woodland walks close to the village and challenging hill walks on Mull. Sea angling, river and loch fishing and of course diving are available locally and it is an ideal location for day trips to the Ardnamurchan peninsula, the mountains of Glencoe, Fort William and the island of Mull.

The Dive Centre overlooks the Sound of Mull and provides self-catering accommodation for individuals and groups in twin rooms with en-suite wash-basins and toilets. There are ample supplies of hot water, an efficient drying room, a fully equipped kitchen with commercial cookers and a lounge with TV and video. The Old Post Office, a stone's throw from the Pier and not much further from the hotel bar, provides self-catering accommodation for groups of 10. Return from your day out to a roaring log fire in the comfy lounge and cooking on a range stove. The bedrooms offer sea views (3 twin rooms, and one family room). All you need to bring for both properties are towels.

DETAILS

■ **Open** - All year, 24 hours
■ **Number of beds** - Centre 24: 12x2, Old Post Office 10: 1x4, 3x2
■ **Booking** - Advisable, with 50% deposit
■ **Price per night** - Dive Centre: £14 pp per night. Old post Office: £140 per night.
■ **Public Transport** - Caledonian MacBrayne ferry runs daily 0745 to 1900 from Fishnish on Mull. Buses run from Corran Ferry, 8 miles outside Fort William.
■ **Directions** - As you descend into the village of Lochaline on the A884, look out for signposts. The Centre is just beyond the shop, up a steep drive.

CONTACT: Mark and Annabel Lawrence
Lochaline, Morvern, Argyll, PA34 5XT
Tel: (01967) 421627
lochaline.divecentre@virgin.net www.lochalinedivecentre.co.uk

CORRAN
HOUSE

Corran House is part of a Victorian terrace with magnificent sea-scapes across the bay to the Isle of Kerrera and the hills of Mull. There is a warm welcome for visitors and reasonably priced accommodation for singles, couples, families and groups. The house has a large self-catering kitchen, spacious TV lounge, comfortable, commodious, well appointed guest rooms and 4 bed dormitories with generous size beds - most rooms have en-suite facilities. Corran House is well situated for exploring Argyll and visiting the inner Hebrides. It is only a short walk along the sea front to the bus, train and ferry terminals. Downstairs is Markie Dans bar with patio and spectacular views. The pub offers great highland hospitality, tasty meals, live entertainment, wide screen TV, pool table and a late licence all year round to enable the discerning drinker to sample the best range of malt whiskies on the west coast. Pony trekking trips now available -prior booking advisable. Photos courtesy of Highland Photos.

DETAILS

- **Open** - All year, reception 10am-9pm. Check in after 3pm.
- **Number of beds** - 36 : 7x4 : 1x2 : 1x6. plus Guest rooms : 11.
- **Booking** - Advisable. Credit card secures bed. Early/late arrival with notice.
- **Price per night** - Bunk room £14-£18 pp. Guest rooms from £25-£40 single.
- **Public Transport** - Oban train, bus and ferry terminals are 900m from the house.
- **Directions** - Corran House overlooks Oban Bay to the west of the town centre. From the Tourist Information and all the Oban transport terminals, with the sea on your left, walk along George Street past the Columba Hotel into Corran Esplanade. Follow the seafront for 300m. Corran House is on your right above Markie Dans Bar.

CONTACT:
1 Victoria Crescent, Oban, Argyll, PA34 5PN
Tel: (01631) 56 6040, Fax: (01631) 56 6854
enquiries@corranhouseoban.co.uk www.corranhouseoban.co.uk

JEREMY INGLIS
HOSTEL

Jeremy Inglis Hostel is only 150 yards from the station and the bus terminus in Oban.

Prices include a continental breakfast with muesli, toast and home made jams, marmalade and Vegemite, etc. Tea and coffee are available at any time.

The rooms are mostly double and family size so you have some privacy, all linen is included in the price.

Kitchen facilities are provided and the hostel is heated by meter.

Smoking is not allowed in the hostel.

DETAILS

■ **Open** - All year, no curfew, access with a key
■ **Number of beds** - 12 to 14
■ **Booking** - Booking preferred. Deposit in certain circumstances.
■ **Price per night** - From £10-£11 per person (in a shared room), including continental breakfast. Single rooms (when available) £17.00 -£18.00
■ **Public Transport** - Nearest train and Citylink drop off 150 metres from hostel. Ferries to Islands 350 metres. For ferry enquiries phone (01631) 566688.
■ **Directions** - The Hostel is in Airds Crescent, one of the streets off Argyll Square. The Hostel is on the second floor, pink door.

CONTACT: Jeremy Inglis or Katrin
21 Airds Crescent, Oban, Argyll, PA34 5SJ
Tel: (01631) 565065, Fax: (01631) 565933
jeremyinglis@mctavishs.freeserve.co.uk

GLENCOE
SCOTLAND INDEPENDENT HOSTEL

Glencoe Independent Hostel, formerly known as Glencoe Hostel & Bunkhouse, is centred around an historic west highland croft in the heart of beautiful Glencoe, offering great value accommodation for groups, families and individuals. It is set in a secluded and peaceful woodland midway between Glencoe village and the Clachaig Inn with immediate access to world class cycling, walking, climbing and kayaking and 20 mins from White Corries ski centre. Relax and enjoy the beautiful surroundings or explore further afield to Ardnamurchan, Mull, Fort William and Skye. The hostel has 3x6 and 1x8 bed rooms, a lounge with open fire in winter, cooking and dining facilities. The self catering Alpine bunkhouse sleeps 20 in a large open plan barn ideal for outdoor activity and school groups. There are also caravans for 4 to 6 people and a log cabin for 2-3 people. Drying room and bike storage. Small shop for 2008.

DETAILS

- **Open** - All year (closed very rarely), 9am - 9 pm
- **Number of beds** - Hostel: 26, Bunkhouse: 20, 4 caravans of 4/6, Log cabin: 2/3
- **Booking** - Booking advised in summer. 30% non refundable deposit required.
- **Price per night** - From £9.50 to £18 per person
- **Public Transport** - 1¼ miles from bus stop in Glencoe Village, served by Citylink 914, 915, 916 from Glasgow/Fort William and by bus 44 from Fort William/ Kinlochleven. West Highland Way bus from Kingshouse Hotel. Pick up also possible.
- **Directions** - 1¼ miles from Glencoe Village bus stop, served by Citylink 914, 915, 916 from Glasgow, via West Highland Way (Kings House Hotel stage) and by 44 from Fort William/ Kinlochleven. Pick up may be possible.

CONTACT: Keith or Davina
Glencoe Independent Hostel, Glencoe, Argyll, PH49 4HX
Tel: (01855) 811906
info@glencoehostel.co.uk   www.glencoehostel.co.uk

BY THE WAY
HOSTEL & CAMPSITE SCOTLAND

By The Way Hostel and campsite can be found in the Loch Lomond National Park halfway between Arrochar's peaks and the grandeur of Glencoe. The site, run by experienced hillwalkers, is aimed primarily at outdoor enthusiasts and with great walking (the West Highland Way passes by the hostel), climbing, white water paddling and gold-panning nearby, there is lots to be enthusiastic about (Munro-baggers can find 50 Munros within 20 miles). Accommodation options range from camping (with an indoor cooking/dining area and campers drying room), through a purpose built hostel (with twin/double rooms and dorms) to fully equipped Scandinavian style mountain huts, or for those wanting more comfort still, a three bedroom centrally-heated timber holiday chalet. By The Way is in Tyndrum with the village pub, shops, café and Tourist Information Centre nearby. The main Glasgow to Fort William road is 250 metres from the site (far from the madding traffic noise) and both the Glasgow Oban and Glasgow Fort William trains pass through (and stop in) Tyndrum.

DETAILS

- **Open** - Hostel open all year. Camping from Easter to October, 24 hours
- **Number of beds** - 26 in hostel; 24 in huts; 50 camping.
- **Booking** - Always phone in advance. Deposit (Visa/Access) guarantees bed.
- **Price per night** - Hostel dorms from £14pp. Huts from £9pp. Camping £6pp
- **Public Transport** - Intercity coach and rail service pickup points in Tyndrum to Edinburgh, Glasgow, Fort William and Oban. Sleeper service to London.
- **Directions** - GR NN 327 302. Travelling on A82 follow sign in village for Tyndrum Lower Station. Hostel is immediately before station.

CONTACT: Jim or Jean Kinnell
Lower Station Road, Tyndrum, FK20 8RY
Tel: (01838) 400333, Fax: (01838) 400243
info@tyndrumbytheway.com www.TyndrumByTheWay.com

BLACKWATER
HOSTEL & CAMPSITE

Blackwater Hostel is in the centre of the scenic village of Kinlochleven surrounded by the Mamore mountains midway between Glencoe and Ben Nevis. An ideal stopover for families, cyclists, walkers, climbers and those who enjoy the outdoors. There are high and low-level, half-hour to full-day walks, all with great views, or if you prefer there is a regular bus service from the village to Glencoe, Ballachulish and Fort William. Water sports are available nearby. Europe's first indoor 14 metre ice/climbing wall is only 200 metres from our door. The hostel offers very comfortable, high-quality STB 4 star bunkhouse accommodation. All rooms have en-suite facilities, TV and central heating. Facilities include self-catering kitchens, lounge, dining conference area and drying room. There are supermarkets, pubs & restaurants within two minutes walking distance. Campsite has drying room, showers & covered area.

DETAILS

- **Open** - All year, 24 hours
- **Number of beds** - 39 - 2,3,4,8 bedded rooms
- **Booking** - Essential (between 8am-8pm)
- **Price per night** - From £13pp including bed linen. £29 for twin.
- **Public Transport** - The nearest train station is Fort William and National Express travels from Glasgow to Glencoe and Fort William. Regular bus service to Kinlochleven all day from Glencoe, Ballachulish and Fort William.
- **Directions** - GR 188 618. OS sheet 41. From A82 Glasgow to Fort William road at Glencoe turn right to Kinlochleven. The hostel is situated near the centre of Kinlochleven. Just past the Co-op a large sign with an arrow will point you to Hostel.

CONTACT: Caroline
Lab Road, Kinlochleven, Argyll PH50 4SG
Tel: (01855) 831253 or 07919366116
black.water@virgin.net www.blackwaterhostel.co.uk

Bank Street Lodge is situated 100 metres from Fort William High Street which has numerous shops, pubs, restaurants, banks etc. There is a fully equipped kitchen with cooker, fridge, microwave and cutlery and crockery is provided. Our common room / lounge has a TV, it also provides tables and chairs for eating self prepared meals, and a snack vending machine. All bedding is provided, we also have en-suite rooms available (twins, doubles and family). The Stables Restaurant, at the front of the building, serves fine food for lunches and dinners - treat yourself.

Fort William is an ideal base from which to enjoy walking, climbing, cycling or mountain biking. The new world-renowned Nevis Range mountain bike trails and ski centre are only a short distance from the town centre.
Three star STB rating

DETAILS

- **Open** - All year, 24 hour reception
- **Number of beds** - 42: 6 x 4 : 3 x 3 : 1 x 7 : 1 x 2
- **Booking** - Booking advised. Deposit required for long stays or groups.
- **Price per night** - £14, £15 or £17.50 per person. Group rates available.
- **Public Transport** - Train and Bus stations at Fort William, 500 metres from Lodge.
- **Directions** - Head for Town Centre via the underpass, turn left after Tesco supermarket on Bank Street, then head up the hill for 150 metres, we are above the Stables Restaurant. Car parking is available.

CONTACT: Kenny/John/Linda
Bank Street, Fort William, PH33 6AY
Tel: (01397) 700070
bankstreetlodge@btconnect.com www.bankstreetlodge.co.uk

CALLUNA

Situated within fifteen minutes walk of Fort William High Street this accommodation is ideal for short or long stays. Free transport from the town centre is available if we are at home, just give us a call. The modern accommodation consists of one flat and two new apartments. Bedding is supplied, along with spacious kitchen and comfortable lounge. Very efficient drying rooms. On the spot advice about Ben Nevis from Alan Kimber (Mountain Guide) who owns and runs Calluna with his wife Sue. Calluna is well known for peace and quiet and fine views over Loch Linnhe to the hills of Ardgour. A popular base for climbing and canoeing groups, families and individual globe trotters. Plenty of parking for mini-buses and trailers. Free lap top connection. For accommodation and mountaineering courses see website.

DETAILS

- **Open** - All year, 24 hours (keys supplied)
- **Number of beds** - 22:- 5 x 2 (twin beds), 3 x 4
- **Booking** - Phone up beforehand
- **Price per night** - £12.00 - £15.00 per person
- **Public Transport** - Fort William train and coach stations are 20 minutes walk from the hostel. Citylink and local bus services operate from the coach station. Alan & Sue offer a free lift from the station when convenient.
- **Directions** - By Vehicle: From roundabout (West End Hotel) go uphill on Lundavra Rd and take third on left (Connochie Rd) between four-storey flats. Follow Connochie Rd (do not take right turns) and arrive at our back door! On Foot: Ask for directions to the West End Hotel and follow the route above (15/20 mins on foot).

CONTACT: Alan or Sue
Heathercroft, Fort William, Inverness-shire, PH33 6RE
Tel: (01397) 700451, Fax: (01397) 700489
info@fortwilliamholiday.co.uk www.fortwilliamholiday.co.uk

Àite Cruinnichidh, 15 miles north east of Fort William, occupies a unique sheltered spot adjacent to the Monessie Gorge; explore remote glens, mountain passes and lochs. Numerous easy walks within minutes of the hostel and seven magnificent canoeing rivers within 20 miles. The location is also ideal for climbing (rock & ice), mountain biking, skiing or just relaxing. A warm, peaceful, friendly, country hostel in a converted barn. Àite Cruinnichidh has been renovated to high standards and sleeps 32 in five rooms of four, one of six, one twin and one double/family room en-suite. All bedding supplied. A fully equipped kitchen/dining room, sitting room, excellent showers. Additional facilities:- sauna suite, garden, seminar room, dark room, use of maps, advice on walking/cycling routes. Groups and individuals welcome. Both of us sign and although we do not have wheel chair access we are glad to accommodate people with all forms of disability whenever we can.

DETAILS

■ **Open** - All year, 24 hours
■ **Number of beds** - 32: 1x6,5x4,1x twin, 1 x family/double en-suite
■ **Booking** - Booking advised, 50% deposit.
■ **Price per night** - £12 per person, discounts for groups
■ **Public Transport** - Roy Bridge train station (2 miles). Citylink coaches drop off all year at Spean Bridge, 5 miles away. Pick up from local transport available.
■ **Directions** - From Fort William follow A82 for 10 miles to Spean Bridge, turn right onto A86 for 3 miles to Roy Bridge. Pass though village and continue for 2 miles. The hostel is on right 100m after Glenspean Lodge Hotel on left.

CONTACT: Gavin or Nicola
1 Achluachrach, By Roy Bridge, Near Fort William, PH31 4AW
Tel: (01397) 712315
gavin@highland-hostel.co.uk www.highland-hostel.co.uk

BEN NEVIS INN
BUNKHOUSE

The Ben Nevis Inn is located in one of the most beautiful and famous areas of Scotland, at the very foot of Ben Nevis, Britain's highest mountain. The Inn sits in Braveheart country at the start of the Ben Nevis path and a mile from the end of the West Highland Way. The bunkhouse offers everything that walkers and mountaineers will need, with self catering facilities including a large kitchen, comfortable bunks, and a separate drying area. All bunks have a duvet and all bed linen (no sleeping bags allowed). The bunkroom sleeps 24 divided into three sections and has some great views onto Glen Nevis. The Inn offers an extensive menu with plenty of local produce and something to suit all tastes. There is frequent live music, check out events on the Inn's website . The bunkhouse is 20 minutes walk from the centre of Fort William which has cafes, provisions shops, outdoor-ware shop, pubs, and a well-equipped and recently refurbished leisure centre with swimming pool.

DETAILS

- **Open** - All year, all day
- **Number of beds** - 24: 3x8
- **Booking** - Strongly recommended. Book online with full payment.
- **Price per night** - £14.00 to £15.00 per person per night.
- **Public Transport** - Trains station and bus stop in town centre, 2 miles (30 mins walks) from bunkhouse. There is a taxi rank outside the station.
- **Directions** - From A82 in Fort William take road to Inverness, just before lights turn right onto Achintee Rd towards Claggan. At Spar shop turn right and follow road.

CONTACT:
The Ben Nevis Inn, Claggan, Achintee, Fort William,
Inverness-shire, PH33 6TE
Tel: (01397) 701227
info@ben-nevis-inn.co.uk www.ben-nevis-inn.co.uk

FARR COTTAGE
LODGE

SCOTLAND

Farr Cottage is situated in Corpach, just 3 miles from Fort William town centre, with a breath-taking view of Ben Nevis and across Loch Linnhe, in the outdoor pursuits capital of Scotland. We specialise in whisky evenings and there is a full range of in-house facilities including; satellite television, video lounge, licensed bar, self-catering facilities, email, laundry and drying facilities, central heating and hot showers. We also organise outdoor pursuits which comprise white water rafting, canyoning, climbing, abseiling, skiing, snowboarding, fishing, golf and many many more! We can provide evening meals, breakfast, picnic lunches and we will ensure you have the break or holiday of a lifetime with us. Our professional team are geared to meet your needs and requirements. The FULL Scottish Experience!!

DETAILS

■ **Open** - All year, 24 hours
■ **Number of beds** - 30: in cottage 2 x 2 : 2 x 8 : 1 x 10. 18: in lodge 1 x 2 : 1 x 4 : 2 x 6. Both buildings fully self-contained.
■ **Booking** - Advance booking advised
■ **Price per night** - £13.00 or £17.00 per person. Group rates available.
■ **Public Transport** - Corpach train station is 200m from the hostel. The nearest Citylink service is three miles away at Fort William. Taxi fare from Fort William centre is approximately £7.50.
■ **Directions** - Follow the A82 north from Fort William centre towards Inverness for 1.5 miles. Turn left at the A830 to Mallaig. Follow this road for 1.5 miles into Corpach. We are on the right.

CONTACT: Cliff or Dee
Corpach, Fort William, PH33 7LR
Tel: (01397) 772315
mail@farrcottage.com www.farrcottage.com

CHASE THE
WILD GOOSE

Chase The Wild Goose Backpackers' Hostel is located on the Great Glen Way and cycle route in the village of Banavie, just 2.5 miles from Fort William and the end of the West Highland Way. You can be sure of a warm welcome, a comfortable bed and the company of like-minded travellers in a pleasant out-of-town environment.

Chase The Wild Goose is ideal accommodation, whether you are on a relaxing holiday break with family or friends, enjoying the adventure of a lifetime, travelling the world or living life in the extreme.
Take time out in the Scottish Highlands. The scenery is breath-taking! The hospitality is second to none!

DETAILS

- **Open** - All year, 7.00am - 10.00pm(late keys)
- **Number of beds** - 50 : 2x8, 3x6, 2x5, 1x4 + 2 bed leaders room.
- **Booking** - Pre-booking is advised. Credit or debit card secures booking.
- **Price per night** - From £9.95 per person. Reductions for under 16s and groups. Exclusive use is available to groups, except in July and August, at excellent rates.
- **Public Transport** - The hostel is located just 100m from Banavie train station. The Fort William-Mallaig-Isle of Skye bus stop is nearby on the A830.
- **Directions** - Travel north from Fort William on the A82, signed Inverness. After 1.5 miles, turn left on the A830 'Road to the Isles' for Mallaig. After 1 mile, cross the canal and take a right turn, then 2nd left. Expect to see a large building with flags on the roof. If walking, take a short-cut to Banavie along the Great Glen Way.

CONTACT: Fergus
Great Glen Way, Lochiel Crescent, Banavie, Inverness-shire, PH33 7LY
Tel: 077095 616 56 or (01397) 772531
enquiries@great-glen-hostel.com www.great-glen-hostel.com

SMIDDY BUNKHOUSE

SCOTLAND

A friendly welcome at our comfortable, family run, mountain hostels in a loch-side location overlooking the Caledonian Canal. Pine clad interior gives a cosy, friendly atmosphere. Stunning mountains and water at the doorstep with the meeting of the West Highland Way and Great Glen Way. Hot showers. Fully equipped kitchens available at all times (food available from local shop until 10pm daily). Use of 2 efficient drying / laundry rooms. Bedding provided. Fully heated for all year round use. Outdoor information / daily snow and avalanche reports. Advice / instruction available from resident mountain and water based instructors and guides for winter and summer walking / climbing; river, loch and sea kayaking; dinghy sailing; hire of kayaks and open canoes; dinghy and other equipment hire. AALA licensed outdoor centre. Group and family accommodation. Meeting/lecture room facilities available by arrangement.

DETAILS

■ **Open** - All year, all day (with key). Key deposit required.
■ **Number of beds** - 26 : 12 + 14
■ **Booking** - Telephone to pre-book.
■ **Price per night** - £10.50 - £14.00 (seasonal) pp (incl. bedding).
■ **Public Transport** - Two minutes walk from Corpach Railway Station on the Mallaig Line. Three miles from Fort William (trains from Glasgow and London).
■ **Directions** - Take A82 north out of Fort William towards Inverness, after one mile take A830 North towards Mallaig and follow for 2 miles to village of Corpach. Turn left immediately opposite "Key" stores, signposted 'Snowgoose Mountain Centre'. The hostel is 30yds on left.

CONTACT: John or Tina
Snowgoose Mountain Centre, Station Road, Corpach, Fort William, PH33 7JH
Tel: (01397) 772467, Fax: (01397) 772467
ihg@highland-mountain-guides.co.uk www.highland-mountain-guides.co.uk

SHEENAS
BACKPACKERS LODGE

The Backpackers Lodge in Mallaig offers a homely base from which you can explore the Inner Hebrides, the famous white sands of Morar and the remote peninsula of Knoydart. Mallaig is a working fishing village with all the excitement of the boats coming in. You can see the seals playing in the harbour waiting for the boats and whale watching trips are available from the harbour.

The hostel provides excellent budget accommodation with two rooms each with six beds, a drying room, full central heating and fully equipped kitchen/common room. It has three star plus grading with the Scottish Tourist Board.
On site is the Tea Garden Cafe open 9am-6pm serving quality meals, snacks, speciality coffee and home baking. In the evening The Garden Restaurant (open from 6pm to 9pm) serves home cooked bistro style sea food. Meals available from April to October. See website for pictures of our food and the beautiful countryside around.

DETAILS

- **Open** - All day, 24 hours
- **Number of beds** - 12: 2 x 6
- **Booking** - Telephone ahead for availability and bookings.
- **Price per night** - £13.50 per person.
- **Public Transport** - Mallaig has a train station and services by Citylink coaches. For information on local buses phone (01967) 431272.
- **Directions** - From railway station turn right, hostel is two buildings along.

CONTACT:
Harbour View, Mallaig, Inverness-shire, PH41 4PU
Tel: (01687) 462764
sam@backpackerspress.com www.mallaigbackpackers.co.uk

A new conversion of a 19th-century building, the Glebe Barn has charm and character whilst providing comfortable accommodation with magnificent views. You can enjoy breathtaking scenery along numerous walks; study fascinating geological formations, or explore varied natural habitats with incredible varieties of plant and animal species. Relax on beautiful sandy beaches, listen to the famous singing sands and watch the eagles soar above the spectacular Sgurr of Eigg. Just a mile away there is a well-stocked shop and café/restaurant with regular traditional music sessions. Facilities at the Barn include a well-equipped kitchen, spacious lounge/dining room (polished maple floor, log fire), a combination of twin, triple, family and dormitory rooms, each with wash hand basins (linen provided), central heating, hot showers plus laundry facilities.

DETAILS

■ **Open** - Individuals April to October, Groups all year, all day
■ **Number of beds** - 22: 1 x 2 : 2 x 3 : 1 x 6 : 1 x 8.
■ **Booking** - Booking essential prior to boarding ferry. Deposit required.
■ **Price per night** - £14- £12ppn (1-3 nights) Twin room £32-£25 (1-5 nights)
Group Bookings:£14-£11ppn (1-3nights)5+ nights £10.50ppn.
■ **Public Transport** - Fort William is the nearest National Express Coach stop. The early train from Fort William to Arisaig and Mallaig meets the ferry. Daily summer sailings from Arisaig or Mallaig.
■ **Directions** - We generally meet visitors at the pier. Follow tarmac road around the shore and up hill until you cross a small stone bridge over a burn. Continue up hill and take first track on right. Taxi/minibus service available on request.

CONTACT: Karen or Simon
Isle of Eigg, PH42 4RL
Tel: (01687) 482417
simon@glebebarn.co.uk www.glebebarn.co.uk

DUNARD
HOSTEL

Dunard is a warm friendly, family run hostel on the beautiful island of Barra in Scotland's Outer Hebrides. The hostel has a cosy living room with a lovely fire, hot showers and spacious kitchen. There are bunk, twin and family bedrooms. Situated in Castlebay the hostel has views over the castle to beaches and islands beyond. We are close to the ferry terminal, a handful of shops, and bars which often fill with live music. During the summer the island is alive for 'Feis Bharraidh' a gaelic festival of music, song and dance. Take time and explore this truly beautiful island with stunning white beaches, quiet bays where otters hunt and seals bask on rocks, dunes and meadows carpeted in flowers, and wild windswept hills home to golden eagles. Join one of our friendly guided sea kayaking trips and paddle amongst sheltered islands for really close-up wildlife encounters (no experience needed) www.clearwaterpaddling.com

DETAILS

■ **Open** - All year, except Christmas and New Year, all day
■ **Number of beds** - 16: 3 x 4 : 2 x 2.
■ **Booking** - Booking advised, especially during the summer. Booking essential for groups.
■ **Price per night** - £12 per person. £30 twin room. £40 family room (sleeps 4). £160-£195 sole use. £5pp camping.
■ **Public Transport** - The hostel is a 3 minute walk from the Ferry Terminal in Castlebay. If using a local bus ask to be dropped at the hostel.
■ **Directions** - From Ferry terminal in Castlebay head up hill, turn left and we are the third house past the old school. (200m from Terminal)

CONTACT: Katie or Chris
Dunard, Castlebay, Isle of Barra, Western Isles, HS9 5XD
Tel: (01871) 810 443
info@dunardhostel.co.uk www.dunardhostel.co.uk

HEB
HOSTEL

SCOTLAND

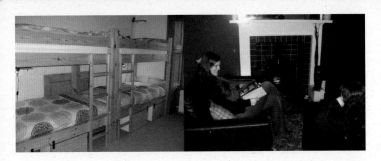

The Heb Hostel is a family run backpackers hostel in the heart of Stornoway on the enchanting Isle of Lewis. It is an ideal stop/stay for travellers visiting the Hebrides & welcomes surfers, cyclists, walkers, families & groups.

Clean, comfortable, friendly and relaxed - Heb Hostel aims to provide you with a quality stay at budget prices.
There are many facilities, including a common room with TV, peat fire, local guides & information.

DETAILS

- **Open** - All year, all day. New arrivals phone to get access code.
- **Number of beds** - 26: 1x8, 2x7,1x4
- **Booking** - Booking is not essential but may be advisable at busier times. Deposits are only required for groups. Payment is due on arrival by cash or cheque.
- **Price per night** - £15 per person per night. 10% discount on booking the whole hostel for more than one night
- **Public Transport** - By plane- From Glasgow, Edinburgh or Inverness(British Airways) Aberdeen(Eastern Airways) Inverness & Benbecula(Highland Airways). By Ferry (Caledonian McBraynes) Ullapool to Stornoway(Lewis), Uig(Skye) to Tarbert(Harris) or Berneray(Uists) to Leverburgh(Harris)
- **Directions** - From Bus station – Exit front door, cross South Beach St & walk up Kenneth St. Pass 1st intersection & we are 2nd on the right. From ferry terminal – come out main exit, turn left, follow pedestrian walk-way to the bus station. From Airport – take bus to Stornoway bus station.

CONTACT: Christine Macintosh
25 Kenneth St, Stornoway, Isle of Lewis, HS1 2DR
Tel: (01851) 709889
christine@hebhostel.com www.hebhostel.com

LAXDALE
BUNKHOUSE

Laxdale Bunkhouse is contained within Laxdale Holiday Park which is a small family-run park set in peaceful tree lined surroundings. Located 1.5 miles away from the town of Stornoway, this is an ideal centre from which to tour the Islands of Lewis and Harris. Built in 1998, the bunkhouse consists of four bedrooms with four bunks in each room and caters for backpackers, families or larger groups looking for convenient, low cost accommodation. A spacious fully equipped dining kitchen which provides two cookers, fridge and microwave. There is a comfortable TV lounge in which to relax. There is also a drying room. Toilets and showers are located within the building and are suitable for the disabled. Outside there is a covered veranda, picnic table and BBQ area.

DETAILS

- **Open** - All year, 8am - 10pm
- **Number of beds** - 16: 4 x 4
- **Booking** - July and August booking advisable one week in advance.
- **Price per night** - £12pp (high season), £11pp (low season). £170 sole use (high season), £150 sole use (low season).
- **Public Transport** - Buses every 30mins stop close to hostel. Taxi fare from town centre approximately £2.50.
- **Directions** - From Stornoway Ferry Terminal take the A857. Take the second turning on the left past the Hospital. Follow camping signs for one mile out of town. The Bunkhouse is located inside the holiday park. From Tarbert or Leverburgh take A859 for 40 miles to Stornoway. Turn left at the roundabout and 2nd left after Hospital then as above.

CONTACT:
Laxdale Holiday Park, 6, Laxdale Lane, Stornoway, Isle of Lewis HS2 0DR
Tel: (01851) 706966 / (01851) 703234
info@laxdaleholidaypark.com   www.laxdaleholidaypark.com

Our comfortable, cosy, fully equipped hostel provides the perfect haven from which to explore the crofting townships of Ness and the west side of Lewis, with sandy beaches, wildlife, historic sites and culture on the doorstep.

Situated within a cobbled stone courtyard enjoying stunning views of the Atlantic Coast towards the Butt of Lewis Lighthouse. A short walk through our croft, with its network of footpaths, takes you to the shore and river, with otters regular visitors. Comprising of one dormitory with up to 8 beds, two shower / toilets and a kitchen / dining room. Bedding can be supplied if required as can meals by order. Bus service to Stornoway, shop within 2 miles. Visit Scotland 4star hostel. Stay a while, for memories of a lifetime.

DETAILS

- **Open** - All year,, 24 hours
- **Number of beds** - 8
- **Booking** - Always phone in advance. Deposit (Visa/Access) guarantees bed.
- **Price per night** - £12pp. Sole use : 2 people £44, up to 8 people £66.
- **Public Transport** - The nearest ferry runs from Ullapool on the mainland to Stornoway which is 20 miles from the hostel. Local buses run from Mondays to Saturdays. Enquire at Stornoway Bus Station.
- **Directions** - GR 437 592. Follow A857 Stornoway to Ness(Nis) road for 20 miles. At Galson (Gabhsann) turn left at phone box. Bunkhouse is ¼ mile.

CONTACT: David and Hazel Roberts
Galson Farm House, South Galson, Isle of Lewis, HS2 0SH
Tel: (01851) 850492, Fax: (01851) 850492
GalsonFarm@yahoo.com www.galsonfarm.co.uk

DUN FLODIGARRY
HOSTEL

The hostel is set in the beautiful Trotternish peninsula of North Skye. The area is famous for the distinctive cliffs and rock formations of the Quiraing and enjoys spectacular views of both the Western Isles and Wester Ross. Pursuits from the hostel - without a car - include Hiking, Hill Walking, Rock Climbing, Painting and Photography. Boat Trips, Fishing, Sea Kayaking and Pony Trekking are available locally. Present day wildlife regularly seen are Otters, Dolphins, Whales and Eagles. Whilst the past has left Dinosaur Footprints and Fossils.

The hostel is centrally heated and fully equipped with all bedding and sheets provided. Phone the hostel for travel information outwith the public bus service times. There is a hotel with a restaurant just 100 metres from our door. Groups are welcome and there is camping available.

DETAILS

- **Open** - All year, but phone from November to March, as we may be closed. All day
- **Number of beds** - 40: 3 x 2 : 3 x 6 : 2 x 8.
- **Booking** - Booking is essential for groups and suggested for individuals during the summer.
- **Price per night** - £12.50pp - £17.50pp. Payment by cash, credit card or cheque with bank card.
- **Public Transport** - Buses come from Portree daily, except Sunday and stop 100 metres from the hostel.
- **Directions** - GR464 720. 34 kilometres north of Portree, 5 kilometres north of Staffin on coast road. Adjacent to the Flodigarry Hotel. Landranger map 23.

CONTACT: Bryan
Flodigarry By Staffin, Isle of Skye, IV51 9HZ
Tel: (01470) 552212
hostel.flodigarry@btinternet.com www.hostelflodigarry.co.uk

PORTREE
INDEPENDENT HOSTEL SCOTLAND

Centrally situated in Portree, the capital of Skye, this hostel provides quality inexpensive self-catering accommodation with a fully equipped kitchen/dining area (continental breakfast is available on request).

Originally the island's main post office it has been converted to an independent hostel sleeping 60 in small family rooms and dormitories. All bedding is provided free. There is also a well-equipped launderette on site. Only 50 metres from the bus terminus it is an ideal base for touring the island. Within easy walking distance there is a wide variety of shops, pubs, eating places, three national banks and post office. From the hostel there are pleasant coastal and woodland walks. Bike and car hire are available locally. Portree holds an annual Folk Festival in July and the Highland Games are in August.

DETAILS

- **Open** - All year, no curfew
- **Number of beds** - 60
- **Booking** - Phone booking held to 5pm. Advance payment guarantees bed. Visa/ Mastercard/Switch accepted.
- **Price per night** - £12.00 to £13.00 per person.
- **Public Transport** - Cross island buses from the mainland to Uig pass through Portree.
- **Directions** - Situated 50 metres from the main square in the town. Approaching Portree on the A850/A87 road from the mainland the hostel is between the long stay car park and the town centre.

CONTACT: The Manager
The Old Post Office, The Green, Portree, Isle of Skye, IV51 9BT
Tel: (01478) 613737, Fax: (01478) 613758
skyehostel@yahoo.co.uk www.hostelskye.co.uk

SKYE WALKER
SCOTLAND INDEPENDENT HOSTEL

Come and visit the Skywalker Hostel on the Isle of Skye and experience a warm welcome and true Scottish hospitality.

Skyewalker Hostel is ideally situated for accessing the Cuillin mountain range and offers real value for money. Our campsite is situated at the rear of the hostel and campers are welcome to use hostel facilities.

Skyewalker Hostel hosts regular Scottish folk music sessions and it is also possible to book the whole place for special occasions such as birthdays, Munro completion parties, family get-togethers etc.

DETAILS

■ **Open** - All year, 24 hours
■ **Number of beds** - 40: (plus 10 tents)
■ **Booking** - Book early to save disappointment. On-line booking available via our website.
■ **Price per night** - From £12 per person.
■ **Public Transport** - Two local buses run each weekday. Running from Portree via Sligachan to Portnalong (hostel) and back. Citylink coaches (from the mainland and north Skye) drop off at Sligachan.
■ **Directions** - The Hostel is easy to get to once you have reached Skye. Simply get to Sligachan which lies roughly in the centre of Skye. From there take the A863 for 5 miles to the turn off for Carbost which takes you onto the B8009. Proceed through Carbost to Portnalong and you have arrived! GR 348 348.

CONTACT: Brian or Lisa
Old School, Portnalong, Isle of Skye, IV47 8SL
Tel: (01478) 640 250, Fax: (01478) 640 420
enquiries@skyewalkerhostel.com www.skyewalkerhostel.com

The Croft Bunkhouse, Bothies & Wigwams comprise 5 fully independent accommodation units and 2 wigwams on a 13-acre croft on the west coast of Skye. Advice on walks and tours, pub 500 yds. Bunkhouse - sleeps 14, built-in bunk beds, hot showers, fully equipped kitchen, washing machine, drying room, large common room and dining area. Bothy - sleeps 6 in first floor dormitory with views over crofts to Portnalong harbour. Ground floor fully equipped kitchen/living room, toilet & hot shower, drying room. Bothy Beag - sleeps 4 in a compact self-contained unit, 2 built in bunk beds in fully equipped kitchen/living room, shower and toilet. But&Ben - sleeps 4, barn to cottage conversion, all facilities. Cabin - sleeps 2 in a small self-contained kitchen/living room with bunk bed, en-suite toilet facilities. Wigwams - sleep up to 5, self contained wooden chalets with access to main hostel facilities. 4-star Visit Scotland QA Grading.

DETAILS

- **Open** - All year, no curfew
- **Number of beds** - Bunkhouse 14. Bothies 6,4 and 2. But & Ben 4.
- **Booking** - By phone : held till 6pm. Payment guarantees bed (Visa/Access).
- **Price per night** - From £10 per person. Camping £4 to £6.
- **Public Transport** - Cross island Citylink coaches from mainland pass through Sligachan. Two buses daily (excl. Sun) from Portree via Sligachan to Portnalong.
- **Directions** - GR 348 353. From Sligachan take the A863 for 4 miles then left onto B8009 for 6 miles through Carbost and Fernilea to Portnalong. Follow signs for Croft Bunkhouse & Loch Harport Gallery, it is 500yds past the pub.

CONTACT: Dave
Portnalong, Isle of Skye, IV47 8SL
Tel: (01478) 640254. Mobile 07841 206 157, Fax: (01478) 640254
skyehostel@lineone.net www.skyehostels.com

Sligachan Bunkhouse overlooks the 'Black Cuillins' and is an ideal base for exploring the magnificent mountains of Skye. Several routes up the peaks pass the Bunkhouse and the path to 'Loch Coruisk' can be seen from the verandah.

The Bunkhouse is surrounded by peaceful mountain scenery on a track easily accessible by car. It is only a 5 minute walk from the bus stop at Sligachan, which sees a regular bus service from the mainland and Portree. The Sligachan Hotel can be seen from the Bunkhouse, about a 5 minute walk, and will provide a hot meal from breakfast through to dinner. The bar is a great place to relax after a long day's trekking and has a great display of malt whiskies and we make our own real ale at the Cuillin Brewery. The Bunkhouse has 4 bedrooms, full kitchen facilities and a lounge with open fire.

DETAILS

- **Open** - March 1st to October 31st, all day
- **Number of beds** - 20
- **Booking** - Booking essential for large groups. Deposit required.
- **Price per night** - £12pp. Block bookings £220 per night. Linen Hire £3.
- **Public Transport** - Train - 1) Fort William to Mallaig, crossing by ferry to Armadale, buses to Sligachan (30m). Inverness to Kyle of Lochalsh, catch bus over Skye Bridge to Kyleakin, connect with bus to Sligachan.
- **Directions** - Inverness: A82 Invermoriston take A887 then A87 to Kyle of Lochalsh, cross Skye Bridge, continue on A87. Fort William: A830 to Mallaig, cross to Skye on ferry, take A851 to Broadford connect A87

CONTACT: Catriona Coghill
Sligachan, Isle of Skye, IV47 8SW
Tel: (01478) 650204
reservations@sligachan.co.uk www.sligachan.co.uk

DUN CAAN
HOSTEL

This warm and friendly hostel, set on the harbour front in the romantic fishing village of Kyleakin, is the ideal base for your Isle of Skye visit. Overlooking the ancient ruins of Castle Moil (once home of a Viking princess known as Saucy Mary) you'll be enjoying beautiful sea and mountain views from every room.

We provide you with a well-equipped self-catering kitchen, free teas and coffees, hot showers, a cosy common room with TV, freshly laundered bed linen, a drying room for wet outdoor clothing, lots of books to read, games to play and advice on what to see and do on this truly magnificent island. Also available at the hostel: laundry services and bike hire. Please note that this is a non smoking hostel. Local facilities include a coffee shop, bars, restaurants and a general store and post office. Let's Go recommended and STB 4-star.

DETAILS

- **Open** - 1st March to 1 Oct, all day
- **Number of beds** - 16: 2 x 6 (dorm): 1 x 4 (quad)
- **Booking** - Booking advisable in June, July and August. All major credit cards accepted. Secure on-line booking.
- **Price per night** - £13 - £15 inc. bedlinen, teas and coffees. No hidden costs.
- **Public Transport** - Kyle of Lochalsh Train station arrivals connect with Skye Bridge bus to Kyleakin(last stop Dun Caan Hostel). City Link coaches stop near to Hostel. Ferries Armadale, Kylerhea (Summer only).
- **Directions** - After crossing the Skye Bridge turn left at the roundabout for Kyleakin. Through village towards harbour and old ferry pier.

CONTACT: Terry or Laila
The Pier Rd, Kyleakin, Isle of Skye, IV41 8PL
Tel: (01599) 534087
info@skyerover.co.uk www.skyerover.co.uk

Kintail Lodge stands at the foot of the Five Sisters of Kintail, right on the shores of Loch Duich. It is an ideal base for touring Skye and the Western Highlands or for bagging some of the 30 Munroes in the area. In the grounds of the hotel there are two budget accommodation units which are especially popular with walkers, climbers and fishermen. The Wee Bunk House has a cosy room with bunks to sleep 6 people and a snack kitchen containing fridge, hot rings, kettle, microwave and basic cooking utensils. There is a shower room with a toilet and the building is wheelchair friendly. The Trekkers' Lodge sleeps 6 people in two twin rooms and two single rooms, each with their own washbasin. There are 2 shower rooms with toilets and a snack kitchen equipped as in the Wee Bunkhouse. After a long day in the hills you can unwind in the relaxed atmosphere of the traditional Kintail Bar, where good food is served and beer is plentiful. Or enjoy the lochside garden and patio. Packed lunches are available if ordered the night before.

DETAILS

- **Open** - All year, all day
- **Number of beds** - Trekkers Lodge 6: 2x2,2x1, Wee Bunkhouse 6:1x6
- **Booking** - Book by phone or email.
- **Price per night** - £13.50pp, 3+ nights £12.50pp, Sole use of Trekkers lodge £75 per night. Sole use of Wee Bunkhouse £60 per night.
- **Public Transport** - See Citylink website
- **Directions** - Kintail Lodge is situated on the A87 between Invergarry and the Skye Bridge.

CONTACT: Reception
Kintail Lodge Hotel, Glenshiel, Kyle of Lochalsh, Ross-shire, IV40 8HL
Tel: (01599) 511275
kintaillodgehotel@btinternet.com www.kintaillodgehotel.co.uk

CRAIGOWER
LODGE

Craigower Lodge is situated in its own quiet grounds in the highland village of Newtonmore within the Cairngorms National Park. Our central Highlands location makes Craigower the ideal base for outdoor activities. Within easy reach of Craigower we have the rivers Spey, Findhorn, Roy and Spean. For the Mountaineer we are halfway between The Northern Corries and Creag Meagaidh. Hillwalkers have an abundance of Munros nearby, for skiers and snowboarders, Cairngorm Mountain is nearby and Nevis Range within an hour. For the cyclist we have Sustrans route 7 coming through the village and the all new Wolftrax downhill trails at Laggan are a must.

Craigower Lodge welcomes individuals, families, groups and clubs to this magnificent part of Scotland where we can quite literally say its all on our doorstep. The Lodge is extensively renovated to STB 3* hostel status and provides self-catering and catered accommodation for up to 68 people. Instruction, guiding and activity breaks available all year.

DETAILS

- **Open** - All year, 8 till late
- **Number of beds** - 68
- **Booking** - Essential, by phone or email
- **Price per night** - £13.00 per person
- **Public Transport** - Newtonmore Train Station ¼ mile. Buses from Inverness, Glasgow and Edinburgh.
- **Directions** - From the main street in Newtonmore, turn into Curleys Lane next to the Co-op, take 1st right after 50m and follow lane around for 50m.

CONTACT:
Golf Course Road, Newtonmore, Inverness-shire, PH20 1AT
Tel: (01540) 673319, Fax: (01540) 673390
info@activeoutdoorpursuits.com www.craigowerlodge.com

HAPPY DAYS
HOSTEL

Happy Days Hostel in the centre of Kingussie has a variety of accommodation with rooms sleeping 2, 4 and 6 all offering en-suite facilities, central heating and individual reading lights. There is also a fully equipped room for our disabled guests. Bedding is included in the price and all rooms are of very high standard. Within the premises there are a range of facilities to help ensure your holiday is a happy one. A drying room and laundry facilities are available on site. A TV lounge and internet access are located on the ground floor. There is a fully eqipped self-catering kitchen and the Happy Days fish and chip shop and restaurant is just next door.

The Harkai family who have over 30 years experience in local tourism offer a warm welcome and at Happy Days we are more than happy to help the planning of your holiday, provide packed lunches and organise local excursions. Four star VisitScotland approved.

DETAILS

- ■ **Open** - All year, 24 hours
- ■ **Number of beds** - 32:
- ■ **Booking** - Advisable, essential for disabled
- ■ **Price per night** - From £13.50pp (dorm) and £15pp (double/twin). We offer special rates for families and discounts for groups.
- ■ **Public Transport** - Kingussie has a train station and Citylink bus-stop.
- ■ **Directions** - Kingussie is 12 miles south of Aviemore. The hostel is also on the High Street, within minutes of all the facilities in the village.

CONTACT: Reception
65 High Street, Kingussie, Inverness-shire, PH21 1HX
Tel: 01540 661175
info@cairngormhighlandhostel.com www.cairngormhighlandhostel.com

Nestling in the wooded valley of Strathspey beneath the often snow covered granite mass of the Cairngorm plateau, is the village of Aviemore. Local attractions include the Cairngorm funicular railway, Strathspey steam railway, fishing in the River Spey (or Rothiemurcus fish farm if you are hungry), dog sledding, off road driving, swimming pools, golf courses, clay pigeon shooting, mountain bike trails and pony trekking.

Aviemore Bunkhouse is the place to stay for friendly, cheap self-catering accommodation in Aviemore. We offer en-suite accommodation comprising bunk and family rooms, for mountaineers, cyclists, walkers, individuals, groups, families and tourists travelling towards Skye, Loch Ness,and Orkney or as a base to explore the Cairngorms National Park.

DETAILS

- **Open** - All year, 24 hours
- **Number of beds** - 44: 3 x family (4), 4 x 6 bunk, 1 x 8 bunk
- **Booking** - Advance booking required with a deposit.
- **Price per night** - From £15 pp.
- **Public Transport** - Aviemore train station and bus stop for Citylink and National Express coaches are 10 minutes walk from the hostel.
- **Directions** - GR 894117, O.S. Landranger 35/36. Arriving in Aviemore from A9 take right turn at junction signposted Cairngorms. Dalfaber Road is next left.

CONTACT:
By the Old Bridge Inn, Dalfaber Road, Aviemore, PH22 1PU
Tel: (01479) 811181
sales@aviemore-bunkhouse.com www.aviemore-bunkhouse.com

NETHY STATION

SCOTLAND

Sharing a car park with the Speyside Way and just yards from the river, this converted station offers all that a group could expect from a bunkhouse. It is well-equipped; fully central heated and has two public areas. Most rooms have triple bunks. We now have 2 bunk rooms with outside access and no store room. We call it Narnia, as you can reach them through a wardrobe! Whether you self-cater or we cook for you as a group you will have access to the kitchen at all times. We never ask people to share the building so you may sleep, walk, ski, board, hike, ride, fish etc…. at your own convenience!

The station is only 200 yards from the centre of Nethy Bridge with its shop, butcher, pubs and interpretive centre and half way between two wintersports areas. Dogs are welcome but please do not let them sleep on the beds!

DETAILS

- **Open** - All year, anytime
- **Number of beds** - 24: 2 x 9 :3 x 2.
- **Booking** - Essential (with deposit)
- **Price per night** - £11pp. Minimum of 6 people.
- **Public Transport** - Take train or Citylink coach to Aviemore. Local buses are available from Aviemore to Nethy Bridge Post Office, phone (01479) 811566.
- **Directions** - GR 002 207.   Hostel is adjacent to the Speyside Way. From the B970, with post office on your right, go over the bridge and turn left immediately. Past the butcher turn second right.

CONTACT: Patricia or Richard
Nethy Bridge, PH25 3DS
Tel: (01479) 821370
info@nethy.org www.nethy.org

SLOCHD MHOR
LODGE
SCOTLAND

Slochd Mhor Lodge is perfectly situated in the spectacular Strathspey in the Cairngorm National Park and halfway between the villages of Carrbridge and Tomatin. The Lodge is on an 'off road' section of the No 7 Sustrans cycle route and surrounded by hills and forests. This is also perfect walking country and in winter there are nordic ski trails from the doorstep. All other outdoor pursuits are within easy reach. Slochd Mhor Lodge offers a genuine welcome in warm cosy surroundings. Fully equipped kitchen with wood burning stove and a spacious dining area together with large lounge/lecture room with woodburner. Other facilities include a drying room and laundry facilities, some en-suite rooms, a room suitable for wheel-chair user, an on-site cycle shop/workshop, MT bike hire, and in winter nordic ski hire. We have basic provisions for sale and there is an outside seating and BBQ area. Ample parking. Visit Scotland 4 star graded. Silver Green Business Award. Cyclists Welcome and Walkers Welcome members.

DETAILS

- **Open** - All year, 24 hours
- **Number of beds** - 28: 1x10 : 1x6 : 2x5 : 1x2
- **Booking** - Booking recommended
- **Price per night** - From £15.00pp. Sole use rates available.
- **Public Transport** - Nearest bus and train station; Carrbridge (4miles). City Link London/Edinburgh and Glasgow/Inverness stop at Carrbridge.
- **Directions** - From south on A9, after mileage board 'Inverness 23' travel 1.5 miles north, take first opening on left marked 'Slochd'. Then first opening on right (¼ mile)

CONTACT: Liz or Ian
Slochd, Carrbridge, Inverness-shire, PH23 3AY
Tel: (01479) 841666
Slochd666@aol.com www.slochd.co.uk

RATTRAY HEAD
ECO-HOSTEL

Rattray Head Eco-Hostel is a former lighthouse shore station among huge dunes on an isolated 11 mile long beach. Come and relax in this gorgeous most easterly part of mainland Scotland, and enjoy one of its driest, sunniest, midge-free areas. The 1892 granite building has been renovated to form a modern, non-smoking, dog-friendly coastal retreat. The hostel has a self-catering kitchen, a double bedroom, and three bunkrooms with four beds in each. It is part of the SIH network and has Visit Scotland 2-star grading. 3 stars, Cyclists Welcome, Walkers Welcome, and Green Business awards are all pending. The North Sea Cycle Route (Sustrans 1) is 17 miles inland and passes through historic Aberdeenshire with stone circles, castle ruins and golf courses.

DETAILS

- **Open** - All year, phone in winter,, Check-in 4–8pm, check-out 11am. No curfew.
- **Number of beds** - 14: 1x2, 3x4
- **Booking** - Photo ID is essential to ensure guest security. Booking is available with first night as deposit.
- **Price per night** - £12 which includes tea, coffee, squash, bedding.
- **Public Transport** - Airport, coach and train stations at Aberdeen (43 miles). Buses 260, 263 run frequently between Aberdeen and Peterhead. Bus 269 runs hourly between Peterhead and Fraserburgh. Taxi from Peterhead about £17.
- **Directions** - NK103577 Rattray is signed from the A90 Peterhead to Fraserburgh road. The hostel is at the end of the lane near the lighthouse, about 3 miles from the A90.

CONTACT: Rob and Val
Lighthouse Cottages, Rattray Head, Peterhead, Aberdeenshire, AB42 3HA
Tel: (01346) 532236
hostel@rattrayhead.net www.rattrayhead.net/hostel

The old Railway Station at Ballindalloch at the junction of the Rivers Spey and Avon provides an excellent base for white water canoeing, walking and cycling, with the Speyside Way passing the door and access to the river just 100 yards away. The hostel sleeps 16 people in rooms of 2 x 4, 1 x 6 and 1 x 2 with 2 shower/bath rooms. There is a large lounge with a wood burning stove, a large kitchen and drying area with the entrance area designed as a drying room. This is a non-smoking hostel for self-catering only. The Post Office, shop and petrol are available 1 mile away. In winter the hostel is available for lets with skiing at the Lecht just 16 miles away. The hostel is unmanned. Keys must be collected from Loch Insh Watersports Centre before travelling to Ballindalloch Hostel.

DETAILS

■ **Open** - All year, after 4pm
■ **Number of beds** - 16: 1 x 6 : 2 x 4 : 1 x 2
■ **Booking** - Required with 25% deposit. Full payment 4 weeks before arrival plus £100 security deposit, refunded 1 week after departure less electricity.
■ **Price per night** - £8 per person with minimum 6 persons
■ **Public Transport** - Trains at Aviemore. Buses to Grantown pass Cragganmore Rd
■ **Directions** - From the south and north travel to Grantown on Spey taking A95 towards Elgin and follow for approx 12 miles. As you drop down towards the Avon River turn left at sign for Cragganmore and Speyside Way. Hostel is opposite telephone kiosk. From north east take road to Aberlour and follow A95 towards Grantown for 12 miles. Half mile after the Ballindalloch Post Office turn right at sign for Cragganmore, then as above.

CONTACT:
SpeysideWay, Ballindalloch, AB37 9AB
Tel: (01540) 651272
office@lochinsh.com www.lochinsh.com

LOCHNESS
BACKPACKERS LODGE SCOTLAND

Loch Ness Backpackers is a warm and friendly little Hostel with a relaxed atmosphere, good music and no curfew. It has grown from an 18th-century farm cottage and barn and provides a warm open fire to greet you on cold nights. The house forms the main area of the Hostel with reception, lounges, dining room, kitchen and toilets/showers on the ground floor, and two dormitories and one double room in the upstairs area. A converted barn (the bunkhouse) contains four more dormitories, toilets/showers and a kitchen/dining area. There is also a great BBQ area, garden & car park.

Loch Ness Backpackers is within easy walking distance of Loch Ness, Urquhart Castle, three pubs, restaurants, a supermarket, a fish & chip shop, post office, bank, gift shops and bus stops. A perfect location for activity or relaxation amongst spectacular scenery. Horse riding, fishing on the Loch and mountain biking can all be arranged locally (great bikes available for hire).

DETAILS

- **Open** - All year, all day
- **Number of beds** - House 16: Bunkhouse 24: (1x2, 2 x family room, 6 x dorms).
- **Booking** - Check availability on website or by phone.
- **Price per night** - From £14 per person.
- **Public Transport** - Nearest trains at Inverness. Rapsons, Megabus and Citylink buses all pass close to the hostel.
- **Directions** - Near the A82 Inverness to Fort William road. Turn off is next to the stone bridge in Lewiston near the Smiddy pub.

CONTACT: Wendy and Neil MacIntosh
Coiltie Farm House, East Lewiston, Drumnadrochit, Inverness, IV63 6UJ
Tel: (01456) 450807
info@lochness-backpackers.com   www.lochness-backpackers.com

MORAG'S
LODGE

Morag's Lodge is set in wooded grounds just minutes walk from the centre of Fort Augustus. The village, situated at the southern end of Loch Ness, is ideally located for hill walking, cycling and kayaking. It's an ideal stop on The Great Glen Way. The hostel offers the best quality budget accommodation for backpackers' and independent travellers. Rooms hold a maximum of six people in huge comfy beds and most have en-suite facilities. There are private rooms available including doubles. You can relax in the sun lounge, watch the television with a selection of great Scottish movies, or enjoy a drink beside the open fire in the bar. A drying room is also available. We offer a well equipped self-catering kitchen and dining room. Breakfast and dinner are available on request (for a modest charge). Parking is available in the hostel grounds. The hostel graded 4 stars by VisitScotland.

DETAILS

- **Open** - All year, all day. Check-in from 5pm(earlier by arrangement)
- **Number of beds** - 85: 6x6, 1x5, 8x4, 4x3
- **Booking** - Booking recommended. Credit card details or cheque required to confirm.
- **Price per night** - £16.50 pp bunk. £45 double or twin.
- **Public Transport** - Bus stop for Fort William and Inverness 300 mtrs from Morag's Lodge.
- **Directions** - From Inverness, arrive at Fort Augustus, turn first right up Bunoich Brae. Morag's Lodge 100mtrs on left. From Fort William, go through village past petrol station and car park. Take next left up Bunoich Brae.

CONTACT: Rebecca
Bunoich Brae, Fort Augustus, Inverness-shire, PH32 4DG
Tel: (01320) 366289
info@moragslodge.com www.moragslodge.com

BCC LOCHNESS
HOSTEL

BCC Lochness Hostel is a top quality purpose-built hostel (newly built in 2007) with superb facilities. All rooms are en-suite and offer the very latest in facilities for the discerning traveller. It lies in the heart of one of Scotland's most stunning glens, enabling you to escape from the routine of modern life.
This is an excellent base from which you can explore the world famous Loch Ness, Urquhart Castle, Glen Affric (National Nature Reserve) and Glen Strathfarrer which are renowned for their stunning beauty and variety of wildlife. Yet you're only 20 mins drive from the Historic city of Inverness. From the hostel there are 6 golf courses all within 30 minutes drive, also it is ideally placed for hill walking, mountain biking, cycling, fishing and horse riding. BCC Lochness Hostel is an ideal stop off point for those travelling to Skye and the Outer Hebridies. The hostel is situated near the main bus route and is within easy walking distance of the nearby tearoom/shop.

DETAILS

- **Open** - All year, all day
- **Number of beds** - 30: 5 x 6/4
- **Booking** - Book by phone or email.
- **Price per night** - From £12 per person. From £30 for twin room.
- **Public Transport** - Buses from Inverness, Drumnadrochit and Fort William stop nearby.
- **Directions** - We are midway between Drumnadrochit and Cannich on the A381 which leads to Glen Affric National Nature Reserve.

CONTACT: Donald MacLean
Bearnock, Glen Urquhart, Drumnadrochit, Inverness-shire, IV63 6TN
Tel: (01463) 230 218, Fax: 0778060945
info@bcclochness.co.uk www.bcclochnesshostel.co.uk

Gerrys Hostel is situated in an excellent mountaineering and wilderness area on the most scenic railway in Britain.

The photo shows the hostel, looking North West.

The hostel has a comfortable common room with log fire and library.

Come and go as you please. No smoking inside or out.

Accommodation for non-smokers.

PLEASE CONTACT THIS HOSTEL BY PHONE OR POST.

DETAILS

- **Open** - All year (check by phone), book in 5pm to 8.30pm. Later by arrangement only.
- **Number of beds** - 20: 1 x 10 : 2 x 5. Double and twin also.
- **Booking** - Prepay to secure bed, or phone.
- **Price per night** - From £12pp, discount for long stay large groups.
- **Public Transport** - Achnashellach Station is 4km west of the hostel. Nearest Citylink coaches drop off at Inverness. Local Bus between Inverness and Lochcarron: Wednesday and Saturday 3pm.
- **Directions** - GR 037 493. 95 miles north of Fort William, 50 miles west of Inverness on A890.

CONTACT: Gerry Howkins
Craig, Achnashellach, Strathcarron, Wester-Ross, Scotland, IV54 8YU
Tel: (01520) 766232
sam@backpackerspress.com www.gerryshostel-achnashellach.co.uk

Ledgowan Lodge is a traditional country house hotel with cosy log fires, original features and friendly bar open to residents and non-residents. The bunkhouse is adjacent to the hotel and bunkhouse guests have full use of the hotels` facilities. Ledgowan Lodge is perfectly situated for the hill walker, climber or anyone wanting low cost basic overnight accommodation. It is within easy driving distance of the Torridon and Fannich Mountain ranges and Fionn Bheinn Mountain is on the door step. The lodge sleeps twelve adults in six separate rooms, each with a set of bunk beds, wash hand basin, chest of drawers and thermostatically controlled heating. There is a one off charge for providing towels and linen. The two bathrooms contain large baths with shower facilities and a toilet. There are basic cooking facilities and a refrigerator for self catering, but it is recommended that guests socialise within the hotel where the welcome provides a restaurant, bar meals, real fires and lively conversation. There is ample car parking in the grounds and an excellent drying room within the hotel. Camping available.

DETAILS

- **Open** - All year, all day
- **Number of beds** - 12: 6 x 2
- **Booking** - Book by phone or email
- **Price per night** - £12pp. £24 for sole use of 2 bed bunkroom. Linen £5 (one off charge). Camper vans and tents (with use of bunkhouse) £5pp.
- **Public Transport** - Achnasheen Station is one mile from the bunkhouse.
- **Directions** - On the A890, 1 mile south of Achnasheen

CONTACT: Reception
Legowan Lodge Hotel, Achnasheen, Ross-shire,Scottish Highlands IV22 2EJ
Tel: (01445) 720252
info@ledgowanlodge.co.uk www.ledgowanlodge.co.uk

Kinlochewe Bunkhouse is part of the Kinlochewe Hotel. The accommodation consists of one dormitory with 12 bunks and individual lockers for each bunk. There are central heating, hot showers, toilets, drying room and a well equipped kitchen. The Bunkhouse is ideally placed for walking and climbing in the Torridon Mountains and the many Munros that they have to offer, indeed there are over 20 Munros within 20 miles of Kinlochewe.

The Hotel Bar is open all the year round, and serves excellent home-made food at affordable prices and it also has a selection of real ales and 50 malt whiskies. We provide pillow and pillow case but ask that you bring your own sleeping bags and towels (and a padlock for the locker). For cyclists we are able to provide secure housing for bicycles.

DETAILS

- **Open** - All year, 8am - midnight
- **Number of beds** - 12
- **Booking** - Essential for groups, deposit required. Advisable for individuals.
- **Price per night** - £10 per person.
- **Public Transport** - Nearest train station is in Achnasheen (10 miles away). Trains run three times a day and the postbus meets the lunchtime train and also comes to Kinlochewe. On Tuesdays, Thursdays and Fridays the 5pm Westerbus from Inverness to Gairloch stops outside the hostel around 6.45pm.
- **Directions** - Kinlochewe is situated at the junction of the A832 Garve to Gairloch road and the A896 north from Torridon.

CONTACT: Andrew and Gail Staddon
Kinlochewe by Achnasheen, Wester Ross, IV22 2PA
Tel: (01445) 760253
bookings@kinlochewehotel.co.uk www.kinlochewehotel.co.uk

BLACK ROCK
BUNKHOUSE

Situated in beautiful Glenglass, sheltered by Ben Wyvis, this comfortable bunkhouse is named after the breathtaking Black Rock Gorge. It is an ideal base for touring the highlands and seeing wildlife, including seals in the Cromarty Firth and dolphins at Cromarty. Highland Games are held throughout the area. It is sited at the eastern end of a hikers' route across Scotland and on the Lands End to John O'Groats route for walkers and cyclists. The village has a general shop, PO, bus service and an inn (serving good bar meals and breakfasts) 250m away. Available to groups or individuals, accommodation is in four rooms of four and one room for 1. Blankets are available and sheet sleeping bags can be hired. There is a self-catering kitchen and dining area with TV, showers and launderette facilities. There is also a camping ground. All areas of the bunkhouse are easily accessible by wheelchair and suitable for the disabled.

DETAILS

- **Open** - April 1st to October 31st, 24hr access. New arrivals 9am - 9pm
- **Number of beds** - 17 : 4 x 4, 1 x 1
- **Booking** - Not always essential. Deposit of 1 night's fee to secure booking.
- **Price per night** - £12- £14 per person. 10% off for groups of 8+.
- **Public Transport** - Nearest train station Dingwall (6 miles) Nearest Citylink drop off Inverness (15 miles). There are local buses hourly.
- **Directions** - Follow A9 north from Inverness, 2 miles north of Cromarty Firth bridge take left turn for Evanton. Follow camping signs.

CONTACT: Lillian
Evanton, Dingwall, Ross-shire, IV16 9UN
Tel: (01349) 830917
enquires@blackrockscotland.co.uk www.blackrockscotland.co.uk

Stay on a first class train in Rogart in the heart of the Highlands halfway between Inverness and John O'Groats. The two railway carriages have been tastefully converted, with many original features. Each sleeps 8, with two beds per room, and has a kitchen, dining room, sitting room and two showers and toilets. They are heated and non-smoking. All bedding is included. We also have a cosy showman's wagon which sleeps two. Three trains per day in each direction serve this small crofting community which has a shop, post office and pub with restaurant. Glenmorangie and Clynelish distilleries, Dunrobin Castle and Helmsdale's Heritage Centre are easy to reach by train or car. See the silver salmon leap at Lairg and the seabirds and seals in Loch Fleet. Or just enjoy the peace of Rogart.

The climate is good and the midges are less prevalent than in the west! Families welcome. Free use of bikes for guests.

DETAILS

- **Open** - March to November inclusive, 24 hours
- **Number of beds** - 24: 8 x 2 : 1 x 4 : 1 x 2.
- **Booking** - Booking is not essential.
- **Price per night** - £12 per person, 12yrs and under £8 per person. (10% discount if you arrive by bike or train).
- **Public Transport** - Wick to Inverness trains stop at the door.
- **Directions** - We are at the railway station, 4 miles from the A9 trunk road, 54 miles north of Inverness.

CONTACT: Kate or Frank
Rogart Station, Sutherland, Highlands, IV28 3XA
Tel: (01408) 641343 Mobile/Text 07833 641226
kate@sleeperzzz.com www.sleeperzzz.com

HELMSDALE
HOSTEL

This small friendly hostel was upgraded for 2006. Although now privately run, it is affiliated to the SYHA and a member of VisitScotland (4 Stars). Set in the small scenic village of Helmsdale, halfway between Inverness and John O'Groats, it is ideal for cycling, coastal walks, hill walks and birdwatching. Backpackers, birdwatchers and families are welcome. Accommodation (all with en-suite showers):1 female dorm with 8-10 beds. 1 male dorm with 8-10 beds. 2 family bedrooms (sleep 4) with a double bed and bunks.

FACILITIES Bed linen provided, towel hire available, fully equipped kitchen, large dining area, comfortable lounge area, solid fuel heating, drying cupboard, internet access, cycle shed, garden / barbecue area.

4 star Scottish Tourist Board graded.

DETAILS

- **Open** - All year, not open during the day.
- **Number of beds** - 24: 2x8, 2x4
- **Booking** - Book in advance
- **Price per night** - Dorm £15pp, Family room for 4 £60.
- **Public Transport** - Helmsdale is served by the City Link bus service and is on the railway line from Inverness to Thurso.
- **Directions** - The hostel is situated on the corner of the A9 and Old Caithness Road (park in Rockview Place). Arriving by bus: Walk up the slope for 100 metres. The Hostel is after the old church on your left. (200 metres). Arriving by train: Cross over the old bridge, turn right along Dunrobin Street, then left up Stafford Street. Hostel is at the top of the slope on the left (half a mile).

CONTACT: Irene Drummond
Stafford Street, Helmsdale, Sutherland, KW8 6JR
Tel: (01431) 821636 or 07971 516287
Irene.Drummond@btinternet.com www.helmsdalehostel.co.uk

Sail Mhor Croft is a small rural hostel which is situated at Dundonnell on the shores of Little Loch Broom. The mountain range of An Teallach, which has the reputation of being one of the finest ridge walks in Great Britain, is right on our doorstep and the area is a haven for walkers of all experience as well as for photographers. Whether you wish to climb the summits, walk along the loch side, visit a beautiful sandy beach or just soak up the tranquillity of the area, you know the scenery cannot be beaten anywhere in the country.

The hostel offers accommodation for up to 16 persons in three dorms which are fitted with anti-midge screens. Guests have a choice of using our self-catering facilities or we can provide a full breakfast. It is advisable to ring in advance in order to book yourself a bed, the next self-catering hostel is many miles away.

DETAILS

- **Open** - All year, except Xmas, New Year and January, flexible
- **Number of beds** - 16:- 2 x 4 : 1 x 8
- **Booking** - Always phone in advance. Groups should book as soon as possible.
- **Price per night** - £12 - £12.50 per person, self-catering. £160 sole use.
- **Public Transport** - Nearest train station is Inverness (60 miles). Nearest City Link bus drop off is Braemore Junction (15 miles). Wester bus passes the hostel 3 times a week; Mon, Wed and Sat., it also provides a service between Gairloch and Ullapool on Thursday afternoon.
- **Directions** - GR 064 893 (sheet 19) 1.5 miles west of Dundonnell Hotel on A832.

CONTACT: Dave or Lynda
Camusnagaul, Dundonnell, Ross-shire, IV23 2QT
Tel: (01854) 633224
dave.lynda@sailmhor.co.uk www.sailmhor.co.uk

BADRALLACH
BOTHY

On the tranquil shores of Little Loch Broom overlooking An Teallach, one of Scotland's finest mountain ranges, Badrallach Bothy and Camp Site with its welcoming traditional buildings offers a fine base for walking and climbing in the hills of Wester Ross, Caithness and Sutherland. You can fish in the rivers, hill lochs and sea, or simply watch the flora and fauna including many orchids, golden eagles, otters, porpoises, pine martens, deer and wild goats. Guests often sit around the peat stove in the gas light (there is now electric here too) and discuss life over a dram or two. Hot showers, spotless sanitary accommodation (STB graded 4 star excellent), an unbelievable price (thanks to S.N.H), and the total peace makes our Bothy and camp site (12 tents only) one that visitors return to year after year. We also have a caravan, 4 star cottage and dinner, b&b. Hire canoes, kites, bikes, boats and blokarts.

DETAILS

- **Open** - All year, all times
- **Number of beds** - 12 plus bedspaces (Alpine style platforms). We have had 20 at a squeeze, mats & sleeping bags required.
- **Booking** - Recommended
- **Price per night** - £5 pp £1.50 per vehicle. £60 sole use (£100 Xmas & New year).
- **Public Transport** - Westerbus (01445 712255) operate Mon/Wed/Sat between Inverness/Gairloch and drop at road end Dundonnell, 7 miles from hostel. Pick-up can be arranged.
- **Directions** - GR 065 915 Located on the shore of Little Loch Broom 7 miles along a single track road off the A832, one mile east of the Dundonnell Hotel.

CONTACT: Mr/Mrs Stott,
Croft No 9, Badrallach, Dundonnell, Ross-shire IV23 2QP
Tel: (01854) 633281
mail@badrallach.com www.badrallach.com

Perched on the cliff tops 12 miles north of Gairloch, Rua Reidh Lighthouse must have one of the most dramatic settings of all the Scottish Hostels. The lighthouse still beams out its light over the Minch to the Outer Isles and Skye, but since its automation the adjoining house, no longer needed for keepers, has been converted into a comfortable independent hostel. The centrally heated house has two sitting rooms with log fires, a self-catering kitchen, a drying room, three private rooms and four dorms (each sleeping four), some rooms with en-suite shower. Meals are available from the main dining room and guided walking and rock sports sessions are also offered. The area of the lighthouse is unspoiled and makes a perfect place to watch for whales, dolphins etc.
For an away from it all experience travel to the 'edge of the world' and Rua Reidh Lighthouse.

DETAILS

- **Open** - All year (except last 3 weeks in Jan), 9am - 11pm
- **Number of beds** - 26: 3 x 4; 2 x 3; 4 x 2
- **Booking** - Pre-booking advisable.
- **Price per night** - From £10pp (dorm) to £20pp (private with en-suite facilities)
- **Public Transport** - Nearest train station Achnasheen (40 miles). Nearest Citylink coaches Inverness (80 miles). Westerbus (01445) 712255 and Scotbus run a daily connection between Inverness/Gairloch (12 miles from hostel).
- **Directions** - From Gairloch take the road signed Big Sands and Melvaig, follow this road for 12 miles to the lighthouse. The last 3 miles is a private road with 20mph limit.

CONTACT:
Melvaig, Gairloch, IV21 2EA
Tel: (01445) 771263
ruareidh@tiscali.co.uk www.ruareidh.co.uk

INCHNADAMPH LODGE

Situated at the heart of the dramatic Assynt mountains, Inchnadamph Lodge has been tastefully converted to provide luxury hostel accommodation at a budget price. Twin, family and dormitory (4-8 people) rooms are available and a continental-style breakfast is included. We have a large self-catering kitchen, a lounge and a dining room (both with real fires), and a games room. Packed lunches are available on request and bar meals are served at the Inchnadamph Hotel. At the foot of Ben More Assynt, and overlooking Loch Assynt, you are free to explore one of the wildest areas in the Highlands. Mountains can be climbed from our door! The Inchnadamph Nature Reserve is right by us - home to a wide diversity of birds, plants, animals and full of exciting geological features. Nearby lochs are popular for trout fly fishing.
Details and photos on our website.

DETAILS

- **Open** - All year - phone November-March inclusive, 24 hours
- **Number of beds** - 38: 8x2 : 7x2 : 4x2 (dormitory) 12 (twin/double)
- **Booking** - Advised, required Nov-March.
- **Price per night** - £14.00-£16.00 (dormitory) £19.00-£22.50 (twin room) inc continental breakfast and linen. Group discounts.
- **Public Transport** - Transport is available to our door from Inverness 6 days a week, either by train to Lairg and then postbus, or by coach to Ullapool and minibus to Inchnadamph. Times vary - please call us for details.
- **Directions** - Inchnadamph is 25 miles north of Ullapool on the Lochinver/Durness road. The lodge is the big white building across the river from the hotel.

CONTACT: Chris
Inchnadamph, Assynt, Nr Lochinver, Sutherland, IV27 4HL
Tel: (01571) 822218, Fax: (01571) 822232
info@inch-lodge.co.uk www.inch-lodge.co.uk

ULLAPOOL
TOURIST HOSTEL

THINGS HAPPEN IN ULLAPOOL !!! Ullapool boasts a number of music friendly pubs and during the summer season there is music in the village most nights. This bustling fishing port is one of the most beautiful villages in Scotland surrounded by sea and stunning mountainous country. A hill walkers paradise.Ullapool also has the main ferry link to Stornoway in the Western Isles. Ullapool Tourist Hostel is family run and facilities include central heating, drying room, multi fuel stove in lounge, TV, radio, laundry facilities, internet access x 4 terminals @ £2 per hour and bike hire. Shared rooms, en-suite rooms, double rooms and a self-catering cottage are all available. STB 4 star Hostel. Quote from the Lonely Planet:-" One of the best backpackers in Northern Scotland"

DETAILS

- **Open** - All year, all day
- **Number of beds** - 22: 1x6, 4x4
- **Booking** - Essential in high season, phone bookings require credit card as guarantee. Cheque deposit required + full payment 21 days before arrival for groups.
- **Price per night** - £15 - £16 per person
- **Public Transport** - Trains at Garve (30 miles) and Inverness. Ferry to/from Stornoway. Bus to/from Inverness. Buses run to meet the ferry.
- **Directions** - By car: drive along shore street keeping the sea on your left. Drive past the pier, take the next right into West Lane and drive to the T-junction. At the T-junction the building on your right is the hostel. On Foot: All buses stop on the pier, from the pier walk up the hill with the Seaforth Inn on your left, turn left into West Argyle Street. The Hostel is the last building on the left. Approx 3 minute walk.

CONTACT: Richard.
West House, West Argyle Street, Ullapool, Ross-shire Scotland IV26 2TY
Tel: (01854) 613126
r.lindsay@btinternet.com www.scotpackers-hostels.co.uk

HOSTEL AND HOUSE SCOTLAND

Stromness - a small friendly town where both the hostel and house are centrally situated in Victoria Street near shops, pubs, restaurants, Post Office, bank. museum and the Pier Art Centre. An ideal base for the tourist, as it is also within walking/cycling distance, to see the wildlife, high cliffs, beaches, beautiful sunsets, the historical sites of Skara Brae, Standing Stones, the Palace and Brough of Birsay etc., and for fishing, golfing, bowling, surfing, to dive on the many wrecks in Scapa Flow, or (for the beginner) to book a Scuba-dive course. Free internet access available. Hostel - very popular with all ages, is praised for its cosy well equipped kitchen, seating all guests at one sitting. In the evenings, the big table is a great gathering place and many enjoyable times have been had. Sleeps 14. House - self-catering, has kitchen, sitting room, en-suite bedrooms and laundry room. Let as a whole or per room. Sleeps 12-14

DETAILS

■ **Open** - All year, all day. No curfew, keys provided.
■ **Number of beds** - Hostel 14: 3 x 1 :2 x 2 : 1 x 3: 1 x 4. House 12-14:
■ **Booking** - Booking advisable during March to October. Pre-paid bookings secure (send sae for receipt). Telephone bookings kept only for limited time.
■ **Price per night** - From £11(inc linen), special rate for groups.
■ **Public Transport** - Train or bus to Thurso, bus 2 miles to Scrabster then boat to Stromness. Alternatively from Gills Bay to St Margarets Hope by boat or John O'Groats by boat to Burwick then bus to Stromness via Kirkwall.
■ **Directions** - Just two minutes along street from harbour in Stromness, next to Royal Hotel.

CONTACT: Sylvia Brown
Stromness, Orkney, KW16 3BS
Tel: (01856) 850661
info@brownshostel.co.uk www.brownsaccommodation.co.uk

SCOTLAND

THE HOY CENTRE

SCOTLAND

Surrounded by magnificent scenery the Hoy Centre is ideally situated for a peaceful and relaxing holiday. The centre was completely refurbished in 2005 and offers high quality, four star accommodation. All rooms are en-suite (with shower) and each room has twin beds and a bunk bed, seats, lockers and all bedding. One room is equipped for wheelchair access. There is a well equipped kitchen, comfortable lounge area with TV and a separate spacious dining hall. Underfloor heating ensures a comfortable temperature. Washing and drying facilities are also available. Much of North Hoy is owned and managed by the RSPB. The reserve comprises 3,500 ha of upland heath and cliffs with a large variety of birds. Off the west coast is The Old Man of Hoy, a 137m sea stack, perhaps Orkney's most famous landmark and a great place to see puffins. The dramatic hills of North Hoy and stunning sea cliffs offer excellent walking. The nearest shop is 16km away.

DETAILS

■ **Open** - All year, all day
■ **Number of beds** - 32: 8x4
■ **Booking** - Preferred. Groups send 25% deposit, balance 28 days prior to arrival
■ **Price per night** - £12.60pp, £9.70 (juniors), £3.15 (under 3's). Family room (4 beds) £30.45. Private rms:- 2 adults £34.65, 3 adults £40.95, 4 adults £50.40. Sole use £269, £1344 a week.
■ **Public Transport** - Short walk from Moaness Pier (pedestrian ferry from Stromness). Ferry details www.orkneyferries.co.uk (01856 872044).
■ **Directions** - Car ferry arrives from Houton to Lyness, which is 16km from centre.

CONTACT:
The Hoy Centre, Hoy, Orkney, KW16 3NJ
Tel: (01856) 873535 ext 2404
recreation@orkney.gov.uk

OBSERVATORY
HOSTEL

The North Ronaldsay Bird Observatory is situated at the south west corner of the island with outstanding views and an adjacent shell sand beach. Seals and the unique seaweed-eating sheep are abundant along the coast which skirts the 34 acres of croft managed by the observatory. The observatory sees spectacular bird migration through the island in Spring and Autumn. It offers a special attraction for those interested in wildlife, but welcomes all visitors. The Observatory Hostel consists of three dormitories and a self-catering kitchen in a converted barn and byre of the croft. The Byre sleeps four in two bunks and has en-suite washing, shower and toilet facilities. It is particularly suitable for family use. The Barn also sleeps four and shares facilities with the Bøl which has a single bunk sleeping two. Adjacent is the Observatory Guest House (3 star) which has a lounge bar and meals which are available to hostellers.

DETAILS

- **Open** - All year, 24 hours, open all day, no curfews.
- **Number of beds** - 10 : 2x4, 1x2 House:8 :2x4 and private rooms
- **Booking** - Advance booking essential
- **Price per night** - Hostel £10-£12, Guest House dorm £21-£27 half board. Guest House private rooms £36-£45 half board
- **Public Transport** - Loganair flights from Kirkwall (Orkney) leave daily. Ferry from Kirkwall on Fridays (subject to tides and weather). Small boats may be chartered. Orkney can be reached by vehicle ferries from Aberdeen, Thurso (Scrabster) and Gill's Bay, and a passenger summer service from John O'Groats.
- **Directions** - Situated at the south west corner of the island

CONTACT: Duty Warden
NRBO, North Ronaldsay, Orkney Islands, KW17 2BE
Tel: (01857) 633200, Fax: (01857) 633207
bookings@nrbo.prestel.co.uk www.nrbo.f2s.com

Gardiesfauld Hostel is on Unst, the most northerly of the Shetland Isles. The island has spectacular cliffs, sculpted by the Atlantic Ocean on the west and secluded, golden, sandy beaches on the east with rocky outcrops where seals and otters appear. The Gulf Stream provides a moderate climate and the clean peaceful setting offers an invigorating chance to relax in a community where crime is unknown. During the summer enjoy long hours of daylight and the twilight of the "simmer dim" while in winter the long nights provide the backdrop for a vibrant cultural life. Situated on the picturesque shore at Uyeasound, this refurbished hostel combines superb facilities with a relaxed atmosphere. There is a kitchen, dining room, lounge, conservatory, coin operated laundry, showers (coin operated) and rooms with ensuite facilities. Caravans and tents welcome.

DETAILS

- **Open** - April to September, Open in winter for prebooked groups, all day
- **Number of beds** - 35: 1 x 11, 2 x 6, 2 x 5, 1x 2
- **Booking** - Book by phone or email
- **Price per night** - Adults £11pp, Children (under 16)£8pp. Camping from £6 a tent.
- **Public Transport** - Ferry from Aberdeen to Shetland (Northlink Ferries). The bus meets the ferry and continues to Unst. Ask for Uyeasound. Flights to Lerwick (BA). From Fetlar catch 7:55am ferry from Oddsta (Bus meets ferry)
- **Directions** - Take the A970 north from Lerwick to Voe then the A968 north to Toft . Take the ferry from Toft to Ulsta in Yell. Take the A968 north to Gutcher. Take the ferry from Gutcher to Belmont. Follow the A968 north and head into Uyeasound (B9084). Follow the road to the pier and look out for the hostel sign board.

CONTACT: Warden
Uyeasound, Unst, Shetland, ZE2 9DW
Tel: (01957) 755279
enquiries@gardiesfauld.shetland.co.uk www.gardiesfauld.shetland.co.uk

Galway

Ennis

387

Limerick

386

Tralee

Killarney

385

384

Cork

Bantry

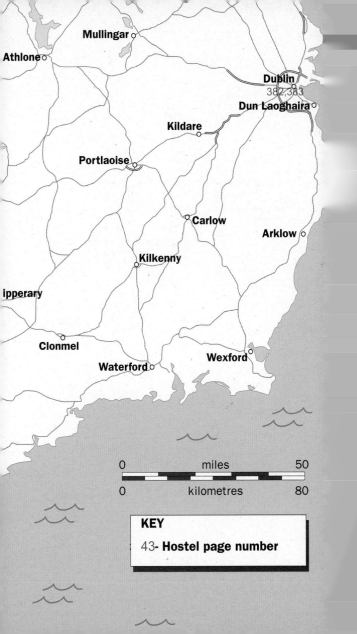

Mullingar

Athlone

Dublin
382,383

Dun Laoghaira

Kildare

Portlaoise

Carlow

Arklow

Kilkenny

ipperary

Clonmel

Wexford

Waterford

0	miles	50
0	kilometres	80

KEY

43- **Hostel page number**

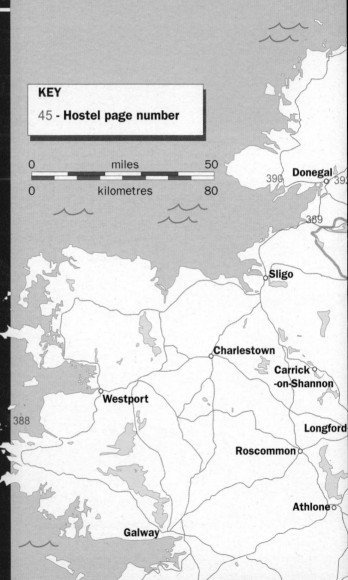

KEY

45 - **Hostel page number**

miles
0   50
0   80
kilometres

Donegal 390 389

Sligo

Charlestown

Carrick -on-Shannon

Westport 388

Longford

Roscommon

Athlone

Galway

ISAACS
HOSTEL

Isaacs Hostel is Dublin's first independent holiday hostel, situated in the city centre, five minutes from O'Connell Street Bridge, and adjacent to the City's central bus and train station. Originally a warehouse, the hostel still retains many of its original features and unique character. Accommodation is in dormitories, triple, twin/double and single rooms with prices starting from €10 per person and includes a light breakfast. For the budget conscious traveller, Isaacs is the perfect choice in Dublin. Food is served all day in the friendly restaurant which offers good value meals. A fully equipped self-catering kitchen is also available. Facilities include sauna, TV lounge, laundry, games room, Bureau de Change, free bed linen, free hot showers, bicycle storage, secure left luggage facilities, internet access and safes. Live music and BBQ's during the summer months. A visit to Dublin would not be complete without Isaacs.

DETAILS

■ **Open** - All year, 24 hours
■ **Number of beds** - 263
■ **Booking** - Recommended especially in high season & weekends. Groups need a deposit. Credit cards accepted.
■ **Price per night** - Dorms €16pp (low season), €18pp (high season). €4 supplement on Fri/Sat nights. Book online for beds from €10. Free light breakfast.
■ **Public Transport** - From Dublin Airport: take the airlink bus to Busaras (central bus station). From Dun Laoghaire Ferryport: take the DART into Connolly Station.
■ **Directions** - Isaacs Hostel is a one minute walk from central bus station. From Connolly Station walk down Talbot Street take third on left for Isaacs

CONTACT:
2-5 Frenchmans Lane, Dublin 1
Tel: +353 (0) 1 8556215, Fax: +353 (0) 1 8556574
hostel@isaacs.ie www.dublinbackpacker.com

Jacobs Inn takes hostel living to new levels with their additional two floors of private rooms, designed to a very high standard with flat screen TVs, laptop safe and ensuite bathroom with shower in all bedrooms. Situated just minutes by foot from the main bus and train station, Jacobs Inn is a short walk from Temple Bar, O'Connell Street and the main shopping areas. Our friendly staff are on hand 24 hours to help with any queries and to make your stay more enjoyable. Accommodation is offered in luxury private bedrooms as well as multi-bed rooms (all ensuite). Facilities include free wifi throughout the hostel, tv lounge with pool table, self-catering kitchen, roof-top patio with views over the city, left luggage facilities, key card access to all rooms, nightly video shows and lift to all floors. Free light breakfast is included in price. Linen is provided in all rooms and towels are provided in private rooms. Towel hire is available.

DETAILS

- **Open** - Closed 23rd to 27th December, 24 hours
- **Number of beds** - 380:   4xtwin : 5xtriple : 4x4 : 2x6 : 12x8 : 15x10
- **Booking** - Recommended in high season and at weekends. Deposit required for group reservations and private rooms. Credit cards accepted.
- **Price per night** - €18 (low season) €20 (high season) pp, for multi-bed rooms. €4 supplement Fridays and Saturdays. Special offers from €10 when you book online.
- **Public Transport** - From Dublin Airport: take the airlink bus to Busaras (central bus station). From Dun Laoghaire Ferryport: take the DART into Connolly Station.
- **Directions** - Jacobs Inn is adjacent to the police station opposite to bus station. From Connolly station go down Talbot St and take 1st road on left.

CONTACT: Reception
21 - 28 Talbot Place, Dublin 1
Tel: +353 (0) 1 8555660, Fax: +353 (0) 1 8555664
jacobs@isaacs.ie www.dublinbackpacker.com

FÁILTE
HOSTEL

Opposite the Kenmare Post Office you will find the warm and welcoming Fáilte Hostel. Our wonderfully clean and well run hostel is an ideal base from which to explore the Ring of Beara and Ring of Kerry.

This home from home has kitchen facilities including an Aga cooker and hot water. Coffee, tea and sugar FREE. Those not wanting to cook will find meals available locally.

The hostel is centrally heated including the common room and also has free hot showers and drying facilities. The beds are to be found in small dormitories, private rooms and en-suite rooms, with sheets and duvets provided. To ensure a good nights sleep a 1.30am curfew is observed.

DETAILS

- **Open** - 2nd May to 23rd October, all day, 1.30 am curfew
- **Number of beds** - 37: 4 x 2 : 4 x 4 : 1 x 5 : 1 x 8
- **Booking** - Please book with Visa / Mastercard Credit Card.
- **Price per night** - €17pp (dorm), €21 to €25pp (double room/twin en-suite), €18 to €22pp (private room for 3/4/5/6)
- **Public Transport** - Bus to Killarney daily. Bus to Sneem, Cork and Castletownbere during the summer season. For details contact Bus Eireann (064) 34777.
- **Directions** - The hostel is opposite the post office in Kenmare town.

CONTACT:
Shelbourne St, Kenmare, Co Kerry
Tel: +353 64 42333
failtefinn@eircom.net www.kenmare.eu/failtehostel/index.html

PORTMAGEE
HOSTEL

IRELAND

Welcome to Portmagee Hostel, located in the fishing village of Portmagee, the gateway to Valentia Island. Opened in 2005, Portmagee Hostel, like it's sister property Skellig Hostel in Ballinskelligs, is a traditionally styled modern hostel with warm, spacious and bright rooms. Groups, families, backpackers, clubs and students are all welcome. There are 2 self catering kitchens with modern utensils and facilities, 2 Dining Rooms, and a Lounge with TV, DVD & Stereo.

Located on the Skellig Ring, "A Secret Ring off the Ring of Kerry", Portmagee Hostel is the ideal place to stay when exploring Valentia and Skellig Islands, and this most beautiful area of Ireland's rugged south west coast. The famous Skellig Island boat trips are only 2 minutes from the hostel and other highlights include the Kerry Way for walkers; magnificent scenery for all to fall in love with; great quiet cycling routes; diving and fishing; horse riding; archaeological sites and Heritage Centres including the Skellig Experience. There is quality music, food & pubs; and best of all, World Famous Irish Hospitality.

DETAILS

- **Open** - All year, all day
- **Number of beds** - 56: 6 x 4 (family), 6 x 2 (dbl ensuite), 2x2 (dbl), 8x2 (twin/bunk)
- **Booking** - Book by phone or email.
- **Price per night** - From €12 pp. Family rooms from €36. Doubles from €32
- **Public Transport** - Trains/Buses at Tralee/Killarney. I hr drive from Kerry Airport.
- **Directions** - 2km outside of Caherciveen on Waterville road, Follow signs for Portmagee, go through village staying on the Skellig Ring road. Hostel is on the left.

CONTACT: Lucy
Portmagee, Co. Kerry
Tel: +353 66 948 0018, Mobile: +353 87 962 8100
info@portmageehostel.com www.portmageehostel.com

MOUNT BRANDON HOSTEL

IRELAND

Mount Brandon Hostel is situated at the foot of Ireland's second highest mountain in one of the most unspoiled areas of Ireland. The beautiful village of Cloghane is on the Dingle Peninsula in the scenic region of Western Ireland.

Mount Brandon Hostel was originally built with the customers' needs in mind. It is built on the waters edge with panoramic views from the television lounge, the dining area and many bedrooms.

All bedrooms are en-suite. There is a fully equipped self-catering kitchen which allows the guests to cater for themselves.

The hostel provides a perfect base for hillwalkers and fishermen, the ideal place to relax and soak up the magnificent views and atmosphere of the area.

DETAILS

■ **Open** - All year, all day
■ **Number of beds** - 31: 1 x 6 : 3 x 4 : 1 x 3 : 2 x double, 3 x twin. Apartment for four persons (only let weekly).
■ **Booking** - Advisable. 2 weeks notice (deposit)
■ **Price per night** - Dormitory €19pp, single room €27, twin €22pp.
■ **Public Transport** - On Fridays there is a bus to and from Tralee.
■ **Directions** - From Tralee follow the main road via Camp to Dingle, follow direction to Conor Pass, turn off at the foot of the Pass to Brandon.

CONTACT: Ingo
Cloghane, Castlegregory, Co Kerry
Tel: +353 (0) 66 7138299
mountbrandonhostel@eircom.net www.mountbrandonhostel.com

JAMAICA
INN

IRELAND

Jamaica Inn is a comfortable, modern hostel located in the village of Sixmilebridge in County Clare.

Nearby are signposted walking routes, numerous lakes and rivers. Visitor attractions are Bunratty Castle and Folkpark, Cragaunowen Celtic site, and Quin Abbey.
Ten miles away are the towns of Limerick and Ennis, and Shannon Airport.

Jamaica Inn has off-street parking, a laundry and drying room, a restaurant, self-catering kitchen, a small TV room and large common room.
There are dorms and private rooms. All rooms are heated and linen is provided.

DETAILS

- **Open** - Jan10th 2008 to Dec 20th 2008,, 08.30 to 22.00
- **Number of beds** - 62: 3 x 10 : 6 x 4 : 4 x 2.
- **Booking** - Groups need to book in advance.
- **Price per night** - €18 to €38.
- **Public Transport** - 3 buses daily from Limerick rail and bus stations and from Shannon Airport to Sixmilebridge. Taxi fare Shannon/Sixmilebridge €15 to €22.
- **Directions** - N18 & R462 from Limerick, N19, N18 & R471 from Shannon Airport. N18 & R471 from Ennis. Hostel is in the centre of the village of Sixmilebridge and is signposted.

CONTACT: Michael McNamara
Sixmilebridge, Co Clare
Tel: + 353 (0) 61 369220, Fax: +353 (0) 61   369377
info@jamaicainn.ie www.jamaicainn.ie

INISHBOFIN
ISLAND HOSTEL

This hostel is situated on one of Ireland's most westerly islands. Inishbofin is a beautiful island with several magnificent sandy beaches which are safe for swimming. The island (population 200) has two hotels, a pub, restaurants, post office and one grocery shop. It is also well known for it's excellent traditional music sessions. The hostel itself was originally a traditional farmhouse which has been converted into a modern hostel which retains all the character and charm of the old building. Its large conservatory offers spectacular views of the Connemara Mountains and coastline. It has a cosy sitting room, complete with a stove and a good selection of books and magazines. We have family rooms, private rooms and small dorms.

DETAILS

- **Open** - April 25th to September 30th 2008, all day
- **Number of beds** - 38
- **Booking** - Can be made on the day - deposit required for advance booking.
- **Price per night** - Dorm €15 per person. Private rooms from €18 to €20 per person based on two sharing. Family room €45-60. Camping €8 per person.
- **Public Transport** - Michael Nee's private bus company runs a daily service from Galway Bus Park (beside tourist office) to Cleggan pier. It connects with the Inishbofin ferry "Island Discovery". For further details contact (095) 51082. Bus Eireann has scheduled runs daily, (091)562000. All ferries leave from Cleggan Pier. For information contact the hostel or phone (095)45819 or (095)45894.
- **Directions** - Turn right at the end of the pier. The hostel is situated 700 metres from the pier on the road to the east village.

CONTACT: Kieran or Theresa
Inishbofin, Co Galway
Tel: +353 (0) 95 45855
inishbofinhostel@eircom.net www.inishbofin-hostel.ie

HOMEFIELD
BACKPACKERS & SURF CENTRE IRELAND

Welcome to Homefield Backpackers situated in Ireland's premier surf capital, Bundoran. Established in 1985 this home-from-home hostel offers competitive rates, friendly well travelled staff, surfing and horse riding instruction, free internet access and wifi and drying room for wetsuits and equipment. Included in the overnight price is a continental breakfast with Leo's famous home-made bread, all bedding, towels and unlimited tea and coffee. Homefield house is family run and has been enjoying the reputation of providing high quality budget accommodation for the past twenty years. Refurbished to a high standard three years ago the house still maintains its three hundred year old character. All rooms are ensuite, clean, comfortable, and tastefully decorated. The hostel has a large modern self-catering kitchen, reading room, TV lounge and there is a restaurant on site. It is 3 minutes walk from clubs, restaurants and pubs. For the surfers the waves are just outside the door and we have our own stables providing instruction, cross-country, beach hacks and trail rides.

DETAILS

- **Open** - All year, all day
- **Number of beds** - 40: 4 & 6 bed dorms, twins, doubles, family rooms
- **Booking** - Book by phone or email
- **Price per night** - Dorm €20pp, Double or twin €25pp. All rooms are ensuite, price includes bedding, towels and continental breakfast.
- **Public Transport** - Buses run regularly from Sligo and Derry through Bundoran
- **Directions** - Coming from Ballyshannon, 2nd turning on the left after the Bridge Bar. Coming from Sligo, 1st turning on the right after the Allingham Hotel.

CONTACT: Leo
Bay View Ave, Bundoran, Co. Donegal
Tel: +353 719841288, Mobile +353 876575161
homefieldhouse@eircom.net www.homefieldbackpackers.com

THE RITZ
ACCOMMODATION

When planning a visit to Killybegs, Ireland's premier fishing port in South-West Donegal, come and stay at The Ritz. This purpose built accommodation is in the centre of town just two minutes walk from the piers and adjacent to pubs, shops and an excellent selection of restaurants. The Ritz offers top quality rooms with twins/doubles and rooms that sleep 4 and 6 which make great family rooms. Continental breakfast is included. Killybegs is an excellent location for touring South West Donegal, Slieve League and availing of the excellent golf courses, equestrian facilities, blue flag beaches, hill walking, angling, scuba diving. Lonely Planet says "as budget haunts go this central place really is The Ritz". It boasts the independence of an IHO hostel with the privacy and comfort of a hotel. Top features include an enormous modern kitchen, colourful en-suite rooms with TV and cosy common areas. A good family choice."

DETAILS

■ **Open** - All year, all day
■ **Number of beds** - 40: 1x6, 4x4, 4x3, 2x2, 1x2 (The rooms contain various mixtures of double beds, bunks and beds - all en-suite)
■ **Booking** - Book early to ensure rooms can be reserved.
■ **Price per night** - From €60 double room. From €70 for family room. €25pp for 3/4 sharing, €20pp for 5 sharing. Group rates are available on request.
■ **Public Transport** - 50 mts from bus stop
■ **Directions** - Approaching from Donegal town turn right into town centre and right again at Ulster Bank. We are on your left. Approaching from Kilcar turn left after the Tara Hotel into town centre then right at Ulster Bank.

CONTACT: Clare or Joe
Chapel Brae, Killybegs, Co Donegal
Tel: +353 (0) 74 9731309 or +353 (0)87 2051452
info@theritz-killybegs.com www.theritz-killybegs.com

THE BLUESTACK CENTRE

The Bluestack Centre is a luxury 28 bed self-catering hostel idyllically located at the foothills of the magnificent Bluestack Mountains in Drimarone, approx 5 miles from Donegal Town. Guests can relax and unwind in the TV lounge and fully equipped self-catering kitchen provided for their comfort. Tennis & basketball courts are among the facilities on offer. Laundry service and towel hire service available. Some concessions are available for large groups and catering can be arranged for visiting groups with pre booking.

DETAILS

- **Open** - All year, all day, Office 9am-10pm Mon-Fri, 4pm-10pm Sat/Sun
- **Number of beds** - 28:1x2, 1x4, 1x10,1x12
- **Booking** - Not essential but recommended. Deposit required for large bookings.
- **Price per night** - Family room (sleeps 4) €50 per room. Dormitory accom €16 per person. Special needs room (sleeps 2) €16 per person. All An Oige (Youth Hostel Association) guests receive a €2 discount on production of a valid YHA card.
- **Public Transport** - Taxi may be found opposite The Abbey Hotel in Donegal Town. The fare to the Hostel is approx €9
- **Directions** - From Donegal Town, take N56 signposted Ardara/Killybegs. At the 1st roundabout adjacent to the Statoil Service Station take the 2nd exit signposted for Letterbarrow/Bluestack Centre. Pass the MillPark Hotel entrance on your right and continue following the signs for Letterbarrow & Bluestack Centre. You will arrive at a small junction; bear right, and after the bridge take a left. You will pass O'Neill's pub on your left and two housing estates on your right.The Bluestack Centre is the large stone building located on the right, adjacent to Drimarone Chapel.

CONTACT: Frances Boyle / Centre Manager
Letterbarrow, Drimarone, Co.Donegal
Tel: +353 (0) 74 97 35564
info@donegalbluestacks.com www.donegalbluestacks.com

GLENHORDIAL FARM [393]
ECO-FRIENDLY HOSTEL   IRELAND

Imagine driving down a country lane, with flowery banks and ancient hedges, into a place that feels like home. Glenhordial Farm hostel welcomes you with a big smile. It is a remote, peaceful, small family hostel. It nestles at the edge of the Sperrin Mountains, here you can breath clean air or wander green valleys, buzzards soar overhead and there is fantastic cycling on deserted roads. Billy and Marella Fyffe have spread their green ethos throughout the hostel from composting to biomass heating. The hostel has single, twin and double rooms, rooms for 3 and 2 small dorms/family rooms. There is a conservatory ideal for drying wet gear. You are free to explore the gardens where vegetables and fruit are grown organically and are available to buy in season. Megalithic sites abound in the area. We are 20 miles from Beagmore stone circle, of enormous European importance, 20 miles from Devenish Island monastic site, 4 miles from Ulster American Folk Park and just 20 miles from the world renowned Janus Statues on Boas Island. We love children and families and children love it here. We have two friendly dogs and a cat called Tigger.

DETAILS

- **Open** - 1st March to 30th September, all day, please arrive before 10pm.
- **Number of beds** - 26:- 1 x 1 2 x 2 2 x 4 2 x 7
- **Booking** - Pre-booking essential for large groups.
- **Price per night** - £12 per adult, Euros accepted.
- **Public Transport** - Free pickup from Omagh bus station by arrangement.
- **Directions** - From Omagh take B48 towards Gortin. Turn right onto Killybrack Road before The Spar Shop. Keep on road and follow signs to hostel.

CONTACT: Marella or Billy
Glenhordial, 9a Waterworks Road, Omagh, Co Tyrone, BT79 7JS
Tel: UK (02882) 241973, Fax: 241973
marella@omaghhostel.co.uk www.omaghhostel.co.uk

RICKS
IRELAND CAUSEWAY COAST HOSTEL

Rick's hostel is situated in the town of Portstewart, only 50 metres from the ocean. It has a mix of accommodation including small dormitories, private rooms for two and family rooms. Some of the rooms are en-suite. All have central heating with duvets and all bed linen provided. There is a self-catering kitchen and it is planned soon to provide meals for those who require them. The spacious common room has an open fire, contains books, games, music, a video-recorder and is overflowing with plants.

Portstewart itself is a relaxed seaside town with a 3.5 kilometre long sandy beach. It contains lively pubs and great value restaurants. There are excellent public transport connections to Belfast, Derry and Dublin. It is an ideal base from which to explore the north coast including the Giant's Causeway, Bushmills whiskey distillery, Carrick-a-rede Rope Bridge and Dunluce Castle or for trips to the glens of Antrim or Derry.

DETAILS

■ **Open** - All year, all day
■ **Number of beds** - 34
■ **Booking** - Recommended by phone or email
■ **Price per night** - £10.50 pp dorm. £13 pp double/twin. £16 pp en-suite
■ **Public Transport** - Nearest train station Coleraine with frequent buses to Portstewart. Direct bus links from Belfast, Derry, Dublin, The Giant's Causeway and Coleraine, all stop at Atlantic Circle Bus Stop 100 metres from Hostel.
■ **Directions** - By car from the A2 take road signposted Portstewart Point/The Herring Pond, the hostel is 100 metres from this turn.

CONTACT:
4 Victoria Terrace, Portstewart, BT55 7BA
Tel: UK (028) 708 33789, IR (048) 708 33789
rick@causewaycoasthostel.fsnet.co.uk

SHEEP ISLAND VIEW

IRELAND

Situated on the Causeway Coast, this family run hostel is ideally situated for exploring this beautiful area including the famous Glens of Antrim.

The modern purpose built hostel offers large self-catering kitchen and communal room. Meals can be prepared for groups on request and there are rooms in a variety of sizes ~ all en-suite.

A ten minute walk takes you to the famous rope-bridge or Ballintoys picturesque harbour. The village has a shop with a post office and two pubs. Both pubs have restaurants and offer entertainment most nights of the week. Often traditional sessions are on offer with everyone welcome to join in.

DETAILS

- **Open** - All year, all day
- **Number of beds** - 100 : variety of size rooms, all en-suite
- **Booking** - Booking is essential in high season
- **Price per night** - £12pp £9 child under 12 (under 2 free)
- **Public Transport** - Coastal bus from Belfast, twice a day No 252. Service No 172 Coleraine/Portrush 6 times a day. Free pick up from Bushmills, Giants Causeway and Ballycastle.
- **Directions** - Ballintoy on main coast road (B15) between Bushmills and Ballycastle. Hostel situated on main street in centre of village.

CONTACT: Seamus or Josephine
42A Main Street, Ballintoy, Ballycastle, Co Antrim, BT54 6LX
Tel: UK (028) 20762470 or 20769391
info@sheepislandview.com www.sheepislandview.com

ARNIE'S
BACKPACKERS HOSTEL

Arnie's is a small, friendly, independent hostel situated in the beautiful Queen's University area of Belfast, just 10-15 minutes walk from the city centre. Belfast, home of sporting heroes and makers of planes and the Titanic, is a great place to explore. Great Craic! Arnie's is the ideal base when enjoying the culture, nightlife, shops and entertainment.

Arnie's Backpackers is in a Victorian town house. You are welcomed with free teas or coffee and biscuits on arrival. There is no curfew or lockout and beds cost as little as £9 a night. There is a self-catering kitchen, real coal fires and a small garden. We recycle. Cab tours of Belfast and bus tours to Giants' Causeway are available from the hostel.
You are welcome !

DETAILS

- **Open** - All year, all day
- **Number of beds** - 22:
- **Booking** - Book by phone, email or online.
- **Price per night** - From £9
- **Public Transport** - Bus - Arnie's is close to the Europa bus centre on Great Victoria Street . Train - closest stations are 'City Hospital' and 'Botanic'. Air - Belfast City and Belfast International are the major airports near Belfast. Walking - 10 to 15 minutes walk from the city centre.
- **Directions** - See map on website

CONTACT: Arnies
63 Fitzwilliam Street, Belfast, BT9 6AX
Tel: UK (028) 90 242867
info@arniesbackpackers.co.uk www.arniesbackpackers.co.uk

Barholm is a Victorian House, it can sleep up to 50 people. The house is tastefully furnished, overlooks Strangford Lough and is situated in an Area of Outstanding Natural Beauty. We can offer our guests a choice of single, double en-suite, family en-suite or group rooms at budget prices. As well as being fully equipped for self-catering we can provide meals on request. A conference room is available for seminars, functions etc and can seat up to 50 people. Portaferry offers typical Irish charm and hospitality and natural interest, it is the home of Exploris, one of Europe's finest aquaria to which our guests are offered concessionary tickets. The area around Portaferry offers sporting activities and the wildlife of the Lough. Strangford Lough is recognised internationally for the quality of the dives, both novice and expert divers alike can enjoy diving all year round, there is a compressor available for airfills.

DETAILS

- **Open** - All year, 9am-2.30 (weekends 10am - 1pm + 5pm - 8pm)
- **Number of beds** - 45: 2 single, 4 double, 4 family (1x3,1x4,2x5). Groups 1x4, 2x8.
- **Booking** - Advised for some rooms and groups
- **Price per night** - From: £13 in group room, £15 single, £35 double, £40 family. Discount for long stays and groups. Whole house from £450. Special offer Oct to Feb, Monday to Thursday stay two nights get third night FREE (except for groups).
- **Public Transport** - No 10 bus from Belfast to Portaferry - drop off point 'The Square' follow ferry signs - Barholm directly opposite ferry terminal.
- **Directions** - By car from Belfast follow directions to Newtownards then sign posted to Portaferry - Barholm is opposite ferry terminal.

CONTACT: Linda Cleland
11 The Strand, Portaferry, Co Down, BT22 1PF
Tel: UK (028) 427 29598, Fax: UK (028) 427 29784
barholm.portaferry@virgin.net www.barholmportaferry.co.uk

Europe

Reykjavik
ICELAND

UK and Ireland maps are on the following pages.
8 England
164 Wales
232 Scotland
336 Ireland

SWEDEN

NORWAY

IRELAND

UK

DENMARK

NETH.

404,405
Berlin

POLAND
40

408
GERMANY

BELG.
LUX.

411,412
CZECH
REP.

402,40

431
Paris

406

409,410

413

SLO
AKIA

FRANCE

SWITZ.
see inset

AUSTRIA

HUN.

SLO,
CRO.

BOS.

PORT.

SPAIN

MONACO

ITALY

Lisbon

433

414
415-417

Rome

421 418-420

ALB

432

430 Zurich

Bern
426

423,424
Geneva

A

428
427

KEY

45 - **Hostel page number**

45 - **Page number of group only accomodation**

| 0 | miles | 500 |
| 0 | kilometres | 800 |

o Moscow

R U S S I A

EST.

LAT.

LITH.

400

BELARUS

KAZAKHSTAN

U K R A I N E

MOLDOVA

ROMANIA

ED
EP
UG.

BULGARIA

GEORGIA

AZER.

ARMENIA

MAC.

422

REECE
443

T U R K E Y

IRAN

SYRIA

IRAQ

CYPRUS

LEBANON

JORDAN

Europe

THE YOUNG TOURIST CENTRE

The Young Tourist Centre is in a XIXth century renovated building on the banks of the river Vilnele, only 10 minutes walk from the Centre of Vilnius.

Vilnius, the most laid-back of the Baltic capitals, has an easy-going provincial charm. The Old Town has amazing baroque and gothic architecture and narrow cobblestone streets. There's a buzz in the evenings when the bars and clubs come alive with youth and style. Vilnius has a well-deserved reputation as one of the safest and friendliest cities in Europe.

The hostel is very convenient to all parts of the city. It is close to public transport and parking is free. There is a self-catering kitchen, public phone and internet access. Bed linen is included in the overnight price. The hostel has lots of info on what to do and where to go and the staff also organise excursions around the rest of Lithuania.

DETAILS

- **Open** - All year, 24 hours
- **Number of beds** - 61: 2x5, 9x4,5x3
- **Booking** - Please book by phone or email.
- **Price per night** - 30 Lt (€ 8.70) per person.
- **Public Transport** - From bus and railway station take bus Nr 34 for six bus-stops to Polocko St.
- **Directions** - The hostel is in the Old Town of Vilnius in Uzupis.

CONTACT: Algirdas Kasparavicius
Polocko St 7, Vilnius, LITHUANIA
Tel: + 3705 2611547; 2613576; Tel/Fax: 2627742
vjtc@delfi.lt www.vjtc.lt

TAMKA
HOSTEL

Warsaw`s Tamka Hostel is one of the most interesting spaces of its kind on the Polish market. The hostel offers 1, 2, and 3 person rooms with or without washrooms, as well as bigger multi-person rooms. That is why so many tourists visiting Warsaw find exactly what they need at Tamka. The hostel also accommodates more demanding tourists: breakfast is included in the price of accommodation, as well as free wireless Internet. In the salon on the ground floor you may also use the hostel`s computers, watch digital TV or DVD`s. These perks attract all to our hostel, including training session participants. The hostel is a free-standing, three storey building in downtown Warsaw. It is a 15 minute walk from the Old Town, and just 5 minutes from the New Town. Located in the heart of the city, the building has its own garden with a barbeque space for guests. Tamka Hostel offers so many perks and is one of the most accessible sites in the capital.

DETAILS

- **Open** - All year, 24 hours
- **Number of beds** - 57: 1x12, 1x7, 1x6, 5x3, 7x2, 3x1
- **Booking** - Book online, by phone or by email
- **Price per night** - Dorms from 30 Zt (low season) to 50Zt (high season). Tiples from 45 to 70 Zt. Doubles from 55 to 90 Zt. All prices per person.
- **Public Transport** - Take bus no 102 (direction 'Olszynka'). Exit the bus on the 5th stop ('Topiel'), go back 200 m. Hostel is on right by crossroad of Tamka / Topiel Str.
- **Directions** - The hostel is by the crossroad of Tamka and Topiel Str. 10 mins to the Old Town, 15 mins from the Railway Station (Warszawa Centralna)

CONTACT: Reception
Tamka 30, 00-355 Warsaw, POLAND
Tel: +48 22 213 29 53, Fax: +48 22 826 30 95
tamka@hostel.pl www.tamkahostel.pl

DIZZY DAISY
DOWNTOWN HOSTEL

Dizzy Daisy Downtown Hostel is a superb hostel with high quality accommodation. Years of experience on the market (the hostel was the third of its kind in Krakow) have resulted in a great upgrades to services and standards, with the goal of making your time spent in Krakow really pleasant.   The hostel offers 2 and 3 person rooms with washrooms, as well as studios (2 rooms with a shared washroom) located towards the rear of the building with a view of the courtyard. We also offer bigger, multi-person rooms for all those looking for the real hostelling experience, while saving a few cents in the meantime. The result of further renovations and the fine tuning of the hostel has produced a cosy common room, linked with the reception, the favourite meeting place of all our guests. You can take advantage of the free Internet, drink free coffee, sit and read a book, or just relax and watch TV. The hostel is close to the railway station and the Galeria Krakowska shopping mall, as well as the Main Square. The hostel is in a quiet corner, however, which guarantees a sound nights sleep.

DETAILS

- **Open** - All year, 24 hours
- **Number of beds** - 52: 1x12,1x10,1x8,4x3,5x2
- **Booking** - Book online, by phone or by email
- **Price per night** - Dorms from 35 Zt (low season) to 60Zt (high season). Triples from 50 to 70 Zt. Doubles from 60 to 85 Zt. All prices per person.
- **Public Transport** - 5 mins walk to the Main Square, 5 min walk to Train Station
- **Directions** - From the Train/Bus Station, turn into Pawia St, turn left on Kurniki St, the follow Filipa Street to end, turn right into Dluga Str and 1st right into Pedzichow.

CONTACT: Reception
Pedzichów 9, 31-152 Krakow, POLAND
Tel: +48 12 398 78 14, Fax: +48 12 634 41 80
krakow@hostel.pl www.krakowhostel.pl

Atlantis offers the cheapest accommodation in the city centre. Here you will spend a night in equally high standards as other hostels, but you`ll pay much less! Atlantis Hostel offers a superb room layout, which makes it attractive for group tours. There are 2, 3, and 4 person rooms, as well as bigger 6 and 8 person ones, in which you can reserve individual beds. The building is located in the very centre of the city, between the Wawel Hill and Kazimierz, an ideal location for all those who, during their stay in Krakow, want to experience both tourists attractions by day and the night life - all located within 5-10 minutes on foot. The space is designed and organised with regard to all tourist needs. Years of presence on the market and therefore an experienced staff have resulted in a hostel which suits the needs of a large majority of tourists visiting Krakow. Attractive discounts for group tours are available.

DETAILS

■ **Open** - All year, 24 hours
■ **Number of beds** - 84: 1x10, 2x8,3x6,1x5,2x4,5x3,6x2
■ **Booking** - Book online, by phone or by email
■ **Price per night** - Dorms from 25 Zt (low season) to 40Zt (high season). Triples from 40 to 60 Zt. Doubles from 50 to 70 Zt. All prices per person.
■ **Public Transport** - Take tram: 3, 13, 19 or 24.
■ **Directions** - Enter the tram no 19 (direction 'Borek Falecki') – the stop is near big shopping centre close to the main hall of the station. Exit the tram on the 4th stop ('Stradom'), turn left into Dietla Street, go 200m, the hostel is on the left side.

CONTACT: Recpetion
Dietla 58, 31-039 Krakow, POLAND
Tel: +48 12 398 78 13, Fax: +48 12 422 99 86
atlantis@hostel.pl www.atlantishostel.pl

GENERATOR
BERLIN

Generator Berlin is the perfect place for all backpackers and groups in the exciting Eastern centre.

Our excellent facilities include:- a funky bar and beer-garden (Happy Hour daily from 5-7 pm), internet café, 24-hour TV lounge, restaurant 6-10 pm and hot showers. Breakfast, bed-linen and towels are FREE!

Free guided walking tour from Generator Hostel Berlin daily at 10.15am.

DETAILS

- **Open** - All year, all day
- **Number of beds** - 904: 1x14 : 119x2 : 88x4 : 7x6 : 26x8
- **Booking** - Book with credit card. Cancellation required 48 hours before visit.
- **Price per night** - From €12 per person. (Groups 1 in 26 free)
- **Public Transport** - Zoologischer Garten or Ostbahnhof: S-Bahn eastbound to Ostkreuz. then Ring S-Bahn northbound get off Landsberger Allee station. The Generator is large white and blue building next to the station! Schönefeld Airport: S9 train to Treptower Park. Change to Ring S-Bahn northbound. Get off at Landsberger Allee. Tegel Airport: Bus X9 to Jungfernheide.Change to Ring S-Bahn eastbound, to Landsberger Allee s-Bahn station.
- **Directions** - Follow signs to Berlin Zentrum, then to Alexanderplatz, pass under railway-bridge and take 2nd street right (Mollstraße). Continue on this road until you're on Landsberger Allee. After approx. 3km turn left onto Storkower Straße (behind the 'Forum' on your left). The Generator is in the courtyard on your left!

CONTACT:
Storkower Straße 160, 10407 Berlin, GERMANY
Tel: + 49 30 417 2400
berlin@generatorhostels.com www.generatorhostels.com

The Heart of Gold Hostel Berlin is the Starship of the Berlin Hostels.

We got off ground in 2003 and met a lot of new friends on our trip through the galaxies since then. Our towels packed we enjoy the two suns outside this unique One out of the state-of-the-art hostels that looks a bit like the spaceship, but then again it doesn't - really, it is mostly harmless.

Inspired by "The Hitchhikers Guide to the Galaxy" by D. Adams.

DETAILS

- **Open** - All year, 24 hours
- **Number of beds** - 108: 10x6, 4x4, 4x3, 8x2, 4x1
- **Booking** - Book ahead for summer, new year, easter and for special events.
- **Price per night** - 14€-17€ 6 bed dorm, 20€ 4 bed dorm, 21€ 3 bed dorm, 28€ 2 bed room, 40€ 1 bed room. All prices per person.
- **Public Transport** - From the main train station "Hauptbahnhof" you take one stop east to Friedrichstrasse. From Airport Schönefeld you take S-Bahn S9 to Friedrichstrasse. From Airport Tempelhof you take the Underground U-Bahn U6 to Oranienburger Tor. From Tegel you take Bus 128 to Kurt-Schumacher-Platz and change into U6 also to Oranienburger Tor.
- **Directions** - The Hostel is near S-Bahn-station Friedrichstrasse. From Friedrichstrasse walk north and cross the River Spree. After the bridge take the second right into Johannisstrasse - 200 m down the street you will find us on the left hand side in number 11.

CONTACT: Reception
Johannisstr. 11, 10117 Berlin, GERMANY
Tel: +49 (0) 30 2900 3300
bridge@heartofgold-hostel.de www.heartofgold-hostel.de

JUGENDGASTEHAUS
STUTTGART

The Jugendgastehaus Stuttgart is half way from Stuttgart's landmark the television tower, to the centre of Mercedes-Benz Town. Just a few minutes away from all the highlights in the valley it is a well known place with plenty of elbow room, multicultural atmosphere and friendly staff.

We are known to have excellent prices for international groups, backpackers and for all young and feeling young individuals from every continent. Lounges and games rooms provide an opportunity for meeting the other guests.

We sell the Three Day Ticket for public transport, please ask our friendly staff for details about reduced weeks for groups or families.

DETAILS

- **Open** - closed 22nd Dec to 6th Jan, 6.30 - 23.00
- **Number of beds** - 110
- **Booking** - Book by phone, fax or email.
- **Price per night** - €16.50 to €32
- **Public Transport** - Public Street cars:- Downstairs at Main Station street cars take line 15 direction Ruhbank/Fernsehturm. Step off at 7th stop Bubenbad.
- **Directions** - By car exit A81 Zuffenhausen/Zentrum. Follow signs to Zentrum. Stay on B27 (direction Tubingen). 1 km after Hauptbahnhof turn right, drive underground, turn left Olgaeck at sign S-Ost follow rails uphill. From Highway A8 exit Flughafen or Degerloch pass the TV tower, then direction Zentrum to Bubenbad.

CONTACT:
Richard Wagner Str. 2, 70184 Stuttgart, GERMANY
Tel: +49 711 241132. Fax +49 711/2 36 11 10
JGH-Stuttgart@internationaler-bund.de www.hostel-Stuttgart.de

PENTHOUSE
BACKPACKERS

Penthouse Backpackers is a homely hostel situated in the centre of Osnabrueck, close to shops and pubs. The whole area is rich in history with the Jewish museum, designed by the famous architect Daniel Libeskind, the medieval city centre and Roman battlefields. The area also caters well for nature lovers with the beautiful Teutoburg Forest where you can see the million-year-old dinosaur tracks or many romantic castles and watermills. The history of coal mining can be explored by glass-walled lift which takes you deep into the old mining shafts. Specialities are the 'Maiwoche' (for 1 week in May there are free open air concerts) or the Christmas markets from 1st of December in the wonderfully lit heart of the City Centre.

The hostel has both private rooms and dormitories and a fully equipped kitchen. After a day's sightseeing or activities come back and join our other guests on the roof top terrace.

DETAILS

- **Open** - All year, all day. Check-in 8-11am and 5-8 pm
- **Number of beds** - 30
- **Booking** - Call ahead/arrive at check-in hours.
- **Price per night** - €14/15 Dorm, €18 Twin, €16 Quad, €20 en-suite.
- **Public Transport** - Osnabrueck train station is 300m straight from the hostel.
- **Directions** - From the 'Hellern' Autobahn turn, take right into the town centre. Pass the Castle, City Centre and before the brick red Post Office building turn right. The hostel is the 3rd building on the left side.

CONTACT: Cathy
Moserstraße 19, 49074 Osnabrueck, GERMANY
Tel: +49 541 600 9606
info@penthousebp.com www.penthouseBP.com

4 You Munich hostel/youth hotel is 150m from the central train station, in the heart of this beautiful city and near to all the sights and places of interest. The hostel has been ecologically built and has facilities for the disabled. Bed linen and breakfast is included. So that our guests can make the most of their stay and experience all the atmosphere there is no lockout or curfew and we have a reception area which is open 24 hours a day to provide you with all the information you need. If you wish to relax after a hard day's sightseeing you can stay within the hostel which has table soccer and internet facilities. The hostel is famous for our superb breakfast buffet. Our house also features two floors of single and double rooms. All these rooms are equipped with a private bath or shower, toilet, desk, radio/alarm clock and telephone.

DETAILS

- **Open** - All year, all day
- **Number of beds** - 2 x 12 : 10 x 2 : 12 x 6 : 2 x 8 : 2 x 4 plus hotel
- **Booking** - Please phone, fax or email
- **Price per night** - Hostel: €17.50- €38.00. Hotel: €44.00- €102.50. October Fest, Hostel: plus €3.50 and Hotel: €79.00 - €140.50.
- **Public Transport** - The main train station (Hauptbahnhof) is just 150m from the hostel. This is also the base for a lot of Metros, S-Bahns and Travis Busse.
- **Directions** - By car please ask for the City Centre. On foot we are three minutes from main station. At the end of the platform turn left and take the exit Arnulfstr. Across the road is hotel Eden Wolf. We are in the street behind, 100m on your left.

CONTACT:
Hirtenstr 18, 80335, Munchen / Munich, GERMANY
Tel: +49 89 55 21 660, Fax: +49 89 55 21 6666
info@the4you.de www.the4you.de

HAUS
INTERNATIONAL

The guest house for young people and those who remain young at heart, Haus International is more than a place to stay. It is a centre for students and a lively meeting-point for people of any age. This is the place for you if you are thinking about spending a few interesting days in Munich. Haus International is in the heart of Munich Schwabing which is close to the city centre and really easy to reach by public transportation. The well known tourist sights of Allianz Arena, Olympia Park and Theresienwiese are just a heartbeat away. Also to explore close by is the old part of Schwabing with the English Garden. Haus International provides private and shared rooms of one to seven beds, equipped with linen and towels. The overnight price includes breakfast in the in-house 220 seat restaurant. Lunch and evening meals are also available in the restaurant and a bar and Discovery Discotheque operate in season. No age restriction, no membership requirement, 24 hour reception, all year.

DETAILS

- **Open** - All year, 24 hours
- **Number of beds** - 200+
- **Booking** - Book by phone, email or online
- **Price per night** - From €25pp. Private rooms from €28pp. Prices include breakfast, linen and towels.
- **Public Transport** - Public transport: Take the U2 from 'Hauptbahnhof' to 'Hohenzollernplatz' and then the number 53 bus or number 12 tram to 'Barbarastraße'.From the airport: Take the S-Bahn or bus transfer to 'Hauptbahnhof'.
- **Directions** - From any motorway take the 'Mittlerer Ring' until exit 'Schwabing'.

CONTACT: Reception
Elisabethstrasse 87, D-80797 München/ Munich, GERMANY
Tel: +49 - 89 -12 00 60, Fax: +49 - 89 - 12 00 66 30
info@haus-international.de www.haus-international.de

ARPACAY is perfect if you are looking for a cosy and comfortable room including bedding and breakfast in the centre of Prague (only 10-15 mins by direct tram or underground to all the sights). The hostel offers 2 to 8 bed rooms with shared facilities or apartments with private bathroom, toilet and kitchens. It has 2 individualistic common rooms, satellite TV and a roof terrace with a beautiful view of Prague. There are 3 fully equipped guest kitchens and a new laundry at the hostel, also left luggage and a safe. At ARPACAY hostel you pay just once. All the services below are included in the overnight price. Free internet access (5 PCs), WIFI in all rooms, luggage room, good hearty breakfast, personal lockers, bed linen and towel, safe at reception, guest kitchens, hot showers. Book ARPACAY hostel and enjoy your stay in Prague.

DETAILS

■ **Open** - All year, reception 7.00-24.00. Key provided for stay (with €10 deposit).
■ **Number of beds** - 78: 5x2 : 6x3 : 1x4 : 3x5 : 1x 6 : 1x7: 1x8: 1 apartment for 2: 1 apartment for 8
■ **Booking** - Book through hostel website.
■ **Price per night** - €8.9 to €14 dorm, €10.9 to €23.6 private room.
■ **Public Transport** - Underground station Smichovske nadrazi (line B) 150m from hostel. Tram stop (No. 14) for down town right in front of hostel.
■ **Directions** - From the international airport Ruzyne take bus No 100 to the final stop Zlicin. Then take underground (line B) and go to Smichovske nadrazi. Go left along the bus lane and cross foot bridge over the track. From the main train station (hl.n.) take underground line C, change to line B at Florenc and then as above.

CONTACT:
Radlicka 76, 150 00 Prague 5, CZECH REPUBLIC
Tel: +42 0/251 552 297, Fax: +42 0/251 552 297
prague@arpacayhostel.com www.arpacayhostel.com

RITCHIE'S
HOSTEL AND HOTEL

Ritchie's Hostel is located in the very centre of Prague, between Old Town Square and Charles Bridge (both just a minutes walk from the hostel). It is situated in Karlova street which is part of the historical King Route. Ritchie's has 2 parts - a hotel with private rooms and a hostel with mixed dormitories. It is ideal for couples of all ages as well as for larger groups, looking for accommodation in the heart of Prague at reasonable prices. To learn more take a look at our website. We are looking forward to your visit.

DETAILS

- **Open** - All year, 24 hours
- **Number of beds** - 113: 1x12, 2x9,1x7, 3x6, 2x5, 3x4, 2x3, 2x1
- **Booking** - Booking should be made at least 2-3 days in advance by email or fax. It may also be possible to book by phone shortly before arrival. A deposit is only required in special cases such as Easter, Christmas, NewYear, and for group bookings.
- **Price per night** - Dorms from €10 per person, doubles from €25 per person. Discounts available for long term stay (4+ nights). Discount for ISIC and IHC members. 5% discount or more for groups.
- **Public Transport** - There are 2 underground stations nearby (2 minutes by foot): line A (Staromestska st.), line B (Narodni trida st.). Tram stops: Staromestka or Karlovy lazne.
- **Directions** - The hostel is located in the very centre of Prague Old Town, in Karlova street that leads directly to the Charles Bridge. Close to Old Town Square. Nearest underground parking on Palachovo nam.

CONTACT: Receptionists
Karlova 13 and 9, 110 00 Praha (Prague), CZECH REPUBLIC
Tel: +420 222 221 229, Fax: +420 222 220 255
info@ritchieshostel.cz www.ritchieshostel.cz

YOHO
INTERNATIONAL HOTEL EUROPE

The Yoho Salzburg is one of the best and most traditional youth hostels in Austria, maybe in Europe. It is one of the most popular meeting points for travellers of all countries of the world. Coming here makes you feel like coming home. NEW IN 2008 : new reception, new lounge, new internet cafe, new kitchen, new beds, new lockers for each bed!!!

The hostel offers an excellent breakfast and the swinging bar provides excellent food, a happy hour everyday and the best music to take care of our hungry and thirsty guests. There are daily films, CNN, internet access and the friendly staff are always willing to assist. The Busabout stops directly at the Yoho and the best tour operators for sightseeing, adventure and skiing tours pick up from the front door.

DETAILS

- **Open** - All year, all day
- **Number of beds** - 160
- **Booking** - Please ring the same day or day before your stay. You can also book by email or fax
- **Price per night** - €17 dorm to €23 twin room.
- **Public Transport** - We are near to the train station, where you will find a big poster in the Hall giving full details.
- **Directions** - Car: Go down from the highway at 'Salzburg Mitte' straight ahead, under the train underpass, then turn second right. Another 100 metres and you will see the hostel. Train Station: 200m to the city, at train underpass turn left (Gablesberger Straße), then as above.

CONTACT: Renate or Gottfried
A-5020 Salzburg, Paracelsusstraße 9, AUSTRIA
Tel: +43 662 879 649, Fax: +43 662 878 810
office@yoho.at www.yoho.at

"...the place for a real holiday in Italy, somewhere you do not feel obliged to go someplace everyday..." For a true taste of Tuscan life come and stay with us in Certaldo. Fattoria Bassetto is a family owned guesthouse located in Certaldo, a lovely medieval town of the Tuscan countryside. A great place to relax from busy cities and experience the true taste of Tuscan life. Our family home was formerly a convent of Benedictine monks, most recently it was a working farm producing wine and oil. In 1998 Fattoria Bassetto became a guesthouse for travellers with the same notion of hospitality as the monks centuries ago. Meander through landscapes, rolling hills and farms on foot, bicycle or mini-van. Or day trip to see the splendours of Florence, Siena, Pisa, Volterra and other towns which are less than an hour away. Enjoy some Tuscan recipes from our cooking classes, sample local wines, or do little more than put your feet up by the swimming pool. There is something for everyone here! Ciao from Dafne, Ale, Cecio & Guido.

DETAILS

- **Open** - From Mar to Dec, office 8.30-12.30 & 17.00-20.00
- **Number of beds** - Dorms 14: + Family room 5: + 6 private rooms.
- **Booking** - By phone or email or online. 10% deposit charged with online booking.
- **Price per night** - Dorm €24 per person. Family room for 5 (en-suite) €95, single room €60, double/twin room €70, triple room €90. Includes self service breakfast
- **Public Transport** - Pick up service from Certaldo train station. See www.trenitalia.com for trains. Bus N°9 (half hourly) from the train station, ask for Fattoria Bassetto.
- **Directions** - See website.

CONTACT: Alessandro
Via delle Cilla, 4, 50052 Certaldo (Firenze), ITALY
Tel: +39 0571 668 342
info@fattoriabassetto.com www.fattoriabassetto.com

BellaRoma Hostel is a brand new backpackers' heaven founded by the people behind Hotel Sandy and Pensione Ottaviano. We have used our years of experience (since 1956) to open a new hostel in a quiet, safe residential area, still close to the city centre and its many sights. It is easy to reach with public transport.

BellaRoma Hostel offer free DSL internet access, satellite TV, free bed linen and blankets, cooking facilities, hot showers, lockers, a refrigerator in each room, no curfew and just around the corner you will find a 24 hour supermarket and bakery. Our friendly, English-speaking staff will provide you with maps, arrange walking/bus tours, pub crawls and all the information you need to have a great stay in the eternal city. Ideal for those between 13 and 40 years.

DETAILS

- **Open** - All year, 24 hours
- **Number of beds** - 50
- **Booking** - Booking in advance is advised at least two weeks prior to arrival. Credit card details required.
- **Price per night** - From €10 pp
- **Public Transport** - From Termini Station you exit platform 24 to via Giolitti, where you get bus number 70. Get off at end station, Piazzale Cladio and follow instructions below or get Metro line A to Ottaviano stop and follow instructions below.
- **Directions** - From St Peters follow Viale Leone IV until you reach Piazzale Clodio. Look for the Mitsubishi shop. We are beside it, via E. Accinni, 63.

CONTACT: Reception
Via E, Accinni 63, 00195, Roma / Rome, ITALY
Tel: +39 063 975 0599, Fax: +39 0639740809
info@bellaromahostel.com www.bellaromahostel.com

The Pensione Ottaviano is the longest running hostel in Rome today. Established in 1956, we have seen generations of backpackers. Since the hostel opened it has been recommended in all the main guide books of the world and we suppose there is a reason for it! The hostel is located in a nice quiet area, one inch from St Peter's Square and from our windows there is a view of the Dome.

Pensione Ottaviano is a clean, budget-wise place to crash, close to the main sights. There are several transport options, underground, buses etc. Our international atmosphere and English speaking, friendly and energetic staff help make us a backpackers' heaven. We help our guests enjoy their days in Rome with all the necessary information. You will find rooms with refrigerators, a lounge with satellite TV, individual lockers, book exchange and much more.

DETAILS

- **Open** - All year, 24 hours
- **Number of beds** - 100
- **Booking** - Booking advised by phone or email
- **Price per night** - From €12 per person
- **Public Transport** - From Airport Fiumicino take the train to Termini station (30 mins).
- **Directions** - From Termini take metro line A (Direction Battistini) to Ottaviano. Exit station at via Ottaviano and we are No.6 on the 2nd floor.

CONTACT: Slim
Via Ottaviano, 6, 00192 Roma / Rome, ITALY
Tel: +39 063 973 7253 or 063 973 8138
info@pensioneottaviano.com www.ottavianohostel.com

SANDY
HOSTEL

Established in 1990, Sandy Hostel has grown up to be one of the most popular and well-known places to stay for young backpackers. Since the hostel opened it has been recommended in all the main guide books of the world.

The hostel is located in a nice quiet area close to the Colosseum and Roman Forum. We know what travelling on a budget demands. Close by are a variety of shops, supermarkets, grocery stores, laundromat, information stands and other essential services.

In our international atmosphere, with English speaking, friendly and energetic staff, always willing to help, you will find book exchange, individual lockers, guide books, maps, a secure luggage store and much more besides. Walking tours can be arranged.

DETAILS

- **Open** - All year, 24 hours
- **Number of beds** - 100
- **Booking** - Booking advised by phone or email
- **Price per night** - From €12 per person
- **Public Transport** - From Fiumicino Leonardo Davinci Airport take train to termini station (30 mins).
- **Directions** - Exit Termini on Piazza Dei Cinquecento and immediately turn left to Via Cavour 136. Hostel Sandy is on the left. Take metro line B to Cavour.

CONTACT: Slim
Via Cavour, 136, 00184 - Roma / Rome, ITALY
Tel: +(39) 064 884585 or 0648906772
info@sandyhostel.com www.sandyhostel.com

PENSIONE MANCINI
HOSTEL

Hostel Mancini is a small cosy safe backpackers located right in front of Naples Central Railway Station. The staff will make you welcome and tell you about cheap day trips to Pompei, Sorrento Capri and the Amalfi coast and also where to go for a really good Pizza. There is a self catering kitchen and free breakfast for everyone. The accommodation is in single beds (no bunks) in mixed and single sex dorms, or in single, double, twin, triple and quad rooms. There are also big rooms for families or small groups. The hostel is run by the family Alfredo, Margherita and Lello who between them can speak Italian, English, Spanish, Polish and French. There is a helpful tourist information desk with free maps of the City and surroundings. The hostel offers a 24-hour reception, free luggage storage and all the dorms have lockers, private showers and TV. Free Internet. No curfew. No lockout.

DETAILS

- **Open** - All year,, 24 hours
- **Number of beds** - 36: 2 x 5 : 4 x doubles (can be triples)
- **Booking** - Please book by telephone or fax or email with credit card number.
- **Price per night** - Dorm: €15-20, Quads: €20-22pp, Triple €22-27pp, Double/Twin rooms: €23-28pp, Double/Twin ensuite: €23-28pp. 10% discount for school groups.
- **Public Transport** - Within walking distance from Napoli central train station. 15 minutes by bus from the airport and only 15 minutes walk from the ferries.
- **Directions** - Coming out of Napoli train station cross the Garibaldi Square. Behind the Garibaldi Monument cross into Via Mancini. The hostel is the last building on the left hand side, just buzz!

CONTACT: Alfredo
Via P.S Mancini 33, 80139 Napoli / Naples, ITALY
Tel: +39 081 553 6731, Fax: +39 081 554 6675
info@hostelpensionemancini.com www.hostelpensionemancini.com

BELLA CAPRI
HOSTEL AND HOTEL

Hostel and Hotel Bella Capri is conveniently located in the centre of Naples right in front of the port for ferries and hydrofoils to the islands of Capri, Ischia, Procida, Sicily, Sardinia, Tunisia and Aeolie. Just a few minutes walk from the hostel is the historical centre of Naples with the famous Piazza Del Plebiscito, opera house San Carlo and the Royal Palace. Only 2 minutes walk to the "SITA" Bus station with buses to Pompei, Sorrento, Positano and the Amalfi coast. Bella Capri provides clean and friendly bed and breakfast. Rooms are available with single, double, triple, quad and 6 beds, with and without private bathrooms. Some rooms have balconies which look over the beautiful Bay of Naples. All rooms have bed linen, TV, lockers and air conditioning. There is a large common area with TV, public phone, free internet access, free luggage store and maps. The English speaking staff will tell you about Naples.

DETAILS

■ **Open** - All year, 24 hours (no curfew)
■ **Number of beds** - 50:(dorms)2x4,2x6(pr)single,tple,dble, quad.
■ **Booking** - Fax or book online with credit card. For cancellation give 48 hrs notice.
■ **Price per night** - €16-€20pp 6 bed dorm, €25-€30pp private rm. €33- €40pp private en-suite. Inc.breakfast, bed linen and tax. Student, school & group discounts.
■ **Public Transport** - From Central railway station: take bus R2 to Piazza Municipio. From airport catch the ALIBUS shuttle to Piazza Municipio (last stop).
■ **Directions** - Opposite to the Ferry Terminal in the port of Naples. From Piazza Municipio face the port and turn left into Via Colombo. After two blocks turn left again and you will see the hostel (2 mins walk).

CONTACT: Alfredo
Via Melisurgo 4, 80133 Naples, ITALY
Tel: +39 081552 9494, Fax: +39 081552 9265
info@bellacapri.it www.bellacapri.it

Hostel of the Sun is the most central hostel in Naples. Located just in front of the ferry port to Capri, Ischia and Sicily, and in front of the terminal for buses to Pompei, Ercolaneum and the Amalfi Coast.

Hostel of the Sun is also very close to the most famous and historic places in Naples. The friendly and international staff are ready to help you with anything you need, especially recommendations on where to get the best Napolitan pizza.

DETAILS

- **Open** - All year, 24 hours
- **Number of beds** - 35 : 3x6; 5x2; 2x3.
- **Booking** - Advisable
- **Price per night** - Per person: Dorms €18; Doubles €25; Triples €28
- **Public Transport** - From the central train station: exit the station, cross the square and take the R2 bus. Get off at the 2nd stop in via de Pretis. Via Melisurgo is just by this stop. From the airport : take the bus called Alibus from outside the arrival terminal to Piazza Municipio, the last stop. The hostel is just 2 minutes walk.
- **Directions** - From the train station take the R2 bus and get off on Via De Pretis (8 bus stops from the station). Once off the bus on Via De Pretis the street in front of the bus stop is via G. Melisurgo. We are at number 15 . From The Airport: outside the arrival terminal there is a shuttle bus called 'ALIBUS' that runs from the airport to the main square of the city. Get off at Piazza Municipio and in less than 2 mins walk you will be at Via Melisurgo 15 where Hostel of the Sun is located .

CONTACT: Coda
via Melisurgo 15, Napoli / Naples, ITALY
Tel: +39 08142 06393, Fax: +39 08142 06393
info@hostelnapoli.com www.hostelnapoli.com

Ring Hostel is situated in Forio, on the west coast of the Ilse of Ischia, perfect for day trips to Capri, Pompeii or the Amalfi Coast. The hostel is owned by three Italian brothers who also operate a small family hotel and beach side apartments. Guests can use the facilities at each of the properties. In the evenings, the brothers provide free transport to La Casereccia where their mama, Tina, cooks traditional Italian cuisine using freshly grown produce from their gardens. Snorkel, Mountain Bike, Hot Springs,Cliff Jumping, Spas, rent a moped, learn to make Pizza, Limoncello, Pasta; enjoy the hostel Trivia night; Beach Bonfires and SO MUCH MORE...Relax and soak up the sun during the day on some of the most beautiful beaches in the world, and then party at night.
Stay with them and have the best time you will have on your holiday.
Ring Hostel has private rooms for 1 to 4 people and dorm rooms for 4, 6, 8 and 12 people, with or without en-suite. Linen is included and towels are available.
The hostel has no curfew and no age restrictions.

DETAILS

- **Open** - All year, 24 hours
- **Number of beds** - 56: 1x12, 1x8, 2x6, 4x4, 4x2
- **Booking** - phone, email or book online
- **Price per night** - Dorms from €17 to €27, Private pp €21 to €60
- **Public Transport** - 50 mins by hydrofoil from Naples. 24hr buses on the island.
- **Directions** - When leaving the Port of Forio follow main road leftwards to Captain Morgan Biglietteria. Turn right here & straight on till you reach a store called Bollicine. Turn left at the store. Hostel is after 300 m (a yellow building with numbers 1828)

CONTACT:
Via Gaetano Morgera n.72, Forio, Island Ischia, Gulf of Naples, ITALY
Tel: + 39(0)81987546, Mobile +39 333 6985665
info@ringhostel.com www.ringhostel.com

PAGRATION
YOUTH HOSTEL

Pagration Youth Hostel is one of the founding members of the Greek Youth Hostel Organization. It is family operated, safe, clean and offers the comfort of a "home" near the heart of the city. Facilities include central heating in the winter, colour TV, table games, luggage storage, kitchen facilities, exchange book service, safe deposit for valuables, information desk, washing machine and dryer, 24 hours hot water, safety camera at entrance, no curfew, roof and open air yard. The Hostel is within walking distance of the main square, Syndagma or Constitution Square, and many other tourist sites such as the Akropolis and the ancient city of Athens, the old quarters of Plaka, the Temple of Zeus, the Parliament, the Kallimarmaro Stadium where the first Olympic games of modern times took place, the National park. Also, one block away, are cafes, tavernas, cinemas, supermarkets, shopping centres, and the stop for the bus to the seashore with charming swimming areas and organized beaches.

DETAILS

■ **Open** - All year, 24 hours
■ **Number of beds** - 60
■ **Booking** - Please phone or email
■ **Price per night** - €12 High Season
■ **Public Transport** - The nearest Metro stop is Evangelismos. Around the corner from hostel Trolley bus stop Filolaou (Pagrati) for trolley buses numbers 2 and 11, and for blue buses numbers 203, 204 and 054.
■ **Directions** - Located near the centre of the city, at walking distance (1500 m) of the main Square " Syndagma ".

CONTACT:
75 Damareos Street, Pagrati 116 33, Athens, GREECE
Tel: +30 210 7519530, Fax: +30 210 7510616
skokin@hol.gr www.athens-yhostel.com

LAUSANNE
GUESTHOUSE & BACKPACKER EUROPE

Lausanne is in the very heart of the Lake Geneva Region. Our Guesthouse is in the heart of Lausanne. Our lucky location is only 2 minutes walking time from main train station. Our peaceful garden and barbecue, our breathtaking views on the Alps, on Lake Geneva and our extremely low price policy contribute to your best souvenir of Switzerland.

Respectfully restored in 2001 our town house built in 1894 complies with the strictest and newest ecological regulations and preserves all the charm of this lovely old European establishment. All our bedrooms face Lake Geneva and the Alps, six of our ten double rooms have private bathrooms, we have a further fifteen four-bedded dormitory rooms. The hostel is equipped for the disabled, it also has high speed internet stations.

DETAILS
- **Open** - All year, reception 07.30-12.00 / 15.00 -22.00
- **Number of beds** - 80: 15 x 4 : 10 x 2.
- **Booking** - Book by email, internet, phone or fax
- **Price per night** - €21 dorm without sheets, €24 with sheets. Double/single rooms from € 55 to €70.
- **Public Transport** - Local train and bus stations
- **Directions** - Two minutes walk from main train station. Exit the station, when facing the Place de la Gare take the next left down, walk through the railroad tunnel, take the first right.

CONTACT:
Chemin Des Epinettes 4, 1007 Lausanne, SWITZERLAND
Tel: +41 21 601 8000, Fax: +41 21 601 8001
info@lausanne-guesthouse.ch www.lausanne-guesthouse.ch

RIVIERA
LODGE

Only 50 min by train from Geneva airport, on the shores of the Lake of Geneva, Riviera Lodge welcomes you in a heritage 19th-century town house. Accommodation in rooms for 2, 4, 6 or 8 people. Toilets and showers on each floor, fully equipped kitchen, breakfast buffet, laundry facilities, TV/video, internet access, parking facilities and a panoramic roof terrace with views of the lake and vineyards.

Vevey is the ideal base to discover the Lake of Geneva region. Cruise the lake on a steam boat to the world-famous Chateau de Chillon. Reach the surrounding hill tops with funicular or cogwheel trains. Discover the ancestral winemaking villages and practise some wine tasting. Chocolate passion in Vevey, home of the first world's milk chocolate. Tour, taste and shop…

DETAILS

- **Open** - all year, 0800-1200 and 1600-2000
- **Number of beds** - 60:
- **Booking** - Tel, fax or email in advance please
- **Price per night** - From CHF27 to CHF44 per person.
- **Public Transport** - Bus/train every 15 mins Montreux/Lausanne, every 50 mins by train from Geneva airport.
- **Directions** - From highway exit at Vevey, following signs to town centre and Place du Marche. From the train station walk about 2 mins towards the lake and you will join the market place. Riviera Lodge is on the right side.

CONTACT: Francois Commend
Vevey - Montreux, Place du Marche 5, 1800 Vevey, SWITZERLAND
Tel: +41 21 9238040, Fax: 9238041
info@rivieralodge.ch www.rivieralodge.ch

BACKPACKERS VILLA
SONNENHOF INTERLAKEN

Backpackers Villa Sonnenhof is centrally located in a villa with a park, just ten minutes walk from either the West or Ost train stations in the town of Interlaken. Our staff have plenty of ideas for what to do and adventure activities can be arranged like river rafting, canyoning, bungee jumping, paragliding, skiing and snowboarding.

Backpackers Villa has a friendly atmosphere. All rooms are clean and most come with Jungfrau-view balconies. There is no curfew or lockout and membership is not required. Facilities include free hot showers on every floor - just what you need after all those activities - fully equipped kitchen, laundry, table soccer, billiards, internet access or you can get away from it all and refresh in the meditation room. Visit our website where you can book online.

DETAILS

- **Open** - All year, reception 7.30-11am and 4-9pm
- **Number of beds** - 90: 4 x 2 2 x 3 4 x 4 10 x 6
- **Booking** - Please book online using your credit card.
- **Price per night** - CHF35-42 (€22-27) dorm, CHF49-54 (€30-36) double, Triples and quads available too. Prices are per person and include taxes, sheets, breakfast, free entry to public swimming pool and minigolf
- **Public Transport** - Walking distance from Interlaken West or Ost train stations or take bus No2 to Sonnenhof.
- **Directions** - In the centre of Interlaken at Hohematte (large greenfield). Follow the brown signs from the stations - just 10 minutes walk.

CONTACT:
Alpenstrasse 16, 3800 Interlaken, SWITZERLAND
Tel: +41 (0)33 826 71 71, Fax: +41 (0)33 826 71 72
mail@villa.ch www.villa.ch

Downtown lodge is situated in the heart of Grindelwald centre, with a breathtaking view of the mountains and glaciers. Cable cars, trains, shops and bars are just around the corner.

Downtown Lodge provides clean and comfortable dorms and double rooms, a great breakfast buffet, self-catering kitchen, TV, laundry facilities, games room with pool, billiards and table football, free entrance to the swimming pool nearby and .. and .. everything that a backpacker's heart wishes.

For groups there are three lodges with own dormitories, fully equipped kitchen and lounge room.

DETAILS

- **Open** - All year, reception open 7.30 till 12 and 4 till 10.
- **Number of beds** - 92: 2x2, 4x4, 6x6, 5x8
- **Booking** - Book on our web page, by email, fax or phone
- **Price per night** - CHF35 (approx €23.50) Price includes sheets, breakfast buffet and taxes
- **Public Transport** - Grindelwald train station is 5 minutes walk from hostel.
- **Directions** - From the train station follow the main street to the city centre. After 5 minutes you will see the hostel sign on the right in front of the 'minigolf' place.

CONTACT: Edi Portman
Dorfzentrum, 3818, Grindelwald, SWITZERLAND
Tel: (0041) 33 853 08 25
downtown-lodge@jungfrau.ch www.downtown-lodge.ch

GIMMELWALD
MOUNTAIN HOSTEL

Gimmelwald Mountain Hostel is a beautiful old renovated building with a lot of charm, where we aim to give you a happy holiday.

The hostel is in the centre of the skiing area in a small village where 150 people live all year round.

Come up and check it, you will love it.

Gimmelwald lies on a sunny mountain-side in the heart of the marvellous winter sports and hiking paradise of the Schilthorn area.
This small mountain village is an ideal starting point for hikes in the romantic countryside with its towering rock faces, cascading waterfalls, mountain forests, meadows ablaze with flowers and a wonderful variety of fauna.

DETAILS

- **Open** - All year, 8.30am to 23.30pm
- **Number of beds** - 50:
- **Booking** - Book by E-mail or phone
- **Price per night** - CHF25pp inc entrance to indoor pool and ice rink
- **Public Transport** - Interlaken Ost change train to Lauterbrunnen. In Lauterbrunnen take bus to Stechelberg, from here take cable car to Gimmelwald. Interlaken to Gimmelwald 1 hour cost: CHF25 round trip.
- **Directions** - Ask for Mountain Hostel.

CONTACT: Petra or Walter
3826 Gimmelwald, SWITZERLAND
Tel: +41 033 855 17 04, Fax: +41 033 855 17 04
mountainhostel@tcnet.ch www.mountainhostel.com

CITY BACKPACKER
HOTEL BIBER

The City Backpacker is a friendly hostel situated in the heart of Zurich's picturesque Old Town. Most of the tourist sites and many places of interest are within walking distance including a lake, museum, bars, disco, nightlife and parks. All the things that a backpacker needs are available at the hostel. We have a self-catering kitchen, showers and washing machine. There is also a nice terrace and common room with internet station and a book-exchange. We have a luggage store and offer discounts on Swiss army knives.
For information and reservations just phone, write or send an email. Check it out and see you soon.

DETAILS

- **Open** - All year, check in 0800 to 1200 and 1500 to 2200 hrs.
- **Number of beds** - 65: 6 x 6 : 4 x 4 : 5 x 2 : 3 x 1
- **Booking** - Booking by phone, fax or email is advisable in summer months. You can book online on our website.
- **Price per night** - CHF33 (€22) dorm, CHF49 (€33) double, CHF 45 (€30) triple, CHF44 (€30) quad. Prices are per person and including new City Tax CHF2.50pp
- **Public Transport** - Zurich is well connected to mainland Europe by rail and coach services. The hostel is in the Old Town and only 10 minutes walk from the main railway station.
- **Directions** - From the main railway station cross the river Limmat and take a right into the old town. Follow Niederdorfstrasse until No. 5. (Niederdorfstrasse is the main walking street in the Old Town).

CONTACT: Receptionist
Niederdorfstrasse 5, 8001 Zurich, SWITZERLAND
Tel: +41 44 251 9015
sleep@city-backpacker.ch www.city-backpacker.ch

Our cheerful hideaway lies in the very heart of Paris. Thanks to it's convenient location between Les Halles, the Marais, the upscale opera district and the Picasso Museum, it is the ideal base from which to explore the unique atmosphere of Paris and its stunning attractions. In the evening enjoy the nightlife and many restaurants or take in a movie at Europe's largest cinema palace, Le Rex, just across the street. We have no curfew.

Bed and Breakfast is comfortable and respectable and its owner, Michael, who is fluent in English, Spanish, Hebrew and Arabic welcomes all ages, groups and families. The hostel offers four, six and eight bed rooms all with satellite TV, stereo and heaters. There are full toilet facilities and hot showers are also available if you need to freshen up after a busy day of sightseeing. Sheets, blankets, towels and a copious breakfast are included in the price..

DETAILS

- **Open** - All year, all day
- **Number of beds** - 50
- **Booking** - Recommended by phone or fax - best to phone to arrange arrival time.
- **Price per night** - €15 per person (inc. breakfast and bedding). No credit cards.
- **Public Transport** - Gare du Nord and Gare de l'Est, are 10 minutes from the hostel. From Airport or Rail stations take the Metro line 8 or 9 to Bonne Nouvelle.
- **Directions** - From Bonne Nouvelle Metro station, take exit marked Boulevard Poissonnière. Walk to Rex cinema, (you can see Rex sign from the metro exit). At Rex cinema turn left to Rue Poissonnière.

CONTACT:
42 rue Poissonnière, 75002 Paris, FRANCE
Tel: + 33 14 02 68 308, Fax: + 33 14 02 68 791
bedandbreakfast1973@yahoo.co.uk 42ruepoissonniere.tripod.com/

PURPLE NEST
HOSTEL

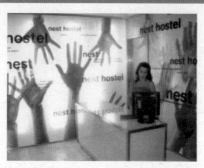

Purple Nest Hostel is in Valencia's city centre, between the commercial area and the bohemian el Carmen district, and just one step from the biggest green area in the city. There's a wide choice of bars and nightlife all around Purple Nest. Don't worry about the heat!! Purple Nest has air conditioning in every room, is very close to 2 swimming pools and just a few metres away from the bus stop to the beach. There are spacious dorm rooms with 4, 6, 8 and 10 beds and private rooms of 2, 3 and 4. Each room has key card access and air conditioning. There are clean, single sex bathrooms on each floor. Purple Nest has an easy, laid back atmosphere with helpful staff to steer you to the beaches, bars, sites and sounds of Valencia and get you free city maps and reservations for tours. The hostel bar has some of the cheapest pints in town and is a great place to meet other travellers and enjoy the great atmosphere of the Valencian night. If Purple Nest is full check out Red Nest Hostel in La Paz.

DETAILS

- **Open** - All year, 24 hours
- **Number of beds** - 186: 3x10, 6x8, 8x6, 12x4. 2x3, 3x2
- **Booking** - Book online, by phone or by email.
- **Price per night** - From €14 per person
- **Public Transport** - From bus station catch No8 and get off at Plaza Tetuan. From train station take metro line 3 or 5, get off one stop later at Colon.
- **Directions** - From train station turn right and follow Xativa street. This changes to Colon, keep walking to Colon metro in front of a shopping mall. Walk around shopping mall to Plaza Alfonso el Magnanimo. Walk through the Park to Plaza Tetuan.

CONTACT: Reception
Plaza Tetuan 5, 46003 Valencia, SPAIN
Tel: +34 963 532 561, Fax: + 34 963 427 128
info@purplenesthostel.com www.nesthostelsvalencia.com

Barcelona loves to indulge in the fantastic. The city pushes the limits of style in everything it does, and gets away with it. Barcelona Mar Hostel has a great location in this vibrant city. In the heart of the Raval neighbourhood, a multi cultural, trendy area close to the museum of Contemporary Art (MACBA). Just 10 minutes from Plaza Catalunya (main square) and 5 minutes from the famous Ramblas & Liceu theatre. All the rooms at Barcelona Mar Hostel are en-suite with heating, A/C and lockers. It also has a brand new section of double rooms. There is a self catering kitchen and a beautiful common room with T.V. and DVD. You get free breakfast, free locker, free internet, and free Barcelona maps. The hostel has helpful international staff and organizes beach parties, pub crawls, sightseeing tours, flamenco show & live concerts. Also available - tailor made accommodation to suit large groups.

DETAILS

- **Open** - All year, 24 hour reception
- **Number of beds** - Double rooms and dorms of 2, 6,8,10,14 and 16 beds
- **Booking** - Book online. Groups of 17+ contact groups@barcelonamar.com
- **Price per night** - Dorms €16-to €23. Doubles extra €5pp. Sheet rent 2,5€.
- **Public Transport** - Coming from the Barcelona Airport catch the train (RENFE) to Sants Station: Barcelona´s central station. Then take the metro. Coming from Girona Airport take the bus that brings you to Estació del Nord. Then take the metro.
- **Directions** - From the metro stop Paral-el, take the exit Ronda Sant Pau. In the street you will find the beginning of el Carrer Sant Pau. From the metro stop Liceu go to the exit and see the Theatre Liceu, where the Street Sant Pau begins.

CONTACT: Reception
Carrer Sant Pau 80, 08001 Barcelona, SPAIN
Tel: +34 93 324 85 30
info@barcelonamar.com   www.barcelonamar.com

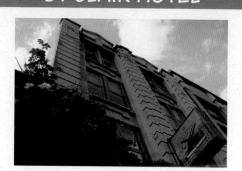

Located right downtown close to Chinatown and Gastown. You may walk to restaurants, nightclubs, buses (local for Vancouver Island), skytrain, north Vancouver Ferry, Stadium and Ice Hockey Arena. This heritage listed building was built in 1911 by Henry Pybus, captain of the Canadian Pacific steamship 'Empress of Japan' which took the blue ribbon while setting the Trans-Pacific crossing record 1887. The hotel originally accommodated railway and ocean going travellers back to both Pacific and Atlantic.

A nautical theme is retained, 34 private rooms, 12 per floor, showers on each floor, no dorms, all linen provided, parking facilities in same block. City bus from airport one block at 'The Hudson Bay Department Store'.

DETAILS

- **Open** - All year, 24 hours. Check in 8-30am/10-30pm, no curfew
- **Number of beds** - 77: 3x1 : 24x2 : 6x3 : 2x4
- **Booking** - Book ahead if possible
- **Price per night** - C$44 double room, C$54 triple room. Weekly double C$275, weekly triple C$325. All private.
- **Public Transport** - Buses operate from local Airport, Greyhound and Rail Station.
- **Directions** - From train station or Greyhound take Sky Train to Granville Station, at The Hudson Bay Department Store. From Airport take bus #424 change at Airport station, board 98 B line to Granville Station (skytrain stop). Walk to Dunsmuire, turn right, first left into Richards Street.

CONTACT: Manager
577 Richards Street, Vancouver, British Columbia V6B2Z5, CANADA
Tel: +1 604 684-3713. Toll free (USACanada) 1-800-982-0220.
sourceentvan@telus.net www.sourceenterprises.bc.ca

32 hostels in 24 cities all over Switzerland

6677 Aurigeno, **Baracca Backpacker**, +41 (0)79 207 15 54

4053 Basel, **basel back pack**, +41 (0)61 333 00 37, info@baselbackpack.ch

4008 Basel, **YMCA Hostel Basel**, +41 (0)61 361 73 09, info@ymcahostelbasel.ch

3011 Bern, **Backpackers - Hotel Glocke**, +41 (0)31 311 37 71,info@bernbackpackers.ch

3013 Bern, **Landhaus - Backpackers Paradise**, +41 (0)31 331 41 66, landhaus@spectraweb.ch

8784 Braunwald, **adrenalin backpackers hostel**, +41 (0)79 347 2905, info@adrenalin.gl

3992 Bettmeralp, **Backpacker Venus**, +41 (0)27 927 25 85, info@venustourist.ch

6558 Cabbilo/Lostallo, **Humanita Backpackers**, +41 (0)91 830 1481, info@humanita.ch

7002 Chur, **JBN Hostel**, +41 (0)81 284 10 10, info@justbenice.ch

1202 Genève, **City Hostel Geneva**, +41 (0)22 901 15 00, info@cityhostel.ch

3826 Gimmelwald, **Mountain Hostel**, +41 (0)33 855 17 04, mountainhostel@tcnet.ch

3818 Grindelwald, **Downtown Lodge**, +41 (0)33 853 08 25, downtown-lodge@jungfrau.ch

3818 Grindelwald, **Mountain Hostel**, +41 (0)33 854 38 38, info@mountainhostel.ch

7130 Ilanz, **Gasthof Mundaun**, +41 (0)79 200 1742, ernstforrer@mundaunpub.ch

3800 Interlaken, **Backpackers Villa Sonnenhof**, +41 (0)33 826 71 71, mail@villa.ch

3800 Interlaken/Matten, **Balmer's Herberge**, +41 (0)33 822 19 61, mail@balmers.ch

3800 Interlaken/Unterseen, Low Budget Hotel & Backpacker Falken, +41 (0)33 822 30 43, falken@quicknet.ch

3800 Interlaken, **Happy Inn Lodge**, +41 (0)33 822 32 25, info@happy-inn.com

3800 Interlaken, **Hua Villa**, +41 0(33) 821 16 28, huavilla@bluewin.ch

3800 Interlaken, **River Lodge**, +41 (0)33 822 44 24, welcome@riverlodge.ch

3718 Kandersteg, **Gemmi Lodge**, +41 (0)33 675 85 85, info@gemmi-lodge.com

7031 Laax-Cons, **Backpacker Deluxe Capricorn**, 41 (0)81 921 21 20, info@caprilounge.ch

1007 Lausanne, **Guesthouse & Backpacker**, +41 (0)21 601 80 00, info@lausanne-guesthouse.ch

3822 Lauterbrunnen, **Valley Hostel**, +41 (0)33 855 20 08, info@valleyhostel.ch

6005 Luzern, **Backpackers Lucerne**, +41 (0)41 360 04 20, Fax +41 (0)41 360 04 42

2560 Nidau b. Biel, **Lago Lodge**, +41 (0)32 331 37 32, sleep@lagolodge.ch

6430 Schwyz, **Hirschen Schwyz**, +41 (0)41 811 12 76, info@hirschen-schwyz.ch

7554 Sent, **Backpacker Hotel Swissroof**, +41 (0)81 864 17 22, info@swissroof.ch

9657 Unterwasser, **Saentislodge**, +41(0)71 998 5025, saentis@beutler-hotels.ch

1800 Vevey-Montreux, **Riviera Lodge**, +41 (0)21 923 80 40, info@rivieralodge.ch

6484 Wassen, **Gotthardbackpacker**, +41 (0)79 306 54 23, www.gotthardbackpacker.ch

8001 Zürich, **City Backpacker/Hotel Biber**, +41 (0)44 251 90 15, sleep@city-backpacker.ch

»german hostels are like two peas in a pod«

we colour your holidays.
more than 45 unique quality
hostels throughout germany.

BACKPACKER GERMANY NETWORK

hospitaly »Made in Germany«

use our free booking service! confirmed OFFline bookings.
free, fast, secure ... no creditcard needed ...

www.backpackernetwork.de

Scottish Independent Hostels

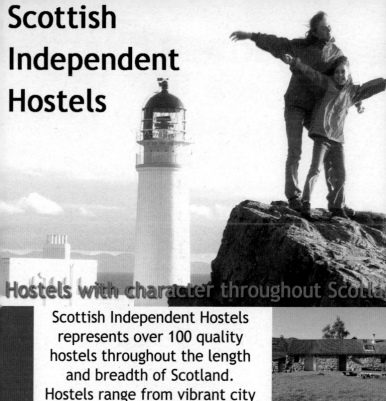

Hostels with character throughout Scotland

Scottish Independent Hostels represents over 100 quality hostels throughout the length and breadth of Scotland. Hostels range from vibrant city centre locations to converted barns on tranquil islands, each with its own very special character.
Our Blue Hostel Guide is published every year giving an up to date listing of all member hostels. For a copy visit our website.

www.hostel-scotland.co.uk

IndependentHostelsUK.co.uk

IHUK

ommodation for backpackers · adventurers and groups

GREEK YOUTH HOSTEL OGANIZATION

75 DAMAREOS STR.-PAGRATI
ATHENS 116 33, GREECE
TEL:+30 210-7519530 FAX: +30 210-7510616
E-MAIL: SKOKIN@HOL.GR
WEBSITE: WWW.ATHENS-YHOSTEL.COM

THE MEMBERS OF THE GREEK YOUTH HOSTEL ORGANISATION WELCOME YOU TO GREECE AND ARE HAPPY TO OFFER YOU ACCOMMODATION WITH THE FAMOUS TRADITIONAL GREEK HOSPITALITY, IN THE FOLLOWING PLACES:

ATHENS YOUTH HOSTEL
5, DAMAREOS STR. 11633
MAN: IOANNIS TRIANDAFILLOU
TEL: +30 210-7519530
FAX: +30 210-7510616
E-MAIL: Y-HOSTELS@OTENET.GR
WWW.ATHENS-YHOSTEL.COM

MACEDONIA

THESSALONIKI YOUTH HOSTEL
44, ALEXANDRE SVOLOU STR
MAN: FEDON SISKOS
TEL: + 30 2310-225946
FAX: +30 2310-262208

PELOPONNESE

PATRA YOUTH HOSTEL
62, HEROON POLITECHNIOU STR
MAN: THEODOROS VAZOURAS
TEL: +30 2610-427278, 222707

OLYMPIA YOUTH HOSTEL
18, PRAXITELOUS – KONDILI STR.
MAN: DIMITRIOS LOLOS
TEL/FAX: + 30 26240-22580

CRETE

HERAKLIO YOUTH HOSTEL
, VIRONOS STR.
MAN: IOANNIS KOUKOULAKIS
TEL/FAX.+30 2810-286281
FAX: + 30 2810-222947

RETHIMNO YOUTH HOSTEL
45, TOBAZI STR.
MAN: EMMANUEL KALOGERAKIS
TEL: + 03 28310-22848
EMAIL: INFO@YHRETHYMNO.COM
WWW.YHRETHYMNO.COM

PLAKIAS YOUTH HOSTEL
PROVINCE AGIOU VASSILIOU
NOMOS RETHIMNOU
MAN: FREDERIKOS KALOGERAKIS
TEL: +30 28320-32118, 31560
FAX: +30 28320 31939
WEB SITE: WWW.YHPLAKIAS.COM
EMAIL: INFO@YHPLAKIAS.COM

CYCLADES

FIRA YOUTH HOSTEL
FIRA SANTORINI
MAN: GEORGIOS KOUSTOULIDIS
TEL: +30 22860-23864

PERISSA YOUTH HOSTEL
PERISSA SANTORINI
MAN: FEDRA KONDAXAKI
TEL: +30 22860-82182 & 81943

OIA YOUTH HOSTEL
OIA SANTORINI
MAN: MANOLIS KARVOUNIS
TEL: +30 22860-71465

Backpackers Hostels Canada
Auberges Backpackers Canada

Visit Canada!
Visit ... www.backpackers.c

INDEX

INDEX